C94

THE FIVE BROTHERS

THE STORY OF THE MAHABHARATA

THE FIVE BROTHERS

BROTHERS

THE STORY OF THE MAHABHARATA

Adapted from the English translation
of Kisari Mohan Ganguli
by
ELIZABETH SEEGER

Illustrated by
Cyrus le Roy Baldridge

an ASIA book
The John Day Company:
New York

CHARACTERS IN THE STORY
in the order of their appearance

KUNTI.   Wife of King Pandu of the Báratas, mother of Yudíshtira, Bima, and Arjuna

YUDÍSHTIRA.   Eldest son of Pandu and Kunti

BIMA.   Second son of Pandu and Kunti

ARJUNA.   Third son of Pandu and Kunti

NÁKULA.   Eldest son of Pandu and his second wife Madri

SAHADÉVA.   Twin brother of Nákula, son of Pandu and Madri

KURU.   King of the Báratas, elder brother of Pandu and Vídura

BISHMA.   Uncle of Kuru, Pandu, and Vídura

GANDÁRI.   Wife of Kuru, sister of the King of Gandára

DURYÓDANA.   Eldest son of Kuru and Gandári

DUSHÁSANA.   Second son of Kuru and Gandári

VÍDURA.   Younger brother of Kuru and Pandu

DRONA.   Teacher of the Pándavas and the Kúravas

ASHVATTÁMAN.   Son of Drona

KARNA.   Son of Kunti and Surya, God of the Sun

THE KING OF PANCHÁLA.   Father of Dráupadi, Dyumna, and Shikándin

PURÓCHANA.   Counselor of Duryódana

VYASA.   A sage, kinsman of the Pándavas and the Kúravas

DRÁUPADI.   Daughter of the King of Panchála, sister of Dyumna, wife of the Pándavas

DYUMNA.   Son of the King of Panchála, twin brother of Dráupadi

KRISHNA.   Nephew of Kunti, cousin of the Pándavas, friend of Arjuna

SUBÁDRA.   Sister of Krishna, wife of Arjuna, mother of Abimányu

ABIMÁNYU.   Son of Arjuna and Subádra

THE FIVE SONS OF DRÁUPADI AND THE PÁNDAVAS

NÁRADA.   A sage

JARASÁNDA.   King of Mágada

SHÁKUNI.   King of Gandára, brother of Gandári

v

VIRÁTA.   King of Matsya, friend and ally of the Pándavas
UTTAR.   Youngest son of Viráta
ÚTTARA.   Daughter of Viráta, wife of Abimányu
KÍCHAKA.   Commander of Viráta's army
SHALYA.   King of Madra, brother of Madri, uncle of the twins
SÁNJAYA.   Charioteer and trusted friend of Kuru
SHIKÁNDIN.   Son of the King of Panchála, brother of Dyumna and
Dráupadi

PRONUNCIATION OF PROPER NAMES

a = ah, like the a in father
e = ay, like the e in obey
i = ee, like the i in police
o = o, as in hole
u = oo, like the oo in fool, except before two
    consonants, when it is like the oo in book
au = ow as in now
All consonants may be pronounced as in English.

CONTENTS

CONTENTS

CONTENTS

INTRODUCTION

The great epic stories of the world are few and their number will probably not increase—unless, for our sins, a new flood washes mankind from the face of the planet, leaving only another Noah or a Manu to start the long course of civilization over again.

For the great epics came out of the dawn of the world, when everything was new: before man wrote or read, when intuition and experience were the only sources of his knowledge; when, amazed and stirred by the cosmic drama in the midst of which he found himself, he tried to find his part in it, his relation to the earth and its creatures, to the heavenly bodies and to his fellow men. He searched his memory to find a cause and a beginning and cast his vision far ahead to seek a purpose and an end. His findings were infinitely important to him and to all who have come after him. In order to record them he put them into stories that caught the rhythm of the turning earth. There is no better way to remember and to make others remember than to make a story and to put it into rhythmic speech.

Because the epics were composed before writing was known or before it was widely used in the country of their origin, they were not individual works but collective; for they were told by teacher to disciple, by parent to child, by storyteller to storyteller, each generation, each unusual person adding something until the story grew, like a Gothic cathedral, including many centuries in its final form. And, like a Gothic cathedral, it gathered in its growth the history, the beliefs and customs, the economy and the arts of the times it passed through, and preserved them for us. Only a great framework can hold all these things together and keep its own shape through so much handling; the epic, therefore, is always a magnificent story.

For these and other reasons it seems unlikely that further stories of this magnitude will be produced, and for these reasons the ones we have are particularly precious. There are none greater or more precious than the two epics of India, the Mahabhárata and the Ramáyana.

The Mahabhárata in its entirety is the longest of all scriptures and of all poems; for it is three times as long as the Bible and eight times as long as the *Iliad* and the *Odyssey* put together. For two or three thousand years the story that forms its nucleus has been the vehicle for the moral philosophy and for the highest spiritual teaching of Hinduism; it has acquired not only enormous elaboration in the telling, but also enormous digressions amounting to whole volumes that are purely philosophical and only tenuously connected with the story. It has become the very encyclopedia of Hinduism: "The storehouse," as one scholar says, "of Indian genealogy, mythology and antiquity."

Since history, as understood in the West, has not been congenial to the Hindu mind, it seems impossible to find out, even approximately, the time when the events of this story may have taken place. Some Hindu scholars say 3000 B.C. and others about 1500 B.C.; Western scholars, after exhaustive research, say any time between 1700 B.C. and 700 B.C. There is no mention of the great battle in the vague historical records, although the Bháratas were known in very early times as powerful rulers of northwestern India who, indeed, gave it its early name—Bhárata-varsha. There seems to be no doubt, however, that the story is based on actual events, though they were not of the colossal proportions claimed by the poem. For one of the quaint results of its long growth is the contrast between the claim of the Bhárata kings to be "lords of the whole earth with its belt of seas" and a certain incident which proves them to be no more than tribal chieftains who raid each other's borders to steal cattle.

The poem, on the other hand, has its place in history. Professor Edward Washburn Hopkins in his book, *The Great Epic of*

India, states that lays, or song cycles, about the Bháratas were current by 400 B.C., that this story, with its familiar characters, was known between 400 and 200 B.C., and that the poem had attained its present form and length at some time between 200 and 400 A.D. By that time it was written in Sanskrit and was available to priests and scholars.

During those many centuries and afterward, the story, its incidents and characters, became known to everyone in India and in those countries colonized or influenced by India: Ceylon, Southeast Asia, and the Indies. It was and is now told in the homes, chanted in the temples, recited under the village tree; it was carved on the walls of Angkor and in the temples of Java; it was and is now shown in the shadow plays of Burma, Siam, and the Indies, played by living actors and danced in exquisite ceremonial dances. Indeed, it is so well known in the Indies that the Javanese began their history with these stories, believing them to be their own tradition.

The great arts of India, Indonesia, and Southeast Asia are as hard to understand, if one is ignorant of the two Hindu epics, as the arts of Western Europe would be if one were ignorant of the Greek myths and the Bible. Kunti and Dráupadi are of the stature of Penelope, Antigone, and Alcestis; Yudíshtira and Arjuna, Bishma and Vídura stand beside David and Solomon, Odysseus and Achilles, Arthur and Galahad and Roland. Is it not time for us to become as familiar with these great figures of Indian tradition as we are with those of our own? Is not the Aryan heritage ours also? And is it not well to know the sources of the culture of a great people whose newly won independence will make them increasingly important in the world?

The Indian epics do not belong so much to the past as ours do: they are alive and active in the life of India today. The grandmother or the mother tells them to the children; bands of actors and of minstrels travel about presenting them in town and village, where amateurs, too, love to enact them; priests recite the sonorous Sanskrit verses while interpreters translate them for the listeners; scholars and poets rhapsodize on solemn or festive occasions, taking one incident and improvising upon it, after the manner of the ancient Greek rhapsodes. The Pándavas, Kunti and Dráupadi are the great examples of noble and virtuous behavior, held up to children and adults; their misfortunes still draw tears from the listener or spectator, and their victory brings an ever returning joy.

I seem to have forgotten that it is not the mighty Mahabhárata that I am introducing, but my own humble version of its story. Yet even this volume has its place in the great tradition, for the noble tale has been in the hands of every sort of storyteller; many versions and condensations of it have been made in all the vernaculars of India and the many stories included in it—the stories of Sakuntala, Nala and Damayanti, Savitri, for example—have been told and retold in India and abroad. That great spiritual poem, the Bhagavad Gita, which is contained in the Mahabhárata and yet is complete in itself, is known to all the world.

The whole of the text has been translated from the Sanskrit into several of the modern languages of India, such as Bengali, Hindi, Tamil, and Canarese, and other editions are in progress. Two complete translations into English have been made by Hindus: one—which I have used, since I am ignorant of Sanskrit—by Kisari Mohan Ganguli, published in thirteen volumes by Pratap Chandra Roy, from 1883–1893; and another by M. N. Dutt, published in eighteen volumes from 1895–1904; the labor of translation and publication covering, in both instances, ten years. To my knowledge, only one complete translation has been made in the West: a translation into French, made by Hippolyte Fauche in 1863.

There is great need of a readable version of the epic story by someone who is master of both Sanskrit and English and who can do justice to the beauty and nobility of the subject. It seems to me that until this is done, any version which might make this living story more familiar to us is justified.

When I first read the edition so devotedly published by Pratap Chandra Roy, I was amazed and delighted to find that the story, which I was primarily seeking, ran through the vast accumulation of digression, repetition, and accretion as a clear brook might run through marsh, meadow, and forest, never losing its direction and falling at last into a mighty river. The story never loses its logic or its continuity; after disappearing from view for two or three hundred or even more than a thousand pages, it emerges in all its purity, rises to a mighty climax, and ends more beautifully than any story known to me.

In the same way, the characters are completely consistent throughout. They are so clearly drawn, so human, admirable, and lovable that one feels that they must either have been real people whose powerful personalities have come down to us unchanged or that the original dramatis personae were recreated by so great a poet that no other dared to alter his conception of them. For they, like the story but unlike the chaotic whole, emerge pure and convincing after millennia of handling.

It is this story and these characters that I have wished to bring to the knowledge of Western readers in this book, together with the moral philosophy of India which is inseparable from the story, which is built upon it, and from the characters, who exemplify it. Following the thread of narrative through the labyrinth of text I have chosen those incidents which seem to me essential to the story or to the understanding of one or another of the characters. This has been my only purpose in selecting, perhaps, one incident from a hundred incidents, one conversation from fifty conversations, one significant paragraph from innumerable ones. Much that is very beautiful has had to be left out so that this book might not be too long.

My hope is that other people may find the same delight in it that I have found. I believe that children are particularly attuned to epic stories, which came out of the youth of the world, and I believe that the best education for children is to relive the world's life, through its folk and fairy tales and its heroic stories. Therefore this book has been written with the utmost simplicity, so that children may enjoy it; and, for the same reason, I have avoided all unnecessary complication, knowing that the setting and circumstances and the names are already alien and may present obstacles to the reader.

If a Sanskrit scholar or, indeed, anyone familiar with the Mahabhárata in any form, takes up this book he will surely be shocked at the spelling that prevails in it. The aspirate after consonants (excepting s) has been omitted, for the reason that not one out of a thousand readers would pronounce it and it might discourage the nine hundred and ninety-nine. The aspirate is a nice distinction of sound and Gand-hára is more beautiful than Gandára; but, if one *h* is left in, surely all must be left in, and then the name of the person most often mentioned will be written "Yudhishthira." If it were so written, I am sure that most children and many adults would simply skip the word rather than struggle with its unfamiliar appearance.

To make reading easier, I have given his family name to the blind king who is so important a personage in the tale, calling him Kuru instead of Dhritarashtra. This will also make clearer the constant differentiation between his sons, known as the Kúravas (or Kauravas) and the Pándavas, the sons of Pandu. So also the name of Dhrishtadyumna, which means Clear Light, has been simplified to Dyumna, Light. All unnecessary names have been omitted, even that of Drupada, King of Panchala, in order not to confuse it with Draupadi, his daughter's name, which is derived from his.

Since my purpose has been to tell the story, religious doctrines that are not relevant to it have not been touched upon. From the Bhagavad Gita only those verses that give the necessary answer of Krishna to Arjuna have been included, for there is no place in a condensed narrative for that great poem. The part of Krishna himself, which is believed to be a later accretion, is also not given the supreme importance that it has in India. Krishna appears as the wise and powerful friend of the Pándavas, not as an incarnation of God, as that idea might complicate and obscure rather than clarify the story. The miracles attributed to him have been omitted: in the famous incident of the unclothing of Dráupadi, although she called upon Krishna, it was Darma, God of Righteousness, who clothed her in miraculous garments; I have simplified this situation by making her call upon Darma.

Since these liberties have been taken, not only with the utmost love and reverence, but with the sole purpose of making the story as clear and familiar as possible to its destined readers, I hope that both Hindu and foreign scholars will be willing to forgive them.

If I have been high-handed in omitting, I have not been so presumptuous as to add anything of my own. Only in the first two pages have I even made any rearrangement. It was necessary there, since the text has three distinct beginnings and the third starts with the creation of the world, for which my modest volume has no room. But even in those pages I have only rearranged what has been told on various other pages; I have not added or invented anything. My part has been to select, to reduce thirteen large volumes to one comparatively small one, to connect intelligibly the selected episodes, and to change the rather formal, stiff, and complicated style of the Hindu translator into what I hope is clear and simple English.

I wish to express my gratitude to Dr. S. Chandrasekhar for reading and approving the manuscript; to Swami Aseshananda of the Ramakrishna-Vivekananda Center in New York for his vivid assurance of the importance of the Mahabhárata in the life of India today; to Professor Louis H. Gray for his help with the pronunciation of the Sanskrit names; to Richard Bloomenstein for his careful and critical reading and approval of the manuscript from the twelve-year-old point of view; and to the Dalton School, without whose generosity the book would not have been written.

THE FIVE BROTHERS

THE STORY OF THE MAHABHARATA

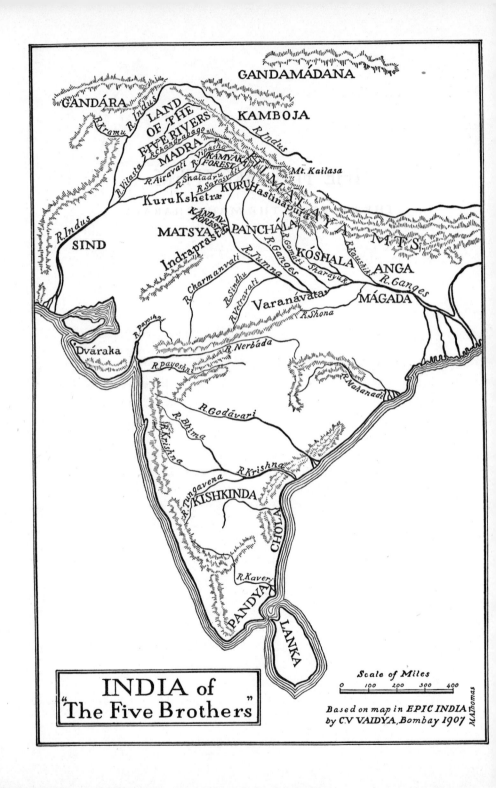

GANDAMÁDANA

GANDÁRA

KAMBOJA

LAND OF THE FIVE RIVERS

MADRA

R.Xramu

R.Indus

R.Chandrabaga

R.Vitasta

R.Airavati

R.Shaladru

Vipasha

R.Sarasvati

KÁMYAKA FOREST

R.Indus

Mt. Kailasa

HIMÁLAYA MTS.

KuruKshetra

KURU Hastinapura

KÁNDAVA FOREST

Indraprasta

MATSYA

PANCHÁLA

R.Gomati

KÓSHALA

R.Kaushiki

ANGA

R.Indus

SIND

R.Ganges

R.Sharayu

R.Ganges

R.Charmanvati

R.Sindhu

R.Jumna

R.Vetravati

Varanávata

MÁGADA

R.Payoshn

R.Shona

Dváraka

R.Payoshn

R.Nerbáda

R.Mahanadi

R.Godávari

R.Bhima

R.Krishna

R.Krishna

R.Tungavena

KISHKINDA

CHOLA

R.Kaveri

PANDYA

LANKA

Scale of Miles

0   100   200   300   400

M.A.Thomas

INDIA of
"The Five Brothers"

Based on map in EPIC INDIA
by C.V VAIDYA, Bombay 1907

BOOK I

THE SONS OF PANDU

They Come to Hastinápura

THE chariot of the thousand-rayed sun was rising from the eastern hills when the five sons of Pandu, with their mother, Kunti, came to the principal gate of Hastinápura, the City of the Elephant. They had been brought there by the holy sages who dwelt on the Mountain of a Hundred Peaks, where the sons of Pandu had been born and where they had spent their childhood. As they drew near to the city, the boys, who had known no home but the deep forest, beheld with wonder the high white walls, the arched gateways as dark as storm clouds, and the countless palaces surrounded by flowering trees, all touched by the first light of the sun, the maker of the day. This was their father's city, the noble capital of the kings of the Bárata folk.

The eldest of the sages, knocking at the gate, summoned the porter, who looked with amazement at the company that stood before him. He saw the stately lady Kunti and the five boys, as beautiful as gods, who stood beside her with the bearing of young lions. At her right was the eldest, about twelve years old, and beside him his brother, a year younger, broad of shoulder and long of arm, as strong as a yearling bull. At her left was a slender, dark-skinned boy with curling hair, and close to him were the youngest brothers, twins of astonishing beauty.

Around Kunti and her sons stood those mighty sages who had

I

cared for them and brought them to the city. They were very holy men who rarely came down from their sky-piercing peaks into the world of men. Their bodies were thin from fasting and clad only in deerskins bound round their loins; their unkempt hair fell on their bare shoulders; but an inner light shone through their thin bodies, and their flashing eyes were terrible to behold. The porter had heard tales of sages such as these: how they had freed their hearts of anger and fear and all desire and gained such power of soul that they could live as long as they wished to live; that they could travel a thousand miles in the wink of an eye, and could behold the whole universe as if it were a plum in the palms of their hands. He bowed down before them till his head touched the ground and awaited their orders.

"Go at once to the King," said the eldest of the holy ones. "Tell him that we await him here."

The man ran quickly to the palace and was admitted to the audience hall where the blind King Kuru sat, surrounded by his counselors, with his uncle, the wise Bishma, seated at his side. Breathlessly the porter gave the message, describing those who had sent it. The King rose at once and went to the city gate, accompanied by Bishma and his other ministers. The ladies of the royal household followed him, one of them leading the faultless Queen, who, in order to share her husband's blindness, wore over her own eyes a cloth gathered into many folds. The hundred young sons of the King, clad in rich robes and decked with jewels, were led by the eldest, a proud and handsome lad. The citizens, meanwhile, hearing about those who stood at the gate, came forth in crowds, with their wives and children; bowing low with joined palms before the sages, they waited, silent and reverent.

Bishma, since he was the eldest of the Báratas, welcomed the holy ones, offering them water to wash their feet, and honey, curds, and rice to eat, while the King and all his followers saluted them. When they had refreshed themselves, the eldest of the sages rose and addressed all who were assembled there, saying, "You all know that your former king, Pandu, went to the forest many years ago, with his two wives, to disport himself and to hunt the deer.

2

A terrible misfortune befell him there, for one day he killed a stag that was mating with a doe and the dying stag put a curse upon him, that he should never have a son. Then in great grief he gave up his kingdom to his brother Kuru, left the pleasures of the world, and went into the deep forest, eating only fruit and roots, in order to rid his heart of fear and anger and desire, and so to free his soul. His two wives would not leave him; therefore with them he crossed many mountain ranges, reaching at last the Mountain of a Hundred Peaks, where he made his abode with us. He studied with us there, serving us and treading the path of virtue and of wisdom.

"Because of the power of soul that he attained and because of a boon granted to his wife Kunti in her girlhood, his line did not die out. The gods themselves gave sons to his two wives. This eldest child, named Yudíshtira, who stands at his mother's right hand, was begotten by the God of Righteousness himself. This second one, named Bima, the strongest of men, is the Wind God's son. This third son of Kunti was begotten by Indra, chief of all the gods who protect the earth; his name is Arjuna and he will humble all the bowmen in the world. Look here upon these tigers among men, the twin sons of Madri, King Pandu's younger wife; they were born of the lovely Gods of Twilight and of Dawn. These children are our pupils; you will be well pleased with them.

"Seventeen days ago King Pandu died. His wife Madri, seeing him placed upon the funeral pyre, threw herself upon it and was burned with him, going with her lord to the regions of the blessed. Here are their ashes. Here are their children, with their mother, Kunti: receive them with due honor, for they are to you as your sons, your brothers, and your friends."

Having spoken thus, the sages disappeared instantly, before the very eyes of the people, who, filled with wonder, returned to their homes.

The King received with joy his brother's sons, caressing each one of them, and the Queen embraced their mother, Kunti, lovingly, welcoming her as an elder sister welcomes a younger after a long absence. Then the royal household and all the kinsmen, friends, and followers, went to the banks of the holy river Ganges to per-

3

form the last ceremonies, the water rites, for the illustrious dead. The royal canopy was held over the ashes of King Pandu and his wife Madri; priests, clad in white, walked at the head of the procession, pouring libations upon the sacred fire that blazed in a finely wrought vessel. Weeping, Bishma, the King and all his kinsmen, the sons of Pandu and all the Báratas performed the water ceremonies. They remained there, sleeping on the bare ground by the sacred river, till the twelve days of mourning had passed.

When they had been cleansed through these rites from the impurity of death, the Pándavas, with their mother, were taken into Hastinápura. They saw for the first time—their eyes wide with wonder—the busy streets of a city filled with beautiful shops, some full of excellent foods and garlands of flowers, others overflowing with finely woven cloths, jeweled ornaments, perfumes, and goods of every sort. They passed through squares shaded by flowering trees, for it was spring; they saw countless spacious houses, groves of trees, and pools of clear water where the citizens sported and refreshed themselves.

They saw also all the four castes of men. The Brahmans they knew, for these were the priests who learned by heart and taught the holy books, the Vedas, and performed all the sacrifices to the gods. They knew those of their own caste, the Kshatrias, the warriors and rulers of men. But they had never seen the merchants and workmen, the farmers and herdsmen of the Vaisya caste, or the dark-skinned Shudras, who were the servants of all. In the city called after the elephant the four castes lived in harmony together, each doing his own work. The people were honest and happy; there were no robbers among them nor anyone who was sinful, for with the help of Bishma, the King ruled them wisely and protected all living creatures in his realm.

As the Pándavas went through the streets, the citizens thronged out to see them, crying out, "Welcome to the family of Pandu! Through the gods' grace we behold them! May they live among us forever!"

Then the boys entered their father's palace and began to live there in a princely way. The leading men of the Báratas were pleased with their knowledge of the Vedas, with the purity of Yudíshtira, the strength of Bima, the courage of Arjuna, and the humility and sweet nature of the twins. All the people rejoiced in their virtues as they grew up with their hundred cousins like lotuses in a lake.

The Poisoning of Bima

Whenever the boys were playing together it was clear that the Pándavas were stronger than their cousins. Bima alone could beat the hundred Kúravas at any sport as if they had been but one: they were no match for that son of the Wind God in speed, in sureness of aim, and in the amount he could eat. Besides, just to show off his strength he used to torment them without mercy. Sometimes he seized them by the hair, threw them down, and dragged them along the ground after him, bruising their knees and shoulders. He made them fight each other while he stood by, laughing. Sometimes he held ten of them under the water and did not let them go till they were nearly drowned. If the sons of Kuru climbed a tree to pick fruit, he shook the tree with his foot until the fruit and the fruit pickers tumbled down together. All this he did more in mischief than in malice.

The eldest son of the King, however, whose name was Duryó-dana, began to hate Bima. They were of exactly the same age, a year younger than Yudíshtira.

When Duryódana was born he had begun to cry and bray like an ass. Hearing him, asses and jackals, crows and vultures had also cried out; violent winds had arisen and fires had broken out in various places. The King had summoned Bishma and other wise counselors, and they said to him, "O lord of earth, these frightful omens mean that this eldest son of yours will be the ruin of his people. Abandon him, O King; do good to all the world by casting off this one child! It has been said that one person should be cast off for the sake of a family; that a family should be cast off for the sake of a village; that a village may be cast off for the sake of the

5

whole country, and that the whole earth may be cast off for the sake of the soul." Although all the wise men counseled him thus, the king had not the heart to follow their advice, out of fondness for his son. He always favored Duryódana more than his other children, so the boy grew up to be proud and jealous and evil-minded.

Now, seeing the might of Bima, Duryódana thought to himself, "No one can compare in strength with this second son of Pandu. Therefore I shall have to destroy him by treachery. Then I will imprison his elder brother Yudíshtira and his younger brother Arjuna and there will be no one left to trouble me." After that, he was always on the watch for a chance to kill Bima.

He had a beautiful pavilion built on the bank of the Ganges and called it the Water Sport Pavilion. Gay flags waved from its roof; he filled it with all sorts of entertaining games and brought cooks there to prepare the most delicious foods. When it was finished he said to the Pándavas, "Let us go to the river for a day's sport in the water." And all the Kúravas, taking the sons of Pandu with them, mounted elephants and chariots and rode to the banks of the Ganges. When they arrived, they admired the beauty of the gardens and the lotus pools surrounding the pavilion; then they entered into it, like lions entering their mountain caves. They sat down to enjoy the games and other pleasures provided for them, exchanging with each other bits of the delicious food that was served to them.

Now the wicked Duryódana had mixed a powerful poison with a portion of the food. Pretending to be very friendly, he fed Bima with a great deal of the poisoned food; then, feeling sure that he had got rid of his mighty cousin, he made merry and was very happy. When they had eaten, the young princes played in the water until they were tired of the sport; then they dressed in fresh garments and rested in the pavilion or in the gardens.

Bima, who had led all the others in their sports, was the last to step out of the water. He felt so exceedingly tired that he lay down on the ground; whereupon he lost his senses, for the poison was working in his body. The other boys had gone on, all except

Duryódana, who lingered behind them, watching Bima. When he saw him lie unconscious on the ground, he bound him hand and foot and threw him into the river.

Bima sank down until he reached the bottom of the river, which was the realm of the Nagas, those mighty, wrathful snakes who dwell beneath the earth and in the waters. The Nagas rushed at him and bit him with their poisonous fangs all over his body, except on his chest, which was so hard that they could not pierce the skin. The snake poison destroyed the vegetable poison that he had eaten and Bima came to his senses. He broke the ropes that bound him and crushed the snakes with his feet against the bottom of the river.

A few of them escaped and fled to their king, saying piteously to him, "O king of snakes, a boy sank under the water, bound with cords and unconscious, but when we bit him he came to his senses and began to kill us. Pray find out who he is!" The King himself, with several of his courtiers, followed them to the place where Bima stood.

By a fortunate chance, one of the serpents was a friend of Kunti's father; he came forward, embraced the boy, and presented him to the King, who was pleased with Bima's strength and courage. "What shall we do for this young hero?" he asked his courtiers. "Let us give him gold and jewels." But Bima's wise friend said, "O lord of serpents, if you are pleased with him, he will have no need of wealth. Let him, rather, drink of your nectar, for that will give him the strength of a thousand elephants and make him invincible in battle." "So be it!" the King replied.

The Nagas performed the proper ceremonies, while Bima purified himself; then he sat down facing the east and began to drink the nectar. At one breath he drained one of the vessels; then drank seven more, until he could not hold another drop. The Nagas prepared a comfortable bed for him, where he lay down at his ease and slept.

Meanwhile the other princes, after looking for Bima, set out for Hastinápura without him, saying to each other, "Perhaps he has gone ahead of us." The wicked Duryódana, sure that his plan had been successful, returned happily to the city, making little of Bima's absence; but Yudíshtira ran to his mother, asking, "Has Bima come? We looked for him everywhere, in the gardens and in the woods, but could not find him. Dear Mother, have you not seen him?"

Kunti shrieked with fear when she heard his words. "I have not seen him, dear son; he has not come home!" she cried. "Oh, go back quickly and look for him again!"

She sent for the wise Vídura, the King's younger brother, whom she trusted. "O noble one," she said to him, "Bima is missing! All the others have come back from the river and he is not among them. Duryódana hates him: I fear that in a fit of anger he may have slain my darling."

Vídura comforted her, saying, "Blessed lady, do not fear! The sages have said that all your sons will be long-lived: Bima surely will return. Wait patiently and do not accuse Duryódana, lest he harm your other sons; but watch over them all with care."

Bima slept for a long time; when he woke he felt strong beyond measure because of the nectar that he had drunk. The Nagas said to him: "O bull of the Báratas, the nectar has given you the strength of a thousand elephants; no one will ever be able to vanquish you in battle. Bathe now in this sacred water and return home, for your brothers are disconsolate because of you."

So Bima bathed, put on white robes and flowery garlands, and ate the sweetened rice that the Nagas gave him. After saluting them and receiving their blessing, he rose from the water and ran swiftly to his mother. He bowed down to her and to Yudíshtira and embraced his younger brothers; those godlike boys, who loved each other dearly, said again and again, "What joy is ours today! Oh, what joy!"

Then Bima told his brothers about the villainy of Duryódana and all that had happened to him in the Nagas' kingdom. Yudíshtira said, "Do not speak of this to anyone; but from this day on, let us protect one another carefully." After that they were very watchful, and Vídura, their younger uncle, also watched over them and gave them wise advice. Vídura was the brother of Kuru and Pandu, but his mother was a serving woman of the Shudra caste; therefore he could never be king, but he was wise and learned above all men and was beloved by all.

Drona Teaches the Princes

The King, seeing the young princes spending their time in idleness and growing naughty, began to look about for a master who could teach them the science of warfare and the duties of the Kshatria caste, a man of great intelligence and godlike strength.

Now it happened that the illustrious Drona, of world-wide fame, a Brahman skilled in the Vedas and in the use of all weapons, human and divine, had come to the kingdom of Kuru with his wife and his son; he was living quietly in the house of a friend.

One day the sons of Pandu and their cousins ran out of the gates of the city and began to play ball, with much laughter and shouting. Suddenly their ball fell into a dry well. The boys did their best to get it out, but all their efforts were useless. They saw a Brahman, dark-skinned and lean, standing near them, watching them; so they went to him and crowded round him, asking for his help. The Brahman smiled at them and said, "Fie upon your strength and your skill! You are Kshatrias, born of the Bárata folk. How is it that you cannot get your ball from the bottom of that well? If you promise me a good dinner I will bring back the ball that you have lost, and this ring, too." With these words he took a ring from his finger and threw it down the well; then, smiling still, he said, "I shall turn these long blades of grass, by my spells, into powerful weapons. I shall pierce the ball with one of these blades and then pierce that blade with another one and that other one with a third, until I have formed a chain of blades that will bring the ball out of the well."

He did just what he had said; the boys' eyes were round with delight and amazement. "Now, O learned one," they cried, "bring

9

up the ring!" Then the stranger, taking a bow and arrow, pierced the ring with the arrow, which, returning to his hand, brought the ring with it.

The astonished princes saluted him, saying, "We bow to you, O holy one! We have never seen anyone so skillful as you. Who are you and what can we do for you? You have asked us for a dinner, but that is only a trifle. Stay with us always!"

"Go to Bishma," said the Brahman. "Tell him how I look and what I have done. That mighty one will know me." So the boys ran to Bishma and told him all that the man had said and done; and Bishma knew at once that this must be Drona, the best teacher that the princes could have. He sought out the Brahman, who was indeed no other than Drona, and brought him respectfully to the palace. "O wisest of men," said Bishma, "by what good fortune have you come to Hastinápura?"

"Sir," answered Drona, "in my youth I went to a great sage who taught me the science of arms and the use of all weapons, human and divine. At the same time the prince of Panchála came to the hermitage and for many years we lived and studied together in the forest with that mighty sage. We became great friends; he used to say to me, 'Drona, I am the favorite child of my noble father; I am sure that he will make me his heir. When the kingdom is mine, I will share it with you, dear friend; my dominion, wealth, and happiness will also be yours.' When he finished his studies he went back to his own country, but I always remembered what he had said.

"Not long after that I married and my wife gave birth to a boy as splendid as the sun. One day this child, seeing some rich men's children drinking milk, began to cry. At this I was quite beside myself, blaming myself that I could not give him milk to drink. I knew that my former friend was now the king of Panchála; therefore, recalling his words and thinking myself blessed, I went to him with my dear wife and child. Approaching him trustfully, I said, 'O tiger among men, behold the friend of your boyhood.'

"To my horror, he laughed at me and cast me off as if I were a vulgar fellow. 'Friendship does not last forever,' he said. 'There cannot be friendship between a poor man and a rich man; one who is not a king can never have a king for his friend. But, O Brahman, I will give you food and shelter for a night.' I left him at once, filled with anger, vowing to revenge myself on him. I have come to Hastinápura to find able and obedient pupils with whose help I can carry out my vow."

"String your bow, O Drona," said Bishma, "and teach the Bárata princes all the science of war. You are the lord of all the wealth we have and of our kingdom itself; the purpose that is in your heart is already achieved. You have come to us in a lucky hour."

Then Bishma gave that foremost of all bowmen a house that was neat and spacious, well filled with rice and every kind of wealth, and Drona accepted the sons of Pandu and the sons of Kuru as his pupils. They were initiated into the Kshatria caste; they studied the Vedas as well as the science of war and became skillful in all athletic sports. Among them all, Arjuna was most devoted to the study and use of weapons; he stayed close to his teacher's side until he excelled all the others in skill and strength and perseverance. Indeed, although the teaching they received was the same, Arjuna, in lightness of hand, became the foremost of all the princes.

Now Drona's own son was one of his best pupils; therefore he began to favor his son in the hope that he might equal or perhaps surpass Arjuna. For instance, he gave his son a wide-mouthed water jug, while he gave all the others narrow-mouthed jugs. When they went to fetch water, his son filled his jug before the others and ran back to his father; in the time thus gained, Drona gave him some added teaching. Arjuna found this out and filled his own jug by using a divine weapon that gave him control over water and that Drona had taught him to use. After that he, too, returned quickly to the master and profited by the added teaching. He was devoted to Drona and served him in every way he could.

Seeing Arjuna's great skill, Drona summoned the cook secretly and said to him, "Never give Arjuna his food in the dark, and do not let him know that I have told you this." Shortly afterward, when Arjuna was eating his evening meal, a wind arose and blew out the lamp that he was using; but he went on eating, his hand going, from habit, to his mouth. That made him understand the force of habit and he began to practice with his bow at night. Then Drona, hearing the twang of his bowstring in the dark, came to him and, clasping him in his arms, said, "Truly, I shall teach you so well that there will not be a bowman like you in the world!" And after that, Arjuna was the favorite of his master, dearer to him than his own son.

Drona taught his pupils to fight on horseback, in chariots, on the backs of elephants, and on foot. He taught them to fight with the mace, the sword, the lance, the spear, and the dart, as well as the bow and arrow. He taught them how to use many weapons, one after the other, how to fight against many men at once, and how to break or to turn aside the weapons of an enemy. The fame of his teaching spread to all the kingdoms of the world; kings and princes came by hundreds to Hastinápura to learn of him. Bima and Duryódana, who were always jealous of one another, became very skillful in the use of the mace; Drona's son excelled in the science of war, the twins in the handling of the sword, and Yudíshtira in the use of the chariot. But Arjuna surpassed them all, for he was skillful with every weapon; his fame spread over all the earth to the verge of the sea.

One day, when their education was finished, Drona wished to test his pupils in the use of the bow. He had an artificial bird put on the top of a tree, as a target; then he called them all together and said, "Take up your bows and stand here, aiming at the bird on the tree, with your arrows fixed on the bowstring. When I give the order, shoot at the bird's head. I shall give each of you a turn, my children."

He first addressed Yudíshtira, since that prince was the eldest. "Behold," he said, "the bird on yonder tree." "I see it," answered Yudíshtira. But Drona spoke again to the prince standing bow in hand, "What do you see, O prince? Do you see the tree, or me, or your brothers?" "I see the tree and you, my brothers, and the bird," replied the eldest son of Pandu. Drona was vexed with him and said reproachfully, "Stand aside! It is not for you to hit the target."

The master asked the same question of all the sons of Kuru, one after another, of Bima and the twins, as well as the other pupils that had come to him from all over the world. The answer was always the same: "I see the tree, and you, my comrades, and the bird." They were all told reproachfully by their teacher, one after another, to stand aside.

When they had all failed, Drona, smiling, called on Arjuna, saying, "You must hit the target; therefore turn your eyes to it, with an arrow fixed on the string." Arjuna stood aiming at the bird, as the master had commanded, and Drona asked him, "Do you see the bird, the tree, and me?" "I see only the bird," answered Arjuna, "not the tree or you." Then Drona, well pleased, said, "If you see the bird, describe it to me." Arjuna said, "I see only the head of the bird, not its body."

At these words, the hair on Drona's body stood on end with delight. "Shoot!" he commanded, and Arjuna instantly let fly his arrow and struck off the head of the bird. The master clasped him to his heart, exclaiming, "You will never be vanquished in battle; you will win everlasting fame!"

BOOK II

THE TOURNAMENT

The Princes Show Their Skill

WHEN the young princes had mastered every weapon, Drona said to the King, in the presence of Bishma and Vídura, "O best of kings, your children have completed their education. Let them now show their skill before you in a tournament."

The King answered with a glad heart, "O best of Brahmans, you have taught them well. Arrange as you desire the place, the time, and the manner in which the tournament shall be held. My blindness makes me envy those who are blessed with sight and may behold my children's skill in arms. Whatever you command shall be done."

Drona then measured out a piece of land that was clear of trees and thickets and well watered with ponds and springs. Upon the land so measured out the workmen of the King built a splendid arena according to the rules laid down in the scriptures. They also built a beautiful stand, where the ladies of the palace might sit to behold the spectacle. The citizens built platforms, the wealthier ones pitching high and spacious tents all around the arena.

When the day fixed for the tournament came, the King and his ministers, with Bishma walking ahead, came into that theater of celestial beauty, gleaming with gold and hung with strings of pearls and other gems. Gandári, the Queen, with Kunti and the other ladies of the royal household joyfully ascended the stand. The four castes of men, eager to see the princes' skill in arms, left the city and came running to the arena; so impatient was everyone to behold the spectacle that the vast crowd assembled almost in an instant. With the noise of blowing trumpets and beating drums and the sound of many voices, the vast concourse was like the tossing ocean.

When all was ready, Drona, dressed in white, with white locks, white beard, white garlands, his body smeared with white sandalwood perfume, entered the arena with his son: he looked like the moon itself, with the planet Mars, in an unclouded sky. On entering, Drona offered sacrifice to the gods, while Brahmans well versed in the Vedas celebrated the rite with sweet-sounding music.

Then those mighty warriors entered, equipped with finger protectors, bows, and quivers; with Yudíshtira at their head, they entered in the order of their ages and began to show their skill with various weapons. Riding swift horses, which they managed easily, they hit the targets with shafts engraved with their names; they mounted their chariots and displayed their skill in driving and in shooting from the moving car. All the spectators, filled with amazement, cried, "Well done! Well done!"

When they had shown their skill in riding, in the use of the bow and arrow, and the management of chariots, these heroes took up their swords and bucklers and ranged the arena, displaying their weapons. The spectators, their eyes wide with wonder, beheld the symmetry of their bodies, their grace, their calmness, the firmness of their grasp, and their mastery of the sword and buckler. Vídura described to the King all the feats of the princes, while Kunti related them to Gandári, whose eyes were ever bandaged out of love and respect for her husband.

Then Bima and Duryódana, inwardly delighted at the prospect of a fight, appeared with maces in their hands, like two single-peaked mountains. Those mighty-armed warriors, clad in mail, summoned all their energy and roared like two angry elephants fighting for a mate; swinging their maces and maneuvering for place, they moved faultlessly, according to the science of arms, around the arena. When they entered, the crowd was divided into two parties, some crying, "Behold Duryódana!" and some, "Behold Bima!" and suddenly there was a great uproar. Seeing this, the wise Drona said to his son, "Restrain both those mighty warriors, lest the anger of the assembly be provoked by a fight between them." And the son of their master restrained those combatants with uplifted maces, who looked like two oceans driven by tempests, and forbade them to fight.

Drona himself commanded the music to stop and addressed the spectators with a voice as deep as thunder, "Behold now Arjuna, who is dearer to me than my own son; behold the master of all weapons, the son of Indra!" Arjuna, dressed in golden mail, equipped with finger protectors, his quiver full of shafts and his bow in hand, appeared in the arena like an evening cloud reflecting the rays of the setting sun and illumined by flashes of lightning. The whole assembly was delighted; a great uproar arose as the spectators exclaimed, "This is the third son of Pandu! This is the son of the mighty Indra! This is the protector of the Báratas!"

At these cries the tears of Kunti fell upon her bosom, and the King, turning to Vídura, asked, "O sinless one, what is this great uproar, rising suddenly and rending the sky?" "O mighty monarch," Vídura replied, "the son of Pandu and Kunti, Arjuna, clad in mail, has entered the arena." Then Kuru said, "I have indeed been blessed, favored, and protected by the three fires that have sprung from Kunti, who is herself the sacred fuel."

As the spectators became calm again, Arjuna displayed before his teacher his dexterity in the use of the bow, the sword, and the mace. First in his chariot, then walking in circles around the arena, he hit various targets with his arrows, using his left and his right hand equally well. He let fly five shafts at once from his bowstring into the mouth of a moving iron boar; he shot one and twenty arrows into the hollow of a cow's horn hung on a rope and swaying to and fro. Those who watched him could not see when he fixed the arrows on the string and when he let them fly, so light were his hands. Then he took up the celestial

17

weapons that Drona had taught him to use. With one he created
fire and with another water; with a third he created wind, with a
fourth clouds, and by still another he caused all these to vanish.
The assembly was delighted; conchs were blown and other instruments struck up their music.

Karna Appears

The tournament was nearly over, the excitement of the crowd
had cooled, and the music had stopped, when there was heard
from the gate a sound like thunder. The people thought, Are
the mountains splitting, is the earth being rent asunder, or is the
sky resounding with the roar of gathering clouds? And they
all turned their eyes to the gate. Drona stood surrounded by the
five sons of Kunti, like the moon with five planets; Duryódana
stood up in haste and was encircled by his century of haughty
brothers, with Drona's son among them. For they knew the
sound to be a challenge sent forth by some warrior of mighty
strength, who smote his armpits with the palms of his hands.

As the spectators, with wide-eyed wonder, made way for him,
a warrior entered the arena, like a cliff walking. He was as tall
as a golden palm tree and handsome as the full moon; he bore
himself like a bull or a lion or the leader of a herd of elephants.
Looking at all those around the arena, he bowed indifferently to
Drona while the whole assembly, motionless and with steadfast
gaze, was thinking, Who is he? Only Kunti, noticing certain fortunate marks upon his person, knew him to be her son.

For Kunti, when she was a girl in her father's palace, had made
it her duty to serve her father's guests. There was one Brahman,
fierce and splendid to behold, who often visited the palace and
was very hard to please. When he had said that he would come
at one time, he came at another; he often asked for food in the
depth of night, when food was hard to find. Yet Kunti always
served him cheerfully, and he was pleased and taught her a spell

by which she could summon any of the gods to do her pleasure.

One morning as she lay in her bed, she thought to herself, "What sort of spell did the high-souled Brahman teach me? I should like to test its power." As she was pondering thus, the sun rose in the east; overjoyed at its beauty, she decided to summon the Sun God, Súrya, at once. As soon as she pronounced the spell, that glorious god, the beholder of everything in the world, appeared before her, saying, "Here I am, O gentle maiden. Tell me, what shall I do for you?"

With joined palms and downcast eyes, the maid replied, "Forgive me, O adorable one. I summoned you from curiosity, to test a certain spell that I was taught."

"The Brahman who taught you that spell knew that you were to bear celestial children," Súrya answered, smiling. "Now you shall have from me a splendid son, decked with a coat of mail and brilliant earrings, who will become the foremost wielder of weapons."

Now Kunti was afraid that her family and friends would blame her for bearing a child in her maidenhood; therefore she told no one about this except her nurse. When the child was born, looking like a very god and decked in a coat of mail and earrings, she placed him in a smooth and spacious wicker basket, well waxed and spread with soft sheets and a costly pillow. In the dead of night she and her nurse carried the basket to the river, where, weeping long and piteously, she laid it on the water.

The basket floated gently from one river to another until it came to the Ganges; there the wife of a charioteer beheld it and drew it to the shore, where her husband opened it. They were amazed to see the beautiful child. Believing that the gods had sent him to them, they brought him up as their son, naming him Karna. He became a mighty warrior, skilled in the use of every weapon, but everyone believed him to be the son of the charioteer, who was a Suta, belonging to a mixed caste formed by the marriage of Brahmans with Kshatrias.

Kunti, through her spies, knew all that had happened to her son, but she never saw him nor claimed him as her own. Now

KARNA CHALLENGES

ARJUNA

she beheld him standing in the arena, radiant with beauty, but she told no one who he was.

Karna, in a voice as deep as that of the clouds, addressed Arjuna: "O son of Indra, I shall perform feats before this gazing multitude, excelling all those of yours. Beholding them, you yourself will be amazed."

At these words the spectators stood up all at once as if uplifted by some unseen power; Duryódana was filled with delight, while Arjuna was abashed and angry. Asking the permission of Drona, the mighty Karna, delighting in battle, did all that Arjuna had done before. Thereupon, Duryódana embraced him joyfully and said, "Welcome, O mighty-armed warrior! You have come here in a lucky hour! Live here with us and share the kingdom of Kuru!"

"I will take you at your word, O prince of the Báratas," Karna replied. "I long for your friendship and I long also for single combat with Arjuna."

"Enjoy all the good things of life with me!" Duryódana exclaimed. "May you bring joy to your friends and, O slayer of foes, may you place your feet on the heads of all your enemies!"

Arjuna, thinking himself disgraced, approached Karna, who stood like a cliff among the Kúravas, and said, "You shall suffer the fate of an unwelcome intruder and a boaster, O Karna, for I will slay you."

"This arena was meant for all, not for you alone, Arjuna," Karna replied. "The Kshatria respects deeds alone; words are the weapons of the weak. Speak then with arrows, until with arrows I strike off your head today before the eyes of the master himself."

Hastily embraced by his brothers, Arjuna advanced for the combat, while Karna, embraced by Duryódana, took up his bow and arrows and stood ready for the fight. Kunti, seeing her two sons facing each other so, swooned áway, and serving maids hastened to her, sprinkling water upon her and rubbing her hands and feet with sandalwood perfume. But Drona, beholding the two warriors with their bows strung, was mindful of the rules concerning duels and said to Karna, "This youngest son of King Pandu and of Kunti belongs to the Bárata folk. Tell us, O mighty-armed one, the names of your father and mother and the royal line that you adorn. When he has heard them, Arjuna will fight with you, for the sons of kings may not fight with men of inglorious birth."

At this, Karna's face looked like a lotus that is pale and torn under the pelting showers of the rainy season. He was silent, but Duryódana quickly said, "O master, if Arjuna is unwilling to fight with one who is not of royal blood, I will make Karna at once the king of Anga." Then and there he ordered servants to fetch a golden seat and offerings of rice and flowers and much gold; he summoned Brahmans to perform the rites of coronation. A royal canopy was held over Karna's head and yak tails were waved around him; the Brahmans poured sacred water on his head and enthroned him as the king of Anga. While this was being done, Kunti came to her senses; and seeing that her son had been made a king, she was well pleased.

"O tiger among men," said the new monarch, addressing Duryódana, "what shall I give you that can compare with your gift of a kingdom? I will do whatever you bid me do."

"I wish only for your friendship," answered the prince, and they embraced one another joyfully.

At this moment the old foster father of Karna, the charioteer of the Suta caste, entered the arena, trembling and perspiring, leaning on his staff. As soon as Karna saw him, he left his throne and went down into the arena; he bowed his head, still wet with the ceremonial water, before his father, who embraced him with tears of joy. Seeing this, Bima jeered at him, saying, "O son of a charioteer, you do not deserve death at the hands of Arjuna. Lay down your bow and take a whip instead! You are not fit to rule the kingdom of Anga, even as a dog is not fit to eat the sacrificial food."

Karna, with quivering lips, fetched a deep sigh and looked at the God of Day, whose chariot was sinking in the west; but Duryódana rose up in wrath from among his brothers, even as a

23

mad elephant rises from a bed of lotuses. "O Bima!" he cried. "It ill behooves you to speak such words! Might is the only virtue that a warrior needs; if he possesses that, no one should scorn to fight him. The birth of heroes, like the sources of mighty rivers, is often hidden. A doe could not bring forth a tiger like this Karna, who deserves to rule the whole world, not only Anga. If there is anyone here who cannot bear what I have done today to Karna, let him mount his chariot and bend his bow against me!" A murmur arose from the crowd, praising his words.

The sun, however, had already set; Duryódana, taking Karna's hand, led him out of the arena, lighted now with countless lamps. The Pándavas, with Drona and Bishma, returned to their homes; the people, too, came away, some naming Arjuna and some Karna as the victor of the day. Duryódana, having won such a powerful friend, was no longer afraid of Arjuna's excellence in warfare; even Yudíshtira believed that there was no warrior on earth like Karna.

Drona's Reward

The time had come when Drona could demand payment for his teaching. He called his pupils together and said to them, "Seize the King of Panchála in battle and bring him before me! This will be my teacher's fee." They all cried, "So be it!" and prepared joyfully for battle, fastening their weapons upon their chariots, and putting on their coats of mail.

With Drona, they marched out to the kingdom of Panchála and attacked its capital city. Duryódana and his brothers, Karna and the other princes who had come from distant lands, all vied with one another to be foremost in the attack. Driving their chariots and followed by cavalry, they entered the streets of the city. Arjuna, seeing their pride, said to Drona, "We shall fight after the others have displayed their prowess. The King of Panchála can never be taken by any of these!" And he, with his brothers, waited outside the walls of the town.

Meanwhile the King, hearing the clamor, came out of his palace and was at once assailed with a shower of arrows. He mounted his chariot and rushed forth against the Kúravas, pouring a fierce shower of arrows upon them; such was his lightness of hand that the Kúravas, in a panic, thought that a hundred kings were fighting them. While the fierce arrows of the monarch fell on all sides, conchs and drums and trumpets sounded the alarm, and the Panchála army came forth, roaring like a thousand lions, while the twang of their bowstrings filled the air. The citizens also showered upon the Báratas all sorts of missiles; young and old rushed forth to battle, while the King careered among them like a wheel of fire, smiting Duryódana and his brothers and the mighty Karna, and quenching their thirst for battle.

The Kúravas broke and fled, wailing, to the gate, where the Pándavas were waiting. Then Arjuna, begging Yudíshtira not to fight, drove forward in his chariot, with the twin sons of Madri guarding his wheels on either side, while Bima, mace in hand, ran on ahead. Roaring like the ocean in a tempest, Bima rushed toward the elephants and cavalry, felling them with his mace, while Arjuna assailed the host of the Panchálas with his arrows. As a herdsman drives easily before him countless cattle, so Bima drove the chariots and elephants of the enemy; and Arjuna, like a consuming fire, laid countless warriors low.

The King of the Panchálas, seeing his army driven back, aimed all his arrows at Arjuna, who fought furiously in return. The Pándava prince cut the King's bow in two with a broad-headed arrow, smashed his flagstaff, and finally pierced his horses and his charioteer with five arrows. Then, throwing aside his bow, Arjuna took up his sword and, with a great shout, leaped from his own chariot upon that of his foe. Standing there fearlessly, he seized the King as an eagle seizes a mighty snake, making him captive. When they saw this, the Panchála troops fled in all directions.

The Pándava princes took the King of Panchála to Drona, who had been watching the battle. And Drona, beholding him humbled and defeated, said to him, smiling a little, "Your kingdom and your capital have been won by me, brave king. But you need not fear for your life: we Brahmans are always forgiving. My love for you has increased with my years, ever since we played together as boys in our master's hermitage. Do you wish to be my friend again? You told me once that none but a king could be the friend of a king; therefore I am keeping half of your kingdom, but, as a boon, I give you back the other half. You are king of all that lies on the southern side of the Ganges, while I become king of that which lies on the north. Henceforth, O Panchála, let us be friends!"

The King answered, "You have a noble soul and great skill in arms, O Brahman; I am not surprised at what you have done. Truly, I desire your everlasting friendship."

After that, the King lived sorrowfully in the southern provinces of his former kingdom. He knew that he could not defeat Drona by force of arms, although they were equal in skill, having studied under the same master; but Drona had more power of soul. Therefore the King began to do penance and to make sacrifices in order that he might have a son who could defeat Drona in battle.

Drona remained in the capital city and ruled over the northern territory, rich in towns and cities, that Arjuna had won for him.

One day he called that hero to him and in the presence of all the other princes, said, "The master who taught me all the science of arms gave me a weapon, more powerful than lightning, that can burn up the whole earth. Accept it from me now. Never use it against a human foe, for if used unworthily, it might destroy the world; but if any superhuman foe contend with you, you may use it then in battle. Keep it with care, for it has not a peer in the three worlds. Now, in the presence of your brothers and kinsmen, grant me what I ask in return for this gift."

"Whatever you ask of me, O master," Arjuna said, "I will gladly grant."

His teacher said, "O sinless one, if I fight against you, you must fight against me!" And Arjuna, touching his feet, pledged his word that he would do so.

Now that they were warrors, tried and skilled, the princes went forth to battle and, by conquering the territory of other kings,

26

increased the kingdom of the Báratas. The Pándavas brought under their sway kings whom even their father Pandu had been unable to conquer; vassals who had not been obedient to the Báratas felt the edge of Arjuna's power. That third son of Kunti, helped by the mighty Bima, challenged all the kings of the east and made them vassals of his uncle, Kuru; he conquered the kings of the south and sent a great train of horses, elephants, camels, and carts laden with all kinds of wealth, back to Hastinápura.

The Kúrava princes were filled with jealousy as they beheld his mighty prowess; King Kuru's love for the Pándavas was also poisoned and he became so anxious that he could not sleep.

BOOK III

THE HOUSE OF LAC

The Pándavas Are Banished

KING KURU, unable to sleep because of his anxiety and jealousy, summoned to his side one of his ministers, a Brahman well versed in the science of politics. The King said to him, "O learned one, the Pándavas are beginning to overshadow the earth. I am jealous of them because of my sons. Shall I have war or peace with them? I pray you, advise me truly, for I shall do as you bid me."

The clever Brahman answered him in these pointed words: "Listen to me, O King, and do not be angry with me when you have heard all that I have to say. Kings should ever be ready to slay their foes. When your foe is in your power, destroy him by any means, open or secret: by deceiving him, by bribing him, by separating him from his friends and allies, or else by open fight. This is my counsel.

"Listen, O monarch, to the story of a jackal who lived in the forest a long time ago. This wise jackal lived with four friends, a tiger, a mouse, a wolf, and a mongoose. There was in the woods a deer that they could not catch because of its swiftness and strength. So they called a meeting, and the jackal said, 'O tiger, you have often tried to catch this deer, but all in vain, because it is young, swift, and very clever. Now let the mouse eat into its feet when it lies asleep; then you will be able to catch it.'

29

"They did as he said: the mouse ate into the feet of the deer, and the tiger killed it. Then the jackal, ever mindful of his own interests, said to his companions, 'Go and wash yourselves in the river while I watch over the deer.' They all went down to the stream while the jackal sat there, pondering deeply what he should do.

"The tiger returned first; seeing the jackal plunged in thought, he said, 'Why are you so sorrowful, O wise one? Let us enjoy ourselves now and eat the deer.' But the jackal said, 'Listen, O mighty one, to what the mouse said. He said, "O fie upon the king of beasts! It was I who slew the deer; because of the strength of my arm he will feast today!" After hearing these boastful words I, for my part, do not care to touch this food.' 'My pride is also aroused,' answered the tiger. 'After this I will kill my own food.' And the tiger went away.

"The mouse came next and the jackal said to him, 'Listen, O mouse, to what the mongoose said. He said, "The carcass of this deer is poisoned by the tiger's claws. I will not eat of it, but with your permission I will slay the mouse and feast on him."' Hearing this, the mouse was frightened and ran into his hole.

"Soon the wolf came. The jackal said to him, 'The king of beasts is angry with you; he is coming back in a few moments with his wife. Do as you think best!' The wolf, though he was very fond of meat, ran away with his tail between his legs, making himself as small as possible.

"It was then that the mongoose came. 'Behold,' said the jackal, 'I have defeated all the others and they have run away! Fight with me now; then eat as much of this meat as you like!' The mongoose replied, 'If the tiger, the wolf, and the clever mouse have all been put to flight by you, I do not care to fight.' And with these words the mongoose also went away.

"Then the jackal, well pleased with the success of his plans, ate the meat by himself.

"If kings act in this way, deceiving the strong and frightening the weak, they can be happy. O King, if your son, friend or brother, if even your teacher become your enemy, slay him with-

out mercy! The sons of Pandu are stronger than your sons. Therefore, O King, protect yourself from them; free yourself and your
sons from any fear of them!" Having given this evil advice, the
Brahman returned to his home, leaving the King sad and thoughtful.

Duryódana also, seeing Bima surpass everyone in strength and
hearing Arjuna acclaimed as the best of bowmen, was vexed in
spirit. He and his brothers, with Karna, tried in various ways to
compass the death of the Pándavas, but those heroes were watchful; with the help of Vídura they avoided his plots and never
spoke of them to anyone.

At this time the citizens of Hastinápura began to talk about the
sons of Pandu in the streets and in the market places, and whenever
they met together in public gatherings. They praised Yudíshtira
for his firmness and patience, his kindness and unswerving honesty;
they said openly that he should rule the kingdom. "King Kuru,"
they said, "was not given the throne in his youth because he was
born blind; therefore, his younger brother Pandu reigned over us.
Why, then, should Kuru be our king now? Let us put upon the
throne this eldest son of Pandu, who is young, wise, truthful, and
kind. He will always care for the old king and his sons and share
with them his wealth and his pleasures."

Duryódana heard these words of the citizens and was deeply
distressed, for he could not bear these speeches. Burning with
jealousy, he went to his father; finding him alone, he bowed reverently and said, "O Father, I have heard prating citizens utter
words of ill omen. They wish the son of Pandu to be their king,
setting you aside and me also. If Yudíshtira reigns, his son will
reign after him, and so the kingdom will descend in Pandu's line,
while we, O lord of earth, will be despised by all men. O Father,
let us never suffer poverty and shame, depending on others for
our food!"

The King, hearing these words and remembering all that his
minister had said, became very sorrowful and his mind began to
waver. Seeing this, Duryódana consulted his brother Dushásana
and Karna; these evil-minded ones decided that the king must
exile the Pándavas to some distant place. The jealous prince went

again to his father and said: "O King, with some clever excuse, send the Pándavas to the town of Varanávata. Then we shall have no fear of them."

After a moment's thought, King Kuru answered, "My brother Pandu was always dutiful to his family and particularly to me. He cared little for the enjoyments of the world but gave everything to me, even the kingdom. His son, as virtuous as he, is the favorite of the people; how can we exile him from his father's kingdom? The counselors and soldiers of the state, their sons, and grandsons have all been cherished and supported by Pandu. Will they not slay us, O son, with all our friends and kinsmen, if we injure Yudíshtira?"

"All that you say is true, my Father," Duryódana replied, "but we must protect ourselves from the danger that is looming over us. If we win over the people with wealth and honors, they will surely side with us; the treasury and the ministers of state, O King, are still under our control. Therefore, banish the Pándavas now, by some gentle means. Then make me your heir, equal to yourself in power. When that is done, the sons of Kunti may safely return."

"That very thought has been in my mind," his father said, "but because of its sinfulness I have not spoken of it. Neither Bishma, Drona, nor Vídura will ever agree to the exile of the Pándavas. In their eyes, dear son, we and the Pándavas are equal; those wise and virtuous ones make no difference between us."

"Bishma has no great preference for either side and will therefore be neutral," the prince answered. "The son of Drona is on my side and there is no doubt that where the son is, there will the father be also. Vídura secretly favors our enemies, but he alone can do us no harm. Besides, all of of those wise ones are dependent on us for their living. Therefore, exile the Pándavas without any fear; let them go thither this very day! If you do this, O Father, you will end the grief that consumes me like a blazing fire, that robs me of sleep, that has pierced my heart like an iron dart!"

The King, who never could gainsay this favorite son, agreed to his evil plans. Duryódana, with his brothers and friends, began to win the people over to his side by grants of wealth and honors.

He told some clever courtiers to describe the town of Varanávata to the Pándavas as a charming and desirable place. They did so, saying: "The festival of Shiva, creator of the three worlds, has commenced in Varanávata. There is a great concourse of people there, and the procession is the most delightful ever beheld on earth."

While they were speaking, the King perceived that the curiosity of the Pandavas had been aroused and he said to them, "Men often speak of Varanávata as the pleasantest town in the world. If, therefore, my children, you wish to see the festival of Shiva, go there with your followers and friends. Enjoy yourselves like gods; give away pearls and jewels to the Brahmans and musicians assembled there and, when you have enjoyed all the happiness you desire, return to Hastinápura."

Yudíshtira understood the true meaning of the King's words but, knowing that he had neither wealth nor allies, he merely said, "So be it!" Addressing Bishma and the other elders of the Báratas, he said slowly, "We will go to the town of Varanávata at the command of the King. Give us your blessing so that we may not be touched by sin."

The elders all blessed them saying, "You sons of Pandu, may all the elements protect you along your way, and may not the slightest evil befall you!"

The wicked Duryódana was delighted when the King had spoken thus to the Pándavas. He secretly summoned his counselor, Puróchana, took his right hand, and said, "O Puróchana, this world, so full of wealth, is now mine, but I will share it with you; therefore, it behooves you to protect it. Now do as I bid you. Go this very day to Varanávata in a chariot drawn by swift mules. Build there a palace rich in materials and furniture, and guard it from prying eyes. Use, in erecting it, hemp and resin and all other inflammable material that you can find. Mix a little earth with oil and fat and a large measure of varnish of the lac tree to make a plaster for the walls. Scatter all around the house hemp and oil and lac and wood in such a way that no one, even with the closest scrutiny, may behold them there or believe the house to be inflammable. When it is finished, invite the sons of Pándu to live in it with Kunti, their mother; and when you are sure that they are sleeping there in confidence, then set fire to the mansion, beginning at the outer door! The Pándavas must be burned to death, but the people must think that the fire was an accident."

Puróchana said, "So be it!" He drove swiftly to Varanávata, where he did everything that Duryódana had commanded him to do.

The Burning of the House

Meanwhile the sons of Pandu with their mother Kunti, having prepared for their journey, took leave of the King and the elders of their family, sorrowfully touching the feet of Bishma and Vídura and Drona, their master. They saluted reverently the elder men of the King's court and embraced those who were their equals in age; they took respectful leave of the ladies, and the children said farewell to them.

Vídura and many of the citizens followed the chariots of those tigers among men for some distance. The citizens said, "Fie upon King Kuru! He does not honor justice and virtue. The royal sage Pandu cherished us of old with fatherly care; but now that Pandu has gone to heaven, the King cannot abide these princes, his children. Let us all leave this city and our own homes and go wherever Yudíshtira goes."

To these distressed citizens Yudíshtira said, though he himself was filled with sorrow, "The King is our father, our spiritual guide, and our superior. We must do with trusting hearts whatever he bids us do. Give us your blessing now and return to your homes. When we need your help, then indeed, we shall ask you for it."

When the citizens had blessed the Pándavas, the wise Vídura spoke to Yudíshtira in order to warn him; for Vídura was able to read the heart by outward signs and had guessed Duryódana's purpose by watching his face. He knew the language of the barbarians, which Yudíshtira also spoke; he used that language now so that Yudíshtira alone could understand. "He who knows his enemy's plans may escape them," he said. "The consumer of straw and wood, the drier of the dew, cannot burn one who makes his dwelling like the jackal's, with outlets dug under the ground. One who wanders about learns many paths and can guide his steps by the stars. Keep alert; remember that he who controls his five senses will never be overcome by his enemies. "Yudíshtira answered, "I have understood."

When Vídura had bidden them farewell and returned with the other citizens to Hastinápura, Kunti said to her son, "I could not understand what Vídura said to you, because there were so many people about, and he spoke so indistinctly. If it is right for us to know, pray tell us."

"The virtuous Vídura said to me," answered her son, "that the house that is being prepared for us in Varanávata is built of inflammable material and will be burned. He told me how to escape from it and he also said that those who control their five senses can rule the whole world. I told him that I understood him."

When they arrived in Varanávata, the people, filled with joy, thronged out to meet them, blessing them, and crying, "*Jaya!* Victory!" Entering the beautiful city, the Pándavas went first to pay their respects to the Brahmans; then they visited the officials of the city and the principal men of every caste, even to the Shudras. Puróchana came to them and led them to a house that had been made ready for them; he placed food and drink before them and made them very comfortable, and they lived happily in that town, enjoying the festival of Shiva.

When they had been there for ten nights, Puróchana invited them to see the mansion that he had built for them; he called it The Blessed Home, but in truth it was an accursed house.

Those tigers among men entered the mansion and inspected it. Yudíshtira, scenting the smell of fat mixed with lac, said to Bima, "O slayer of foes, this house is indeed inflammable; our enemies, with the help of trusted workmen, have built it so. The wretched Puróchana is staying here in order to burn us to death as soon as he believes that we trust him."

35

"Would it not be well to remain where we are living now?" Bíma asked.

"It seems to me," Yudíshtira said, "that we should live here, seeming to be contented, but all the while with senses wide-awake, seeking for escape. If Puróchana sees in our faces that we have fathomed his designs, he may act suddenly and burn us to death. If, however, from fear of being burned, we fly hence, Duryódana will have us followed and will certainly compass our deaths. We have no power nor favor with the King, while he has both; we have no allies nor armies, while he has both; we are without wealth, while he commands a full treasury. Let us, therefore, deceive this Puróchana. Let us live like hunters, wandering over the earth, so that we may be familiar with all paths. Let us also have an underground passage dug so secretly in the house that neither Puróchana nor any citizen of this town may know what we are doing."

Shortly after this, a friend of Vídura came to the Pándavas and spoke to them secretly, saying: "I am a miner, whom Vídura has sent to serve you. He told me that Puróchana plans to set fire to your house on the fourteenth night of this month, for this is the dark fortnight of the moon, before it has attained its first quarter. When you left, O son of Pandu, Vídura spoke to you in the barbarian language and you answered him in the same tongue. I tell you this as proof that I really come from him."

"O kind one," replied Yudíshtira, "I know you now to be a dear and trusted friend of Vídura, and therefore our friend, too. The danger of which our uncle warned us is at hand. Save us from it without letting Puróchana know how we escape!" "So be it!" said the miner.

Carefully he began to dig a deep underground passage leading from the house into the woods. The mouth of the passage was in the center of the house, on a level with the floor; he covered it with planks during the day, for fear of Puróchana, who kept a constant watch at the one door of the mansion. The Pándavas slept with their weapons beside them; during the day, they went hunting from forest to forest, in order to learn their way through every part of the country roundabout. Thus they lived very guardedly, deceiving Puróchana by seeming to be trustful and contented. The people of Varanávata knew nothing of what was in the minds of the Pándavas; in fact, no one knew except Vídura's friend, that excellent miner.

Seeing the Pándavas living cheerfully there with no apparent suspicion, Puróchana was delighted; and beholding Puróchana's pleasure, Yudíshtira called his brothers together and said to them, "I think the time has come for us to escape."

On the occasion of a festival, Kunti invited a great number of Brahmans and also many ladies to a banquet in her house. Eating and drinking, they enjoyed themselves as long as they desired and then, taking leave of Kunti, returned to their homes. Attracted by the food, as if impelled by fate, a woman of mixed caste, accompanied by her five sons, came by chance to that feast. They all drank so much wine that they lay down where they were and slept as if they were dead. Puróchana also slept within the house that night, but the Pándavas and their mother were awake.

At midnight a violent wind began to blow. Bima rose, lighted a torch, and set fire to the house just where Puróchana was sleeping; then he set fire to the door and to all the walls. When the Pándavas were sure that all sides of that house of lac were blazing, they entered the underground passage with their mother, and going swiftly through it, came out into the night and fled into the woods without being seen by anyone.

The heat and roar of the fire awakened the townspeople. Finding the house in flames, they stood around it and waited there the whole night until the fire died down. As they beat out the embers in the morning, they could see that the house had been built of inflammable material, and they said to each other, "O shame on Kuru's heart, which is so partial! He has burned to death the sinless heirs of Pandu as if they were his enemies." Looking among the ashes to find some trace of the Pándavas, they found the bodies of the innocent woman and her five sons, who had come to the feast. (They did not find the mouth of the underground passage,

37

for the miner had covered it over with ashes.) Believing the six bodies to be those of the Pándavas and Kunti, they bewailed with sorrowful hearts the fate of those sinless ones, saying, "Now let us send word to the King and say, 'Your dearest desire has been fulfilled! You have burned to death the Pándavas!' " And they sent messengers at once to Hastinápura.

When the King heard the evil news, he wept with great sorrow, saying, "King Pandu, my noble brother, indeed died on the day those heroic sons of his, with their mother, were burned to death! Let men go quickly to Varanávata to perform the funeral ceremonies. Let the bones of the dead be sanctified; let everything that is needful be done for the welfare of their souls."

All the people sorrowed deeply and wailed aloud, some crying, "Alas, Yudíshtira, prince of the Báratas!" while others cried, "Alas, Bima! Alas, Arjuna!" And others cried, "O Kunti! O the twins!" Thus they bewailed the Pándavas and offered libations of water to them. Only Vídura did not weep much, for he knew the truth.

The Escape

Meanwhile the mighty Pándavas and Kunti went out of the town of Varanávata into the forest, going toward the south, finding their way in the dark by the light of the stars. Soon they came to the deep forest where even the sky was hidden. They were tired and thirsty and heavy with sleep. Yudíshtira said to Bima, "We cannot go much farther. We do not know whether Puróchana was burned to death or not; we cannot tell how great our danger is. O Bima, you are the strongest and swiftest of us; help us to go on!" Bima took his mother on his shoulder, the twins on his sides, while Yudíshtira and Arjuna held both his hands. So, carrying them all, he fled through the forest, breaking down the trees with his breast, pressing deep the earth with his tread; for his father, the Wind God, had given him speed, and the serpents' nectar gave him immeasurable strength. The trees and their branches trembled before him as he broke a path for himself, treading down everything that stood in his way. Even so passes through the woods, trampling down mighty trees, the leader of a herd of elephants, sixty years old, angry, and filled with excess of energy during the mating season.

All the next day they traveled thus until evening, when they reached a terrible forest resounding with the cries of birds and beasts. Darkness came, the cries of night-wandering animals grew fiercer, and untimely winds began to blow. They sat down under a tree with wide-spreading branches and Kunti said, "I am the mother of the five sons of Pandu and am with them now; yet I suffer from thirst!"

Bima's heart was melted with pity at these words. "Rest here while I go in quest of water," he said. "There must be a pool near by, for I hear the sweet cries of water fowl."

He followed the cries of the birds for a long way, till they led him at last to a lake. There he bathed and quenched his thirst; then, mindful of his mother, he soaked his upper garment and held it in his hands, for he had no other means of carrying the water. But when he retraced his steps he found his mother and his brothers lying asleep upon the ground. This sight filled his heart with distress; sighing like a snake, he said to himself, "Oh, what a painful thing is this, to see our mother, Kunti, the noble Pandu's wife—beautiful as a lotus flower, delicate, and tender, fit to lie only on the costliest bed—sleeping now on the bare ground! To see the virtuous Yudíshtira, who deserves to rule the three worlds, sleeping on the bare ground; to see this Arjuna, dark hued as the clouds, unequaled among men, and the twins, beautiful as the gods of dawn and twilight, asleep on the bare ground!

"He who has no jealous and evil-minded kinsmen lives happily in this world, like a single tree in a village; he, too, who has heroic and virtuous kinsmen lives happily, like a tall tree in a forest. But we have been forced into exile by the wicked Kuru and his sons; we have just escaped a fiery death and where are we now to go? You wicked sons of Kuru, you are alive only because Yudíshtira has not yet told me to take your lives; else this very day I should send you all to the realm of Yama, King of the Dead—you and your friend Karna! But what can I do, you sinful ones, when the eldest son of Pandu is not yet angry with you?" Like a half-extinguished fire, his wrath blazed up in him again and he pressed his palms together, sighing deeply. Then, beholding again those who lay sleeping so trustfully, he thought, "These are all asleep, so I will stay awake. When they rise refreshed from sleep, they can quench their thirst." And he sat there all night, keeping watch over his mother and brothers.

In the morning they awoke and quenched their thirst, and Yudíshtira said, "There is a town not far from this forest. Let us go hence at once so that Duryódana may not trace us."

As they left the forest they met the mighty sage Vyasa, who was their kinsman and therefore watched over them with special care. They saluted him reverently, standing before him with joined palms. "You bulls of Bárata's line," he said to them, "I knew beforehand that you would suffer this exile at the hands of Kuru's wicked son. Do not grieve at what has befallen you: it is all for your happiness. Listen to me! Not far off, ahead of you, is a delightful town where no danger can overtake you. Live there, disguised as Brahmans. I will return when you have need of me."

Thus comforting them, he led them into the town, to the house of a Brahman who received them kindly and let them lodge with him. Then the holy Vyasa returned to the regions whence he had come.

The Pándavas dressed themselves in the skins of animals and let their hair fall on their shoulders after the manner of Brahmans who dwell in the forests and beg for their food. They went from village to village, with begging bowls in their hands, seeing in their wanderings delightful forests, rivers, and lakes. They studied the Vedas and the sciences of government and virtue; they were beloved by the people of that region, for they were pure in deed, kind and sweet of speech. When they came back at nightfall from their begging tours, they placed before Kunti all that had been given them and she divided it among them, each one taking the part allotted to him. She gave to four of her sons, together with herself, half of the food, giving to the mighty Bima alone the other half. In this way the heroic sons of Pandu lived in that town unknown to anyone.

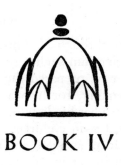

BOOK IV

THE BRIDAL CHOICE

The Princess Is Won

WHEN the Pándavas had dwelt for some time in that town, a wise and holy Brahman came to the house of their host, who, ever hospitable to guests, gave him lodging there. The Pándavas, with their mother Kunti, begged this Brahman to tell them about his travels and his experiences. He spoke to them of various countries, shrines and sacred rivers, of kings and provinces and cities; and when he had finished his stories, he told them that a great festival was about to take place in the kingdom of Panchála. At this festival the King's daughter, the beautiful Princess Dráupadi, would choose her husband from among all the kings and princes who came to win her hand; it was to be her *swayámvara*, or bridal choice.

Now the King of Panchála was the very one who had wronged Drona; it was he whom the Pándavas had defeated in battle and brought captive to their master. Therefore, they asked the Brahman to tell them about him, and he, not knowing who they were, told them all about the King's quarrel with Drona and how he had had to give up half his kingdom to his former friend.

"The King never forgot for a single moment how he had been shamed," said the Brahman. "He began to waste away, thinking only of how he might obtain a son who could defeat Drona in battle. He wandered from place to place, seeking some Brahman

41

who, through his knowledge of sacrifice, might induce the gods to give him such a son. At last he found one. With a delighted heart he prepared the sacrifice and had it performed with great ceremony, for he was willing to give all his wealth in order to have what he desired. And truly, because of that sacrifice, he obtained twin children, a son and a daughter. The son was strong, beautiful as a god and terrible to behold; the Panchálas were mad with joy at his birth. Drona himself took the boy into his house and taught him the use of every weapon.

"The daughter is exceedingly beautiful. Her eyes are dark and large as lotus leaves and her hair is black and curling; her waist is slender and her bosom deep; her body is as fragrant as a blue lotus flower. Indeed, she has no equal on earth in beauty. It is she who will choose her husband at the festival that is to be given in the kingdom of Panchála. Kings and princes from many lands, mighty warriors, young, handsome, and famous, will come to it, eager to win her hand. Actors and dancers, athletes and tumblers, bards and musicians who sing the praises of kings and recite the scriptures, will come there to entertain the guests. The festivities will be like those in the halls of heaven."

When the sons of Kunti heard these words, it seemed as if their hearts had been pierced with arrows. They lost all their peace of mind and became listless and absent-minded. Their mother, seeing this, said to Yudíshtira, "We have lived for many months in the house of this Brahman, passing our time very pleasantly here. I have often seen the lovely woods and gardens of this kingdom, but I have never seen Panchála. If you like, my son, let us go there."

Now Yudíshtira and his brothers were longing to go to Panchála; so they saluted the Brahman in whose house they had dwelt and set out on their journey with joyful hearts, their mother walking before them. They traveled slowly, lingering in the woods and beside the lakes that they found on their way. When they arrived at the capital of Panchála, they found lodging in the house of a potter and no one recognized those heroes as they dwelt in the royal city.

Now the King of Panchála, ever since he had fought against Arjuna, had cherished the wish that his daughter might marry that son of Pandu, but he had never spoken of it to anyone. With this desire in mind, he had a bow made that was so stiff that it could not be bent by anyone save Arjuna. He also had a revolving wheel erected on a tall pole and a golden fish set in the sky above that wheel, for he believed that none save the third son of Kunti could hit such a mark. Then he proclaimed the swayámvara, saying, "He who can string this bow and with these well-adorned arrows hit the fish above the whirling wheel shall have my daughter for his wife."

Hearing this proclamation, the kings and princes of other lands came to his capital. Many great sages and Brahmans from every country came there also to behold the festival. Duryódana, his brothers, and Karna came among the other princes, and all were received with courtesy and reverence by the King.

An amphitheater had been built on a level plain to the northeast of the city, enclosed on all sides by a moat and high walls pierced with arched doorways. It was shaded by a canopy of many colors and scented with the black aloe; it was adorned with garlands of flowers and sprinkled all over with water mixed with sandalwood perfume. Surrounding it on all sides were mansions, white and spotless as the necks of swans or the cloud-kissing peaks of Mount Kailasa. The doors were wide and the stairways easy to ascend; the floors were covered with costly carpets and all the rooms were fragrant with flowers and the scent of aloes and sandalwood. In those mansions, beautiful as the peaks of the Himálayas, dwelt the monarchs who had come to win the hand of Dráupadi.

When the festival began, the citizens and countryfolk, roaring like the ocean, took their seats on stands erected around the arena. The Pándavas, entering the amphitheater, sat among the Brahmans and looked upon the unrivaled splendor of the King of Panchála. The festival, made merry by the performances of actors, dancers, and athletes, and by gifts of great value freely given away by the King, lasted for fifteen days.

On the sixteenth day, when the gaiety was at its height, the

Princess Dráupadi entered the amphitheater. She was richly attired and decked with jewels; she carried in her hands a golden dish with offerings to the gods and a garland of flowers to place around the neck of him whom she would choose as her husband. A holy Brahman lit the sacrificial fire and poured with due rites the libation upon it, uttering blessings as he did so. Then he stopped all the musical instruments that were playing and the resounding trumpets.

When the vast crowd became perfectly still, the twin brother of Dráupadi, Dyumna—that splendid son who had been born to avenge his father—took his sister's arm and spoke in a voice as deep as thunder: "Hear, you assembled kings! This is the bow, that is the mark, and these are the arrows! The mark is to be struck through the spokes of that revolving wheel with these five sharpened arrows. I tell you truly that any man, nobly born and strong and handsome, who achieves this feat shall win today my sister Dráupadi as his wife."

Then he turned to his sister and recited to her the names, the lineage, and the noble deeds of those assembled lords of the earth: "Duryódana and Dushásana, and many others of the mighty sons of Kuru, with Karna, the Suta's son, have come to win you for their bride, O sister. The four sons of the King of Gandára; the noble Ashvattáman, the son of Drona; King Viráta, with his two sons; that mighty charioteer, the King of Madra; the son of Sindu's king and the King of Mágada; Krishna of the Yadu folk, and many other Kshatrias of world-wide fame; all these have come, O blessed one, for you. They will string the bow and shoot at the mark, and you shall choose for your husband him who strikes it and brings it to the ground."

The young princes, vying with one another, each thinking himself the mightiest and most skillful in arms, rose and lifted high their weapons. Filled with pride in their beauty and prowess, their wealth and knowledge, their youth and noble birth, they were like Himálayan elephants in the mating season. Looking at one another jealously, each one cried, "Dráupadi shall be mine!" For all had been pierced by the shafts of the God of Love: each one

44

had lost his heart as he gazed upon the beauty of that maiden. The sons of Kunti also and the twin sons of Madri were pierced by the same shafts as they looked, wide-eyed, at the princess of Panchála.

All those who wished to compete went down into the amphitheater; they bit their nether lips with wrath, looking with jealousy even at their best friends. They began, one by one, to display their strength, but not one of those heroes could bend the bow. Some of them, trying with swelling muscles to string it, were tossed on the ground as it sprang back from their hands, and they lay there motionless. The powerful king of Madra was thrown to his knees as he tried in vain to string it, and the proud ruler of Mágada was flung down, whereupon he rose and left the amphitheater in anger.

Seeing the plight of these princes, Karna came forward; he raised the bow and strung it with ease; then aimed at the mark. The Pándavas, beholding that son of Súrya with the bow drawn to a circle, thought that the target was as good as hit and that the day was lost. But Dráupadi cried out, "I will not choose a Suta for my lord!" And Karna, laughing in vexation and casting an upward glance at the Sun, his father, threw the bow aside.

When all the kings, amid the jeering talk of the crowd, had given up the attempt, Arjuna rose from among the Brahmans who were seated in the assembly. He approached the bow and stood there like a mountain; then he bent his head to Shiva, the giver of boons, and lifted the bow. He strung it in the twinkling of an eye and, taking up the five arrows, he shot the mark, which fell down on the ground between the whirling spokes of the wheel.

A great uproar arose in the amphitheater: all around it, those who had failed cried out in grief and despair, while musicians struck their instruments, and bards and heralds chanted the praises of the unknown hero who had won the bride. Looking upon him, the King was filled with joy; his daughter also rejoiced and, approaching Arjuna, placed round his neck the bridal garland.

But the monarchs who had come to the swayámvara looked at one another, filled with wrath. "This king," they said, "passing us by and thinking nothing of us, is about to give his daughter, the loveliest of women, to a Brahman. Having planted the tree, he cuts it down just when it is ready to bear fruit. According to the Vedas, a Brahman has no part in the swayámvara of a Kshatria maiden. Let us slay this wretch who thus insults all kings!"

Taking up their weapons, they rushed upon the King, to slay him then and there, and he sought the protection of Arjuna. That mighty bowman stepped forward with his bow drawn to a circle, while Bima, with the strength of thunder, uprooted a tree and, tearing off its leaves, stood there like Yama, the mace-bearing king of the dead. Yudíshtira and the twins, not wishing to be recognized, had already left the amphitheater.

Now Krishna of the Yadu folk, whose father was Kunti's brother, had been watching all that passed. He said to his brother, "That hero there whose tread is like the lion's, who bent the mighty bow, is no other than Arjuna, the son of Kunti. There is no doubt of this, if I am Krishna. And that other hero who has uprooted the tree is Bima, for no one in the world except Bima could do such a thing. O brother, that youth with eyes like lotus leaves, who walks like a lion but is humble withal, is the eldest son of Pandu; he left the amphitheater with two others youths who, I suspect, are the sons of Madri. I have heard it rumored that the Pándavas and their mother escaped from the flaming house of lac."

Then Krishna, gently addressing the assembled monarchs, said, "This maiden has been justly won by the Brahman," and he persuaded them not to fight. At his words the angry kings laid down their arms and returned to their own kingdoms, wondering much. All who had come to the swayámvara went away saying, "The festival has ended in the victory of the Brahmans, for the princess was won by one of them."

Surrounded by Brahmans, Bima and Arjuna passed with difficulty out of the throng, while the princess of Panchála, like a female elephant following the leader of the herd, cheerfully followed Arjuna, catching hold of his deerskin garment.

In the Potter's House

Now the sons of Kunti, each day after they had watched the festival, had gone on their usual rounds to beg their food and had brought it to their mother. She did not know that this was the final day of the swayámvara; therefore, wondering why they should return so late, she began to be anxious about them and to think of all the evils that might have befallen them. First she feared that the sons of Kuru might have recognized her children and slain them; then she thought that some cruel and powerful demon might have deceived them and led them astray. As she was pondering these things in the stillness of the late afternoon, her sons returned to the house with Dráupadi. They said to her, "Behold the alms we have received today!"

And Kunti, who was inside the house and did not see them, replied to them as she always did, "Share it among you and enjoy it together!"

A moment afterward she turned and beheld the princess. Knowing at once, from her beauty and her bridal garments, who she must be, Kunti cried, "O, what have I said?" Fearful of sin and wondering how she could undo what had been done, she took the hand of the smiling maiden and said to Yudíshtira, "O bull of the Báratas, when you presented this maiden to me as the alms that you had received, I spoke before I saw her. Tell me now how my words may remain true and yet bring no harm to the princess of Panchála."

Yudíshtira, after reflecting for a moment, said to Arjuna, "O consumer of foes, Dráupadi was won by you. Therefore it is right for you to wed her. Now light the sacred fire and take her hand with all the holy rites."

But Arjuna replied, "O king of men, do not command me to do wrong! You, the eldest of us, should wed first, then the strong-armed Bima, then myself, then Nákula, and last of all Sahadéva of matchless strength. Bima and I, the twins, and this maiden are all obedient to you. Therefore reflect; do what will be right in the

47

eyes of the King of Panchála, and we shall obey your commands."

Hearing these words, so full of love and respect, the Pándavas all looked at Dráupadi, and she looked at them. Then, looking at one another, the princes took their seats, searching their minds for an answer to this question. But, truly, they could think only of Dráupadi, for her beauty was greater than that of any other woman, and the God of Love had invaded all their hearts. Yudíshtira, beholding his younger brothers, understood what was passing in their minds, and fearing that there might be a division among them, he said, "The blessed Dráupadi shall be the wife of all of us!" And the sons of Pandu, hearing these words of their eldest brother, rejoiced exceedingly.

At this moment Krishna, who had recognized the Pándavas in the amphitheater, came to the potter's house. He touched the feet of Yudíshtira, saying, "I am Krishna, the son of Kunti's brother." Then he touched the feet of Kunti, his father's sister.

The Pándavas welcomed him with great delight, asking, "How, O Krishna, were you able to trace us, living here as we do in disguise?"

"O king of men," Krishna answered, smiling, "fire, even when it is covered, can be perceived. Who but the Pándavas could have shown such might as you displayed at the swayámvara? By good fortune you have escaped from the house of lac; by good fortune the wicked son of Kuru and his counselors have not succeeded in their plots. May you be blessed with wealth and joy! Now, lest the other monarchs recognize you, give me leave to return to my tent."

When Krishna had left the potter's house, the illustrious Pándavas went out to beg their food and, returning, gave everything gladly to their mother. She said to Dráupadi, "O lovely one, first devote a portion of this food to the gods and give it away to Brahmans and to those who are hungry. Divide the rest into two halves: give one of them to Bíma, for this strong youth, equal to a king of elephants, eats a great deal; divide the other half, O blessed one, into six parts, four for these youths, one for myself, and one for you." The princess cheerfully did all that her mother-

48

in-law had told her and they all ate the food that she prepared.

Then Sahadéva, the younger son of Madri, spread on the ground a bed of grass and those heroes, each spreading thereon his deerskin, lay down to sleep, with their heads toward the south. Kunti laid herself down along the line of their heads, while Dráupadi lay along the line of their feet. The princess, although she slept on a bed of grass along the line of their feet as if she were their nether pillow, grieved not in her heart nor thought unkindly of those heroes. The brothers began to talk together, and their conversation was exceedingly interesting, since each of them was worthy to lead an army; it was all about celestial weapons and chariots, elephants and swords, arrows and battle-axes.

And all that they said was overheard by Dyumna, the brother of Dráupadi, who lay concealed in the potter's house.

The Weddings

For the son of the King, wishing to know what manner of men had won his sister's hand, followed them out of the amphitheater to the house of the potter, and hiding himself there, saw and heard all that happened. When morning came, he left his hiding place and ran to tell his father all that he had learned. He found the King sitting sadly in his palace, not knowing who had taken away his daughter. Seeing his son, he cried, "Oh, where has Dráupadi gone? Who has taken her away? Has any Shudra or anyone of mean descent, has any tax-paying Vaisya, by winning Dráupadi, placed his left foot on my head? O son, has that wreath of flowers been thrown away on a grave? Or are the sons of the noble Pandu yet alive? Was it Arjuna who took the bow and hit the mark?"

Dyumna gladly told his father all that had happened after the swayámvara was over, saying, "O King, I followed those two heroes to the house of a potter in the suburbs of the city. There sat a lady like a flame of fire who, I suppose, is their mother; and around her sat three other men each of whom was like fire in splendor. After they had eaten, they all laid themselves down for sleep, Dráupadi lying along the line of their feet as their nether pillow. Before going to sleep they talked on many subjects in voices as deep as those of stormy clouds; O Father, no Vaisya or Shudra or Brahman could talk as those heroes did! Without doubt they are Kshatrias, for they spoke only of weapons and of war. It seems that our hope has been fulfilled, for I have heard that the sons of Kunti escaped from the fire of the house of lac. When I saw that youth string the bow and hit the mark, and that other one uproot the tree, and when I heard their talk, I felt sure that these were the sons of Pandu wandering in disguise."

The King was greatly cheered by these words of his son. He sent a messenger at once to the potter's house to say, "The King has prepared a wedding feast for the bridegroom's party, and begs you to come to partake of it when you have finished your morning worship. Do not delay. These chariots adorned with golden lotuses and drawn by excellent steeds are worthy of kings and will carry you to the palace." The Pándavas, placing Kunti and Dráupadi on one of the chariots, mounted the others themselves and were driven by skillful charioteers to the royal dwelling.

Meanwhile the King, in order to find out the caste to which those heroes belonged, made a large collection of the gifts that were suitable for the weddings of all the four castes. He had placed in the courtyard of the palace fruits, cattle, seeds, plows, and other farming tools. There were also coats of mail and shields, swords and scimitars of fine temper, beautiful chariots and horses, bows and well-feathered arrows.

When the bridegroom's party arrived, Kunti went with Dráupadi into the inner apartments of the palace; the ladies of the royal household were amazed at her stately beauty and saluted her with joyous hearts. And when those five mighty warriors, the Pándavas, dressed in deerskins but walking like lions, entered the palace, the King and his son, his ministers and his friends were exceedingly glad. They offered the Pándavas handsome seats furnished with footstools, noting that they showed no awkwardness or fear in taking those costly seats, one after another in the order of their ages. Skillful cooks and servants brought them food worthy of the gods, on gold and silver plates; and the sons of Pandu dined and were well pleased.

When the dinner was over, the King showed them the gifts that he had prepared. The Pándavas, passing by everything else, looked with interest at all the weapons of war. Watching them, the King and his ministers understood that their guests must be of royal blood, and they rejoiced.

Then the King, still addressing Yudíshtira as if he were a Brahman, inquired of him, "Are we to consider you Kshatrias or Brahmans, or are you gods who, disguised as Brahmans, are ranging the earth and have come hither for my daughter's hand? Tell us truly, O chastisers of foes, for I must prepare Dráupadi's wedding according to the caste to which you belong."

"Let joy fill your heart, O King," answered Yudíshtira, "for your long-cherished desire has been fulfilled. Know me to be the eldest son of Pandu and these, who won your daughter among that concourse of princes, to be Bima and Arjuna. These are the twins, Nákula and Sahadéva. We are Kshatrias and your daughter has only, like a lotus, been carried from one lake into another. O King, you are our father and our refuge."

At these words, Dráupadi's father raised his eyes in ecstasy and for some moments he could not speak for joy. Then he answered Yudíshtira with fitting words and asked him how he and his brothers had escaped from the house of lac. Hearing everything that the son of Kunti told him, he blamed Kuru, that ruler of men, and vowed then and there to place Yudíshtira on his ancestral throne. "Now, O mighty-armed one," he said, "let Prince Arjuna, on this blessed day, take my daughter's hand, and the rites of marriage shall be performed."

To this Yudíshtira replied, "I, too, O ruler of men, must marry." "If it please you," said the King, "do you take my daughter's hand yourself." But Yudíshtira answered, "Your daughter, O lord of earth, shall be the wife of all of us, for so my mother has declared. I am not married, nor is Bima, and Arjuna is younger than we two. It is true that Arjuna has won this jewel, your daughter, but it has always been a rule among us to share equally any jewel that we may win. O best of kings, we cannot swerve from that rule now! Let Dráupadi become the wedded wife of all of us, taking our hands in turn before the sacred fire!"

"O son of Bárata's line," answered the King, "it has been said that one man may have many wives, but it has never been heard that one woman may have many husbands. You, who are pure and know the path of virtue, can never do a sinful thing that is contrary to custom and to the Vedas!"

"Virtue is subtle," Yudíshtira said. "We do not know its course; we can only follow in the path trodden by the wise in former ages. My heart has never turned to what is sinful; my mother commanded this and my heart approved it. Therefore, O monarch, let us proceed without fear or scruple."

The King said, "Let your mother, my son, yourselves, and me discourse upon this matter and decide what should be done."

While they were talking, the high-souled sage Vyasa came there and they all rose and saluted him with reverence. Saluting them in return, he sat down on a golden carpet. The King asked him about Dráupadi's marriage, saying, "How, O sinless one, can one woman become the wife of five men without being defiled by sin? Oh, tell me truly what we ought to do!"

"It is true," Vyasa said, "that such a marriage is contrary to custom and to the Vedas, but it was not always so. This proposal of Yudíshtira's is virtuous because it was ordained of old by Shiva himself, the god of gods, the giver of boons. I will tell you how it came to pass.

"A noble sage, who lived long ago in a hermitage, had a daughter beautiful and chaste, but no husband came to woo her. Sorrowful at heart, she fasted and disciplined her mind and body so that she might please the lord Shiva and obtain a boon. At last the mighty god was pleased and appeared before her, saying, 'O blessed one, ask whatever you desire, for I am Shiva and will grant your wish.'

"The maid, in her joy, said again and again, 'Oh, give me a husband graced with every virtue!' And the god replied to her, 'You shall have five husbands from among the Bárata princes.' 'O lord,

DRAUPADI

through your grace,' she said, 'I desire only one husband.' 'Maiden,' the god replied, 'you have said fully five times, "Oh, give me a husband!" Therefore, in a future life of yours, it shall be even as you have asked.'

"O lord of men, this daughter of celestial beauty is that maiden; the faultless Dráupadi has been destined to become the wife of five husbands. Therefore let these heroes with happy hearts perform the rites and take her hand."

When Vyasa had spoken thus, the King and his son made preparations for the wedding, and brought forth Dráupadi beautifully attired and decked with many pearls and jewels. There came to witness the wedding all the friends and kinsmen of the King, his ministers of state, and many Brahmans and citizens who took their seats according to their rank. Then those princes of the Bárata line, adorned with earrings, dressed in costly robes, perfumed with sandalwood, accompanied by a priest of flamelike splendor, entered the wedding hall, one after another, in due order and with glad hearts, like mighty bulls entering a cowpen. The priest, knowing well the Vedas, lit the sacred fire and poured libations upon the blaze. Calling Yudíshtira there, he united him and Dráupadi who, hand in hand, walked around the holy fire.

Day by day, one after another, those mighty chariot warriors, those princes dressed in splendid robes, took the hand of that best of women and were united with her in marriage. When the weddings were completed, the King gave to the Pándavas a hundred chariots set with rows of tinkling bells and golden standards, each chariot drawn by four horses with golden bridles; a hundred elephants all having favorable marks on their temples and faces, like a hundred mountains with golden peaks; a hundred serving girls in the prime of youth, dressed in costly robes and ornaments and wreathed with flowers; and to each one of those princes he gave much wealth, rich robes, and splendid jewels. After this alliance with the Pándavas, the King of Panchála had no fears; indeed, he no longer stood in fear even of the gods.

And the sons of Pandu, after they had obtained Dráupadi, passed their days in joy and happiness, like so many gods, in the kingdom of Panchála.

BOOK V

THE KINGDOM OF INDRA PRASTA

The Reconciliation

THE kings who had attended the swayámvara soon heard that the beautiful Dráupadi had been wedded to the sons of Pandu. They wondered much, for they had heard that Kunti and all her sons had been burned to death in the house of lac. Everyone believed that the cruel plot had been contrived by Duryódana, with his father's consent. They remembered it now and said, "Shame on Bishma, O shame on Kuru of the Bárata realm!"

Duryódana heard the news as he was returning with his brothers and his friends to Hastinápura; grief and despair filled his heart. He was his father's heir, equal to him in power; indeed, he was the ruler of the Báratas and thought himself superior to any other king. Now the mighty sons of Kunti had appeared again, allied with the King of Panchála and his kinsmen, who were powerful warriors possessing large armies. Dushásana, his brother, said to him softly, "Fate rules all things and our efforts are fruitless. Fie upon all our efforts, brother; fie upon Puróchana for his carelessness! For the Pándavas are still alive!" Talking with one another thus, they entered Hastinápura with cheerless and sorrowful hearts.

Vídura, the wise uncle of the Pándavas, hearing that they had won Dráupadi and that the sons of Kuru were returning with their pride humbled, was filled with joy. "Good luck attends the Báratas, O King!" he said to Kuru.

"What good luck, O Vídura, what good luck?" asked the monarch in great glee, for he supposed that Duryódana had been chosen by Dráupadi. He had had many fine ornaments made for the bride and had planned that she and his son should be brought with pomp to his city. Vídura told him that the Pándavas had won the princess; that those heroes were alive and prospering and were allied now with the King of Panchála and his kinsmen and friends, all possessing large armies.

"Those children, O Vídura," Kuru said shamelessly, "are to me as dear as they were to Pandu—nay, more so! Now my love for them increases, for they are well and prosperous and have wealthy and powerful friends. Who would not like to have the ruler of Panchála as an ally?"

"O King, may your mind remain unchanged for a hundred years!" Vídura replied, and returned to his abode.

The moment he had left, Duryódana and Karna entered; they had overheard all that had been said. "We cannot, O King," Duryódana began, "speak any evil in the presence of Vídura, but now that we are alone with you we shall speak as we like. Why, O foremost of men, do you praise the Pándavas in the presence of Vídura? Do you look upon the good fortune of your foes as if it were your own? We should do everything we can to weaken the strength of the Pándavas. The time has come for us to take counsel together, so that they may not swallow us up with all our children and our kingdom."

"I will do whatever you advise," replied Kuru. "I did not want Vídura to know by the slightest word what was in my mind. Tell me, Duryódana, what plan you have hit upon, and give me your counsel also, O Karna!"

Duryódana said, so hastily that the words tumbled together out of his mouth, "Let us, O Father, send trusted spies to stir up trouble between the sons of Kunti and the sons of Madri, making them jealous of one another. Or let them speak evil to Dráupadi about her lords or make the Pándavas dissatisfied with her; this should be easy, since she is married to them all. Or let, O King, some clever spies secretly bring about the death of Bima, for Bima is the strongest of them all; without him they will no longer seek to regain their kingdom. Or let messengers be sent to bring them hither so that, when they arrive, we may, through trusted agents, cause them to be slain. Or let the King of Panchála and his sons and all his ministers of state be tempted by presents of great wealth to abandon the cause of Yudíshtira and to ally himself with us. O Father, use any of these means that seems best to you. Time passes! It is better to deal with our enemies before they are too firmly settled in Panchála. These are my plans for their discomfiture. What do you think of them, Karna?"

"Your plans will fail, brave prince," Karna replied. "You have before, by various subtle means, tried to slay the sons of Pandu, and you have always failed. It is impossible to make them quarrel with each other, nor can we turn Dráupadi against them through any spies of ours. She chose them as her lords when they were unknown and in poverty; will she abandon them now, when they are prosperous and famous? The King of Panchála is honest and virtuous; even if we offer him our whole kingdom he will not abandon the Pándavas. They cannot be injured by any subtle means within your power.

"This is my counsel, O bull among men! Attack and smite them now until they are all wiped out! Their friends and friendly tribes, their innumerable chariots and animals are not yet mustered together; therefore strike them now without scruple! Put forth your prowess, O King, before Krishna of the Yadus comes with his host to restore the sons of Pandu to their kingdom! Let us, O foremost of Kshatrias, with our great army, grind Panchála to pieces and bring the sons of Pandu hither! Vanquish them by your might, and then rule the wide earth!"

King Kuru applauded these words of Karna. "O son of a Suta, you are gifted with great wisdom and are also mighty in arms," he said. "This speech suits you well. Let Bishma, Vídura, Drona, and you two take counsel together and plan whatever may be best for us." And the King called to him those celebrated ministers to take counsel with them.

"O King," Bishma said, "I cannot give my sanction to a quarrel with the Pándavas. As you are to me, so are Kunti's sons. This is my counsel: make a treaty with those heroes and give them half the kingdom! O Duryódana, just as you look upon this kingdom as your ancestral heritage, so the sons of Pandu look upon it as theirs, having truly a better right to it than you. We are fortunate that they have not perished; from the time when I heard that they were burned to death, I have been ashamed to face any living creature. The Pándavas are virtuous and united; as long as they live, the wielder of the thunder himself cannot deprive them of their share of the ancestral kingdom. If you wish to act righteously, if you wish to do what is pleasing to me, if you seek the welfare of us all, give half the kingdom to them."

After Bishma had finished speaking, Drona said, "O Sire, I am of the same mind in this matter as the noble Bishma. Let a share of the kingdom be given to the Pándavas. This is the way of virtue. Send to the King of Panchála some messenger of pleasant speech, carrying costly presents for the bridegroom and the bride, for the King and all his sons. Let him speak to that monarch of the power and dignity that will arise from this new alliance with him; let him also say again and again that both you and Duryódana are exceedingly glad because of all that has happened. Let him invite the Pándavas to return to Hastinápura and let your sons go out with a noble company to meet them. This, I believe, should be your behavior to the Pándavas, who are to you as your own sons."

Vídura gave the same counsel and Kuru, who ever wavered between good and evil, said at last, "Bishma, Drona, and Vídura have said what is true and beneficial to me. Therefore hasten, O Vídura; bring hither the Pándavas with their mother Kunti and also Dráupadi of celestial beauty, treating them all with loving consideration."

Therefore Vídura repaired joyfully to the King of Panchála and gave that monarch the messages that Drona had advised; he embraced the Pándavas lovingly, and they in turn touched his feet, greeting him with words of love and praise. He gave to Kunti and Dráupadi, to Dráupadi's father and her brothers the gifts of great wealth that Kuru had sent to them. Then he brought the Pándavas, with their mother and their bride, to the city named after the elephant; and Kuru sent out the leaders of the Báratas to welcome them, with Drona at their head. The whole city was radiant with the gay throng of citizens who came out to behold them; the Pándavas, dear to the hearts of the people, heard their shouts of praise and welcome as they went through the streets.

When at last they came to the palace, the Pándavas worshiped the feet of the King, those of the noble Bishma, and of their master Drona; they asked after the welfare of everyone present. Then, at the command of the King, they entered the apartments that had been prepared for them.

After they had rested there for a while, they were summoned to the court by the King and Bishma. Addressing Yudíshtira, Kuru said, "Listen, O son of Kunti, with your brothers, to what I say. In order that no difference may arise again between yourselves and your cousins, let us divide the kingdom! Do you repair to Kándava Prasta and build your city there, where no harm can befall you. Protected by Arjuna, as the gods are protected by the wielder of the thunderbolt, dwell there in peace, king of half the Bárata realm!"

Those tigers among men agreed to what he said and worshiped him; then, content with half the kingdom, they set out from Hastinápura and went to Kándava Prasta.

The Burning of the Kándava Forest

Now Kándava Prasta was no better than a desert. Nevertheless, those heroes of unfading splendor beautified the place, making of it a second heaven. Selecting with Vyasa's help a sacred and favorable region, they asked the blessings of the gods and measured out a piece of land for their city.

Surrounded by a moat as wide as a river, and by walls reaching up to the heavens and white as clouds, that best of cities rose resplendent, like the capital of the nether world of the Nagas.

It was protected by gateways high as mountains and arched like thunderclouds; they were well furnished with weapons of defense, and so strong that the missiles of foes could make no mark on them. The streets were all wide and carefully laid out so that there was no fear of accidents. In a delightful part of the city rose the palace of the Pándavas filled with every kind of wealth, like the mansion of Kúvera, the celestial treasurer himself. Decked with innumerable white mansions, the city looked like a mass of clouds charged with lightning. All around it gardens were laid out, adorned with beautiful trees, their branches bent down with the weight of fruits and blossoms and thronged with singing birds. There were pleasure houses, bright as mirrors, charming knolls, lakes full to the brim with crystal water, pools fragrant with lotuses and lilies, where swans and ducks abounded.

When it was finished, many Brahmans came to that city to dwell there; many merchants came in the hope of earning wealth; artisans, skilled in all the arts, came to that town and took up their abode there. It came to be called Indra Prasta, or Indra's Place.

Thus, because of the virtuous counsel of Bishma and Drona, the Pándavas dwelt in Kándava Prasta, their joy increasing from day to day in that large kingdom peopled by honest and happy men. His subjects had, in Yudíshtira, a king devoted to the Vedas, a performer of sacrifices, a protector of all good people, and their eyes and hearts delighted in him. He gave his mind to the three pursuits—duty, wealth, and pleasure—dividing his time between them as if they were his dear friends. His brothers, all seated on royal thrones, helped him to govern the kingdom or went forth with their armies to bring other kings under his sway.

The Pándavas were well aware that even brothers who loved each other dearly might quarrel because of a woman whom they loved; therefore, they made a rule among themselves in relation to Dráupadi, who was the beloved wife of them all. The rule they made was this: if any one of them saw one of his brothers sitting with Dráupadi, he must not enter the room or the place where those two were sitting, but go his way and leave them by themselves. They kept this rule and no quarrel ever arose among them.

Dráupadi bore to her five husbands five sons, all of whom became great warriors. They were devoted to each other; their behavior was virtuous and they learned from Arjuna the use of all weapons, human and divine.

Arjuna also married Subádra, the sister of Krishna; she bore to him an illustrious son whom they named Abimányu because he was fearless and high-spirited. He was as handsome as the moon, long-armed and broad-chested, with eyes like a bull's; he grew up like the moon in the lighted fortnight, the favorite of his uncle, Krishna, equal to his father in lightness of hand and swiftness of movement, in the knowledge of the Vedas, and the duties of his caste. The Pándavas, beholding these six godlike children growing up before them and becoming great warriors, were filled with joy.

Now Krishna and Arjuna were inseparable friends; indeed, it seemed that they had only one heart and one mind between them, and Krishna came often to Indra Prasta.

One summer day they went to the banks of the river Jumna with a company of friends for a day of sport, meaning to return in the evening. In a pleasant place, surrounded by tall trees, they all took their pleasure, some in the water and some in the woods. Some danced and sang together; some sat about laughing and jesting, while others went apart to talk seriously. After dining on pleasant foods and good wines, Krishna and Arjuna sought a cool spot in the woods, not far from where the others laughed and played. There they sat down and talked about heroic deeds of the past and other things such as warriors enjoy.

While they were talking there, a Brahman came toward them. He looked as tall as a tree; his color was like molten gold, and his beard was yellow. His hair was unkempt and he was clad in rags, yet he seemed to blaze with splendor like the morning sun. The two heroes rose hastily and stood, awaiting his commands.

The Brahman said, "You two who are now so near the forest of Kándava are the two greatest warriors on earth. I am a greedy Brahman who needs much food. O Krishna and Arjuna, I beg of you to give me enough to eat!"

"Tell us what sort of food you desire, O holy one," they said to him, "and we will do our best to give it to you."

"I do not desire ordinary food," answered the Brahman. "Know that I am Agni, God of Fire. I must have the kind of food that suits me. I wish to devour the forest of Kándava, but it is protected by Indra because a Naga, who is a friend of his, lives in it. When Indra sees me blaze forth there, he pours water down upon me from the clouds. Therefore I never am able to devour the forest, although I have tried seven times. Now I have come to you who know all weapons, human and divine. I pray you, keep those showers from falling and any creature from escaping when I begin to consume this forest, for this is the food that I need."

"O exalted one," Arjuna said, "I have several heavenly weapons with which I can fight even the wielder of the thunderbolt. But I have no bow that can bear the strength of my arms, and my hands are so quick that I must have a supply of arrows that can never be used up. My chariot is not strong enough to carry the load of arrows that I wish to keep at hand. I want a chariot that is splendid as the sun and whose wheels roar like thunder. Krishna, too, has no weapons suited to his power. We will do all that we can to thwart Indra from pouring down his showers, but it behooves you, O lord of fire, to give us worthy weapons."

The smoke-bannered Agni called upon Váruna, that god who protects one of the points of heaven and whose home is in the waters. Váruna appeared immediately, and Agni said to him, "Give me quickly the bow and the quiver and the ape-bannered chariot that were made by the architect of heaven, for Arjuna has need of them! Give me also, for Krishna, a mace and a fiery discus!"

Then Váruna gave to Arjuna that jewel of a bow known as Gandíva, beautiful to behold, without any sign of weakness, equal to a hundred thousand bows. He gave him also two quivers whose arrows could never be used up, and a chariot yoked with horses white as silver or as fleecy clouds, decked in golden harness and fleet as the wind. Its flagstaff bore a banner with the figure of a celestial ape, which glared fiercely out as if to destroy all that it beheld; there were lesser flags with figures of animals whose roars and yells would cause the enemy to faint. The god gave to Krishna a mace and a fiery discus which became his favorite weapon. It could slay both men and gods; its roar was like thunder and when he hurled it in battle, it returned to his hand.

Arjuna, walking around that excellent chariot and taking up that splendid bow, was filled with joy. "Now blaze forth as you please, O exalted one," he said, "on every side of the great forest, for now we can withstand the gods themselves!"

Then the illustrious God of Fire took his own form; summoning Vayu, the Wind God, to be his charioteer, he went to the Kándava forest and surrounded it with his seven flames. The trees caught fire with a roar like thunder; that burning forest looked like the king of mountains, Meru, when its snows are lighted by the rays of the setting sun. Krishna and Arjuna placed themselves on opposite sides of the wood to prevent any creature—animal, Naga, or demon—from escaping. They drove around the great forest so fast that the creatures could find no place between the chariots through which they could flee. Arjuna, with his arrows, drove them back into the flames, where Agni consumed them, while the discus of Krishna, hurled by him again and again, came back into his hands after slaying countless demons.

The mighty flames leaped up into the sky till the gods themselves were troubled. They went to Indra and said to him, "O lord of immortals, why does Agni rage so below us? Has the time come for the world to be destroyed?"

Indra, the god of a thousand eyes, himself beholding what Agni was doing, set out to protect the forest in which his friend the Naga lived. He covered the sky with masses of clouds which began to pour their rain on Kándava. But the heat of the fire was so great that the showers of rain were dried up before they fell. Then Indra, growing angry, ordered the winds to trouble all the oceans; they drew together heavier masses of clouds charged with torrents of rain, and roaring with thunder. The flames fought against the downpour, and the forest, filled with smoke and flashes of lightning, was terrible to behold.

Arjuna hurled at these clouds a heavenly weapon that Drona had taught him to use. The torrents of rain dried up; the lightning that played among the clouds flickered and vanished. In a moment the sky was clear; a cool breeze blew and the disc of the sun could be seen again. Agni blazed forth with all his flames and filled the heavens with his roar.

Then Indra rode forth on his white elephant and ordered the leader of his hosts and the mighty storm gods to smite down those two heroes. But Arjuna and Krishna waited calmly and fearlessly, their weapons in their hands; when the celestial host advanced, they assailed the gods with their fiery arrows and discus, driving them back again and again. Indra, seeing their prowess in battle, was well pleased with them both. To test the skill of Arjuna, he sent down a shower of stones, but Arjuna, with his swift arrows, turned them aside. He sent down a heavier shower and Arjuna, with a thousand arrows, broke the stones into dust that the wind carried away.

The gods saw that they could not protect the forest from the might of Krishna and Arjuna, so they retreated, returning to the skies. Indra, the god of a hundred sacrifices, was filled with joy at the power of his son and applauded the two friends. It was known to him that the Naga who lived in the forest was away on that day and had escaped the fire; therefore, he, too, withdrew and returned to his abode in heaven.

Seeing this, Krishna and Arjuna set up a great shout and were filled with gladness. Agni, with blazing eyes, flaming tongue and wide-open mouth, devoured the whole of that mighty forest; his hunger was satisfied and he was greatly pleased.

While Krishna was slaying every creature that tried to escape from the fire, it happened that a demon named Maya rushed forth, with Agni, roaring like thunder, hot on his heels. Krishna raised his weapon, and stood ready to smite him down. Seeing the uplifted discus before him and Agni pursuing him from behind, Maya shrieked, "O Arjuna, protect me!"

64

Hearing the terror in his voice, Arjuna was moved with pity and cried to him, "I will! Do not be afraid!" The merciful voice of Arjuna gave the demon his life, for, when Krishna heard it, he lowered his discus, and Agni burned him not.

When the fire was over, those three, Krishna, Arjuna, and Maya, sat down on the bank of a river to rest. The demon worshiped Arjuna and addressed him humbly, with joined palms and amiable words, saying, "O son of Kunti, I have been saved by you from death. Tell me what I can do for you."

"Your gratitude is enough, O mighty one," Arjuna answered. "Go now wherever you please. May you be blessed and may you always be kind and well disposed toward me, as I am toward you."

"You have spoken worthily, O exalted one," Maya replied, "yet I still desire to do something for you. I am the chief architect of the demons; I should like to build something for you."

"O friend," Arjuna said, "you look upon me as the saver of your life; therefore I cannot ask any favor of you. But do something for Krishna; that will repay me for anything I have done for you."

Maya agreed to this and Krishna, after reflecting for a moment, said, "Build a palatial assembly hall for Yudíshtira, O Maya, if you are indeed so great an architect! Build such a palace that no one in the world of men can equal it; let heavenly, demonic, and human designs be mingled there!"

The Great Assembly Hall

Maya rejoiced at these words and forthwith built for the son of Pandu a peerless palace, renowned throughout the three worlds. It rose, supported by columns of gold, like a mass of new clouds lighted by the sun. It was wide, delightful, and exceedingly handsome, made of excellent materials, with golden walls and archways, adorned with varied paintings; it was so brilliant that it seemed to be on fire. Within the palace he built a pool bordered with marble and set with pearls; a flight of crystal steps led from the marble edge into the water, where lotuses and other water flowers blossomed, while fishes and tortoises of golden hue played in its clear depth. All around the palace were planted tall, ever blossoming trees, giving cool shade; the breezes, entering the wide halls, carried with them the fragrance of the trees outside and of the lotuses within. Maya, having built this great assembly hall in fourteen months, announced to Yudíshtira that it was completed.

Then King Yudíshtira entered the assembly hall after he had fed innumerable Brahmans and given them also new robes and clothes and fresh garlands of flowers. He worshiped the gods with music and fragrant incense. In the hall, athletes and mimes, wrestlers and bards showed their skill, to entertain the son of Kunti, and Yudíshtira sported with his brothers in that palace as the gods do in heaven.

Kings and warriors came to visit him there; learned sages came and discoursed upon sacred matters, gladdening his heart with their wisdom. Even the singers and musicians of the gods, the Gandárvas and the Apsaras, waited upon the son of Pandu in that assembly hall, delighting him and all who gathered there with their heavenly melodies.

One day when the Pándavas were seated in the hall, the holy sage Nárada, having wandered over the three worlds, came to see them. He knew the Vedas and all the histories and sciences; indeed, he was a master of every branch of learning. He had a powerful memory and great eloquence, and was able to behold this universe, above, below, and around, as if it were all before his eyes. This sage of immeasurable splendor came hither with the speed of thought and was filled with joy on beholding the Pándavas. Yudíshtira and his brothers arose and saluted him, bowing humbly before him; they gave him a seat befitting his dignity, worshiping him with offerings of food and rich gifts.

The sage spoke to the King, saying, "O child, do you divide your days wisely between the three pursuits—duty, wealth, and pleasure—well acquainted with the timeliness of each? Does your mind take pleasure in duty? Is the wealth you earn being wisely spent? Are you enjoying the pleasures of life? Does your mind not sink beneath their weight? Have you banished the six evils, O chief of men—sleep, idleness, fear, anger, weakness of mind, and procrastination?

"Do you wake in the small hours of the night and think of what you should do and what you should not do the next day? O son of Pandu, do you rise from bed at the proper time, dress yourself suitably, and show yourself to the people, accompanied by your ministers?

"Is your kingdom protected by ministers learned in the Vedas, who keep their counsel close? Even a single minister, whose passions are under control, who has wisdom and judgment, can bring great prosperity to a kingdom. I ask you, therefore, have you even one such minister? Is your priest humble, pure of blood and renown, without jealousy or greed? Is your astrologer skilled in reading faces, able to interpret omens and to counteract the disturbances of nature? Is the commander of your forces brave, intelligent, able, and devoted to you? Do you give your troops at the appointed time their proper rations and pay; do you support the wives and children of men who have given their lives for you?

"O foremost of victorious kings, do the officers of your government, who are paid from the taxes levied upon the people, take only their just dues? Are merchants coming from distant lands treated with kindness and honesty? Are the thieves and robbers who sack your towns pursued by your police over the smooth and the rough parts of your kingdom? I hope that your officers, having caught a thief with the booty upon him, never, from covetousness, set him free and keep the booty themselves. I hope your officers are never won over by bribes to decide unjustly a case between the rich and the poor.

"Are the four professions—farming, trade, cattle raising, and moneylending—managed by honest men? The happiness of your people depends on these, O oppressor of foes. Are the farmers contented? Do they lack neither food nor seed? Are dams and lakes placed at proper distances so that the farms need not depend entirely on the showers of heaven?

"O King, do you behave with perfect justice to those who deserve punishment and to those that deserve honor, to those who are dear to you and to those whom you dislike? Do you bow down to your superiors, the aged, the gods, the sages, the Brahmans, and the tall banyan trees in the villages that are so useful to the people? O sinless one, do you cause grief or anger in anyone's heart? Do you, like a father, cherish the blind, the dumb, the lame, the deformed, the friendless and homeless? Can all men approach you without fear? Have you faith in the religion taught in the Vedas and practiced by the kings who have gone before you? Do you follow the practices that were followed by them?"

At the conclusion of Nárada's words, Yudíshtira worshiped him and replied, "O holy one, the truths of religion and morality that you have spoken of, one after another, are just and proper. I observe those truths to the best of my power and I desire to walk in the virtuous path of my ancestors. I shall try to do all that you have directed, for my knowledge has increased with your counsel."

Having answered thus, the King, seated beside the sage, said to him, "With the speed of mind you roam over many worlds, beholding everything. Tell me, O sinless one, if you have ever beheld an assembly hall like this of mine, or one superior to it."

Nárada, smiling, answered the King in these sweet words, "O child, O King, I have never seen or heard of an assembly hall like this of yours, among men. But I have seen the halls of all the gods and will tell you about the assembly hall of Indra if you care to listen to me."

The high-souled Yudíshtira, with his brothers and the Brahmans seated round him, joined their hands in entreaty, saying, "Describe it to us, O exalted one! How long and wide is it and of what materials is it made? Who waits upon the wielder of the thunder in that hall?"

"O King," answered the sage, "it is impossible to describe the shape or dimensions of that hall, saying 'it is thus and so,' for I have never seen anything like it. It seems to be made of brilliant gems of many kinds. It seems not to be supported by any columns but, stationed in heaven, it looks like the white peaks of thunderclouds, shaming with its splendor the maker of the day. It moves at Indra's will and may in a moment take a different form that words cannot describe. It is filled with music and fragrant with celestial perfumes. It is neither very cool nor very hot and in it there is neither hunger nor thirst, neither grief nor weakness of age, no fatigue nor any sorrow.

"Sages sanctified by holy deeds, resplendent as fire, their sins washed quite away, wait upon and worship Indra in his hall; King Haris Chandra is also present there. All the gods and the stormy Maruts, the Gandárvas and Apsaras attend the lord of heaven in his hall. The lightning, O son of Pandu, the rain-charged clouds and the winds, the planets and the stars are also there, and the great mountains, rich in jewels, wait in that hall, holding sweet converse together. These and innumerable others come and go, worshiping Indra. As that celestial hall, O tiger among men, is unrivaled among the gods, so is yours unrivaled in the world of men."

"O foremost of eloquent men," Yudíshtira said, "you have told us that the gods and sages, the Gandárvas and Apsaras are seen in the assembly hall of Indra, but you have mentioned only one king, the noble Haris Chandra, who may enter there. What deed was performed by that illustrious king, what steady vows were kept by him, which made him worthy to dwell with the lord of heaven?"

"Haris Chandra was a powerful king," answered Nárada, "who brought the whole world with its seven islands under his sway. Having conquered the earth with its mountains, forests, and rivers, he performed the great Sacrifice of Coronation called the Rajasúya. For this reason Haris Chandra shone more brightly than thousands of other kings; for know, O bull of the Báratas, that those monarchs who perform the Coronation Sacrifice pass their time with joy in Indra's company.

"I have a message for you, O son of Kunti, from your father

Pandu, for I have also visited the hall of Yama, lord of death, where I saw your father among countless other kings. Knowing that I was coming to the world of men, he bowed to me and said, 'Tell Yudíshtira, O holy one, that he can conquer the whole earth, since his brothers are all obedient to him. When he has done this, he ought to perform the grand Sacrifice of Coronation, called the Rajasúya. He is my son: if he performs that sacrifice I may, like Haris Chandra, dwell in the mansion of Indra for countless joyous years.'

"Fulfill, therefore, O son of Pandu, your father's desire and you, too, will dwell with all your ancestors in the realm of Indra." Having spoken thus, Nárada went away, leaving in the minds of Yudíshtira and his brothers the thought of that great sacrifice.

BOOK VI

THE CORONATION SACRIFICE

The Fight with Jarasánda

KING YUDISHTIRA, summoning together his counselors and his brothers, asked them again and again about the Coronation Sacrifice. His minister replied to him, "O great king, your friends believe that you are worthy to rule the world and that the time has come for you to perform this sacrifice."

The King, however, still pondered the matter in his mind, knowing that the wise never come to grief when they act after full deliberation. He longed for the advice of Krishna, to whom nothing was unknown and nothing was impossible. Therefore he sent a messenger to the country of the Yadus to say that he desired to see his cousin, and Krishna, carried by his own swift horses, came to Indra Prasta without loss of time. He was received lovingly by his cousins and his father's sister, Kunti; after he had rested and was fully refreshed, Yudíshtira put the matter before him and begged for his counsel.

"O mighty monarch," Krishna said, "you are worthy, because of all your virtues, to perform the sacrifice, but one thing stands in your way. You know the tradition that has been handed down from generation to generation among the Kshatrias: that king alone who is lord of the whole earth may perform the Rajasúya. O bull of the Báratas, King Jarasánda of Mágada has set himself over the heads of many rulers: some wait upon him, having be-

71

come his vassals; others are allied with him and will always fight for him. The smaller tribes have fled before him, into the east and into the south. He has imprisoned eighty-four monarchs in his hill fortress, as a lion drags the slain bodies of mighty elephants to his mountain cave. When he has captured a hundred he will offer them in sacrifice to Shiva, as if they were so many animals. He, too, desires to be lord of the whole earth. Therefore, O best of men, if you desire to perform this sacrifice, you must set free the kings confined by Jarasánda and compass his death, for you will not be able to celebrate the Rajasúya as long as Jarasánda lives."

Hearing these words, Bima said, "By foresight and wisdom a king may vanquish one who is stronger than himself. In Krishna is wisdom, in me strength, and in Arjuna victory. Like the three fires that consume a sacrifice, we shall accomplish the death of the King of Mágada."

Arjuna also spoke: "O King, there is nothing that I love more than valor. He is a Kshatria who increases his fame and possessions by overcoming his enemies. There is no higher task that we could undertake than the slaying of Jarasánda and the rescue of the kings he has imprisoned for a cruel purpose. Let us three, therefore, fight him; then you shall be king over the whole earth."

"My heart is troubled," Yudíshtira said, "for the Rajasúya seems very hard to accomplish. How, O Krishna, can I send you against Jarasánda? Bima and Arjuna are my two eyes and you are my mind. How shall I live without my eyes and my mind? Yama himself cannot vanquish in battle the mighty host of Jarasánda; what can you three do against it?"

"Truly," Krishna said, "the King of Mágada cannot be vanquished in battle by the gods themselves or the demons, but I believe that he can be vanquished in single combat with bare arms. If we three approach him secretly I am sure that from fear of disgrace and pride of strength he will challenge Bima to a fight. The time has come for the destruction of Jarasánda; therefore, if you have any faith in me, give me, as a trust, Bima and Arjuna and let us set forth without loss of time."

Yudíshtira gave his consent. Krishna, Bima, and Arjuna, dressed as Brahmans, set out for Mágada, blessed by their brothers and friends, while the people beholding those heroes, who had never been defeated in battle, felt that Jarasánda was already slain. Leaving Indra Prasta behind them, they went through the country of the Báratas. Passing over the eastern mountains and the rivers that rise there, they entered the country of Kóshala; crossing the Ganges, still traveling eastward, they arrived in Mágada and from the wooded hills looked down upon the city, rich in cattle and wealth, well watered and beautiful with innumerable trees.

Unarmed, those mighty brothers and Krishna entered the city, beholding the great beauty of its shops filled with excellent foods and flowers and every kind of wealth. They took garlands of flowers from the vendors and, adorning themselves, entered the palace of Jarasánda, like Himálayan lions entering a cattle fold. Passing through three gates crowded with people who looked at them with wonder, they proudly approached the King; and Jarasánda, rising, received his visitors with proper ceremony, welcoming them. Bima and Arjuna did not answer him, but Krishna said, "O king of kings, these two are under a vow to remain silent until midnight. After that hour they will speak with you."

The King housed his guests in pleasant apartments. When midnight came he presented himself to them, for that ever victorious monarch obeyed the rule known throughout the three worlds—that if a Brahman should arrive at his palace, even at midnight, he must immediately grant him an audience. Beholding the strange attire of his guests, the King reproached them saying, "It is well known that Brahmans who are under a vow never adorn themselves with flowers. Who are you, therefore, adorned with garlands and with hands that bear the scars of the bowstring? Why have you entered the city in disguise and what is your purpose in coming to me? Tell me truly who you are."

Krishna replied, "O King, Brahmans, Kshatrias, and Vaisyas may all observe vows. Those who are adorned with flowers always achieve success; therefore, we have adorned ourselves. You have slain many of the Kshatrias of the world and have brought many kings as captives to your city, meaning to offer them as sacrifices to Shiva. We have come, O King of Mágada, to slay you for the slaughter and imprisonment of our kinsmen. Truly we are not Brahmans. I am Krishna of the Yadu folk and these two heroes are sons of Pandu. O King, we challenge you! Either set free all those kings, or fight with us and go to the abode of Yama!"

"I never imprison a king," Jarasánda said, "unless I have defeated him in battle. What captive here has not been vanquished fairly in war? Having brought these kings together to sacrifice them to the god, shall I, O Krishna, from fear of you, free them now at your command? I am ready to do battle with you in any way you choose: with troops against troops arrayed in order of battle, or alone against one, or against two, or against three, at the same time or separately."

"With whom amongst us three do you desire to fight?" asked Krishna; and the monarch of terrible prowess, addressing Bima, said, "O Bima, I will fight with you. It is better to be vanquished by a superior person."

King Jarasánda summoned his son and had him installed upon the throne, while he himself dressed for battle, taking off his crown and binding up his hair.

Then, like an ocean breaking upon the land, he rushed upon Bima and the mighty Bima met him, eager to fight. Those tigers among men smote their armpits with the palms of their hands, making the palace courtyard tremble at the sound. With their bare arms as their only weapons, they seized each other's neck and arms, each pressing every limb of his body against the other's limbs and twining his legs around the other's legs. Roaring like thunderclouds, they struck at each other's breasts with clenched fists, like two mad elephants encountering each other with their trunks. Dragging and pushing each other, they exchanged fierce looks and stinging speeches. Skilled in wrestling, each in turn clasped the other round the waist and hurled him to the ground.

The citizens, even the women and the old people, came out to behold that fight, until the crowd was so great that there was no space between body and body. The sound the wrestlers made with the clapping of their armpits and by dashing each other to the ground was as loud as thunder or as falling cliffs; for these were mighty men who delighted in combat. They fought on terribly for fourteen hours, driving the crowd at times this way and that.

In the fourteenth hour, Jarasánda grew tired, and the son of Pandu, perceiving his plight, resolved to take his life. Summoning all his strength, that slayer of foes lifted the powerful Jarasánda and whirled him round his head until the King lost his senses. Then the mighty Bima pressed his knee against the King's spine and broke his body in two. As he did this, he uttered a terrible roar that made the citizens of Mágada dumb with terror, for they believed the earth itself to be rent asunder.

Krishna ordered the King's chariot to be brought. With Bima and Arjuna, he drove out of the city, leaving the body of Jarasánda lying at the palace gate like one asleep. On that excellent chariot, decked with rows of bells, with wheels that sounded like thunder, they drove to the hill fortress to release the imprisoned kings. Those monarchs worshiped Krishna with reverence, saying, "O tiger among men, command us; we shall do whatever you desire, difficult though it may be." "Yudíshtira, the just king, desires to perform the Rajasúya Sacrifice," Krishna said. "Help him to accomplish it. That is my one command." All the kings gladly answered, "So be it!"

The son of Jarasánda, with his kinsmen, his ministers, and his priest, came forth from the city to meet them and was installed at once upon the throne of Mágada. Having won the friendship of Krishna and the two sons of Kunti, he re-entered his father's city joyfully, while the two princes and Krishna, laden with gifts, returned to Indra Prasta.

Yudíshtira embraced Krishna and his brothers with joy; he welcomed also the liberated kings, entertaining them with merriment and pleasure until those kings with joyful hearts set out for their own kingdoms.

The Ceremony

Shortly after this, when Yudíshtira and his brothers were sitting in the assembly hall, Arjuna said, "We have celestial weapons, strength, allies, territory, and armies. Therefore, O King, we should now make all the kings of the earth pay tribute to you and so increase your treasury. Permit me, O best of monarchs, to set out on a holy day of the moon, under a favorable constellation, to conquer the north and make the kings of that direction, presided over by Kúvera, the lord of treasures, pay tribute to us."

With his elder brother's leave, Arjuna set out, surrounded by a large host, making the earth tremble with the sound of his drums, the thunder of his chariot wheels, and the roar of the elephants in his train. He conquered the mountain passes and the hilly regions, vanquished the robber tribes on the northeastern frontier, and those that dwelt in the woods. And having overcome all the countries that lay to the north, having taken from them much wealth and excellent horses with the speed of the wind, he returned to Indra Prasta to offer all that wealth to Yudíshtira.

Bima, also, and those bulls among men, the twins, set out, each at the head of a large army. Bima subdued the east, Sahadéva the south, and Nákula, skilled in all weapons, the west. Many kings willingly paid tribute to Yudíshtira; many gladly became his allies, and many were vanquished in battle. All the barbarian kings dwelling on the marshy eastern seacoast paid tribute in sandalwood and aloes, pearls and gold and coral. Sahadéva, with his host, marched down beyond the Nerbáda River, past the celebrated caves of Kishkínda, and fought with the monkey kings that dwell in the southern forests. When he reached the seacoast he sent messengers to the illustrious Vivíshana, lord of Lanka, who willingly accepted the sway of the son of Pandu, sending as gifts many kinds of pearls and jewels. Nákula conquered all the countries of the west; there he visited the family of Krishna and the kingdom of Madra, ruled by his uncle, Shalya, Madri's brother, who from affection gladly accepted the sway of Yudíshtira. After subduing the fierce barbarians dwelling on the seacoast and the wild tribes of the hills, he retraced his steps to his own city, bringing with him so much treasure that ten thousand camels carried it with difficulty on their backs.

The great treasury of the King was so full of wealth that it could not have been emptied even in a hundred years. The friends and ministers of Yudíshtira, each separately and all together said to him, "The time has come, O exalted one, for your sacrifice. Let it be prepared without loss of time!"

Directed by Vyasa, Yudíshtira and his brothers began to collect all the materials that were necessary for the occasion, as well as food and many articles of pleasant taste and smell to delight the hearts of the Brahmans, for many Brahmans and sages had gathered in Hastinápura for the celebration of that sacrifice. The sinless Vyasa himself was the chief priest; he appointed other exalted Brahmans to perform the different parts of the ceremony and to chant the Vedic hymns. All of them, having uttered blessings and announced the purpose of the sacred festival, worshiped the enclosure where it was to take place. Directed by them, builders and artists erected halls and pavilions that were spacious and fragrant, like the temples of the gods.

When these were finished, Yudíshtira said to Sahadéva, "Send out swift messengers now to invite all the Brahmans in the land and all the Kshatrias, all the Vaisyas and the Shudras, to come hither!" Speedily then those messengers invited everyone, and returning, brought with them many guests, both friends and strangers. The King sent the ever victorious Nákula to Hastinápura to invite Bishma and Kuru, Drona, and Vídura, and those among his cousins who were well disposed toward him. The elders of the Báratas came with joyous hearts to that sacrifice, with Brahmans walking before them. The sons of Kuru, with Duryódana at their head, Ashvattáman, Karna, Shákuni, King of Gandára and brother to Gandári, the King of Madra, and the King of Panchála with his sons: all of these came to the sacrifice of the son of Pandu, and hundreds of other kings and Kshatrias, knowing the nature of the sacrifice, came with joyous hearts from many countries to pay homage to King Yudíshtira, bringing with them gifts of many kinds.

Yudíshtira, having worshiped Bishma and the other elders among the Kurus, said to them and to his cousins, "Give me your help in performing this sacrifice. This great treasure that is here is yours as well as mine." He appointed each one of them to different offices, under the direction of Bishma. Dushásana took charge of the distribution of food, while Drona's son attended the Brahmans; Drona himself took charge of the diamonds and gold, the pearls and gems, and the distribution of gifts; Vídura made all the payments, and Duryódana received the tribute brought by all the kings. Others among the Kúravas served in other ways; while Krishna, at his own request, washed the feet of the Brahmans.

Then Yudíshtira commenced the Sacrifice of Coronation with six fires, presenting many gifts to the Brahmans and pleasing everyone with presents of jewels and every kind of wealth, abundance of rice and pleasant and fragrant foods. The gods were pleased with the worship offered by the great sages, well versed in every rite, by the chanted hymns and the libations poured upon the fires; all the castes of men were pleased with that sacrifice and filled with joy.

On the last day, the great sages and the King entered the inner enclosure, where Yudíshtira was sprinkled with holy water and crowned as lord of the whole earth. There the other kings waited upon the son of Pandu, holding his weapons and his armor, his shoes and headgear and garlands, while Bima and Arjuna fanned him and the twins stood at his sides. Thus that sacrifice, performed in a favorable season, rich in wealth, food, and gifts, blessed by the Brahmans and sages, was in due time completed.

The Kshatria monarchs took their leave of Yudíshtira. "By good fortune you have become king over all kings, O virtuous one!" they said. "By this act you have gained spiritual merit. O lord of earth, cherish your subjects with ceaseless care and patience. As the rain clouds are to all creatures, as a large tree with spreading branches is to the birds, be the refuge and support of all men!"

When the kings had departed, each one of them courteously escorted to the borders of Yudíshtira's domain, when the Brahmans, duly worshiped and laden with gifts, and all the other guests had gone their way, the sons of Pandu returned to their own palace. No one was left in the assembly hall but Duryódana and his uncle Shákuni, the King of Gandára, the brother of Gandári.

Duryódana's Jealousy

With Shákuni, Duryódana slowly examined the whole of the assembly hall, finding there many celestial designs and materials that he had never seen in the city called after the elephant. One day he came upon a crystal floor and, mistaking it for a pool of water, he drew up his clothes; then, seeing his mistake, he wandered on, very much ashamed. Shortly afterward, mistaking a clear pool, covered with lotuses, for land, he fell into it with all his clothes on. Bima saw this and laughed uproariously. So did some servants, who brought him dry and handsome clothes; but Duryódana, who could not bear to be laughed at, would not look at them. Another time, he tried to walk through a closed crystal door; striking his brow against it, he stood there with his head swimming. The twins, who saw this happen, came to him and supported him, saying kindly, "This way, O King; here is the door." But Bima, who was also there, laughed again, saying mockingly, "Here is the door, O son of Kuru! This is the way."

At last, taking leave of the Pándavas, Duryódana returned to Hastinápura, reflecting sorrowfully on all that he had seen and suffered. On the way home his heart was so heavy and his mind so full of grief that he did not answer a word when his uncle spoke to him. "Why are you sighing so deeply?" Shákuni asked.

"O Uncle," Duryádana replied, "when I beheld the wealth of the sons of Pandu and that assembly hall of theirs and their servants laughing at me, my heart burned with jealousy. I am drying up like a shallow pool in summer. I shall throw myself upon a flaming fire or swallow poison or drown myself, for I cannot live! Behold, the sons of Kuru are decaying, while the sons of Pandu are increasing day by day! O Uncle, tell me how I can overcome them!"

Shákuni reflected a moment and then said, "Arjuna and Krishna, Bima and Yudíshtira, Nákula and Sahadéva, the King of Panchála and his sons cannot be overcome in battle. But, O prince of the Báratas, I know how Yudíshtira himself may be vanquished by you. He is very fond of gambling but he is not skillful at dice. Being a Kshatria, he cannot refuse a challenge. Now I am an adept at dice: there is none equal to me on earth, nay, not even in the three worlds. Therefore, challenge him to play at dice and I will win his kingdom and all his wealth for you, O bull among men. Present this plan to Kuru, and I will fulfill your desires."

"O son of Súvala," Duryódana replied, "present it to him yourself, for I cannot do so."

As soon as they arrived in Hastinápura, Shákuni, accompanied by Duryódana, approached King Kuru, and finding him seated on his throne, said to him, "O great king, your eldest son has lost color and become thin and sad. Why do you not find out the grief that preys upon his heart?"

"What is your sorrow, O son?" asked the King. "This vast wealth of mine is at your disposal; your brothers and all your family do everything to please you; you wear rich clothes and eat the best of food. Wherefore, O proud one, do you grieve as if you were destitute?"

"Though I eat fine food and am richly clothed, I enjoy nothing," Duryódana answered, "for I am a prey to fierce jealousy. Having beheld the blazing wealth of the son of Kunti, I have become pale, thin, and sad. I tell you I must be strong, inasmuch as I remain alive after seeing the whole earth under the sway of Yudíshtira. The Himálayas, the ocean, the shores of all the seas, the numberless regions yielding jewels and pearls do not contain as much wealth as fills the mansion of Yudíshtira. O monarch, since I was the eldest of his cousins and entitled to respect, he appointed me to receive the tribute brought by all the kings. Never before has been seen the enormous wealth that was brought to that sacrifice. My hands were so tired by receiving it that those who brought it waited until I was able to take up my task again.

"O Father, listen as I describe that wealth! The people of Valhika gave him as tribute a thousand asses, large and black necked, that daily run a hundred miles. The kings of the west gave each a thousand elephants, dark as rocks, decked with golden girdles and fine blankets, exceedingly patient, and of the very best breed, with tusks like plowshares. The kings of the eastern countries presented costly carpets, armor inlaid with jewels and gold and ivory; thousands of chariots of various shapes and handsome design, adorned with gold, covered with tiger skins, and drawn by well-trained horses. O lord of earth, these kings also brought to the sacrifice heaps upon heaps of jewels and gems for the son of Kunti.

"The King of Kamboja gave innumerable skins of the best kind, three hundred horses with noses like parrots, and a like number of camels and she-asses, all fatted with the olive. The Kings of Chola and Pandya brought numberless golden jars filled with fragrant sandalwood juice from the hills of Malaya and loads of sandal and aloe wood and many jewels of great brilliance and fine cloths inlaid with gold. The King of Singala gave those best of sea-born gems called the lapis lazuli, heaps of pearls, and hundreds of coverlets for elephants. Other kings of the earth brought thousands of kine, with as many copper vessels for milking them, to be given away by Yudíshtira to the Brahmans; they presented to him thousands of serving women with slender waists and luxuriant hair, and thousands of serving men with their wives. Innumerable jewels, horses, elephants, and camels were brought to the son of Pandu.

"Even the barbarous tribes that dwell on the seacoasts, in the woodlands, or in countries on the other side of the ocean waited at the gate with gifts of asses and goats, camels and vegetable honey, blankets and skins, for there was too great a crowd to be contained within the city. The mountain tribes brought soft, black brushes and others white as moonbeams; the cruel huntsmen who live on the northern slopes of the Himálayas brought heaps of valuable skins, and jars of gold that is raised from the earth by ants and hence called ant-gold. Men came from the eastern, western, and the southern seas. O Father, none but birds ever go to the northern sea, yet the Pándavas have spread their dominion even there, for I heard conchs blown that were brought from that ocean and the sound of them made my hair stand on end. Beholding my foes as they received those excellent gifts, I wished for death.

"All these men, of every caste, high, indifferent, and low, of numberless tribes, coming from every land, made the city of the Pándavas seem the center of the earth. In Indra Prasta, thousands of Brahmans, supported by Yudíshtira, daily eat rich food on golden plates within his palace. Thousands of elephants and cavalry, charioteers and horses, and countless foot soldiers are fed there daily, and not a single man of any caste lacks food and drink and ornaments. Dráupadi herself, before she eats, sees that everyone, even the dwarfs and the deformed, have had their food.

"Beholding all this, O chief of the Báratas, I cannot be at peace. Because of this I am pale and thin and plunged in grief."

Then Shákuni said, "O foremost of victorious kings, I can snatch this wealth from Yudíshtira and give it all to you. O King, I am skilled at dice and have especial knowledge of the play. Betting is my bow, the dice are my arrows, the diceboard is my chariot. I will challenge the son of Kunti to play; he cannot refuse and I will defeat him at every throw by deceitful means. I promise to win all that wealth of his, and Duryódana shall then enjoy it all."

"O Father," Duryódana said hurriedly, "this Shákuni is ready to win the wealth of the sons of Pandu. Grant him permission to do so." "I always follow the advice of the wise Vídura," answered Kuru. "He will tell us what is right for both sides, and what we should do." "If you consult Vídura," Duryódana said, "he will not allow you to do it, and if you do not do it, O King, I shall certainly kill myself. When I am dead, you can enjoy your kingdom with Vídura. What need have you of me?"

At these words, the weak-minded Kuru, ready to do anything that his son dictated, summoned his servants, saying, "Let workmen erect without delay a handsome and spacious palace with a hundred doors and a thousand columns. Let it be set with jewels and covered with many-colored carpets. Report to me when everything is complete."

When it was finished the King summoned Vídura, the chief of his ministers, saying, "Repair at once to Indra Prasta and bring Yudíshtira here with you. Let him come hither and behold this handsome assembly hall of mine and let a friendly match at dice be held here!"

"I do not approve, O King, of this command," Vídura said. "I fear it will bring about the destruction of our line. A dispute may arise between your sons and the Pándavas on account of this gambling match, and a quarrel will surely follow."

The King replied, "O Vídura, if the gods are merciful to us, no dispute will arise. When you and I, Drona and Bishma are at hand, no evil is likely to happen. Say no more. The whole universe moves at the will of its Creator; it is not free. Therefore go as I command you and bring the invincible son of Kunti here at once."

Sorrowfully, believing that his line was doomed, Vídura set out for the city of the wise sons of Pandu.

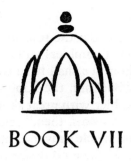

BOOK VII

THE GAMBLNG MATCH

Shákuni's Deceit

WHEN Vídura arrived at Indra Prasta, he entered the palace, beautiful as that of Kúvera, the God of Wealth, and approached Yudíshtira. The King saluted him reverently, seating his uncle beside him. "O Vídura," he said, "your mind seems troubled. Do you come here in happiness and peace? Are the sons of Kuru obedient to their old father? Are the people obedient to his rule?"

"The King, with his sons, is well and happy," answered Vídura. "He reigns like Indra himself; his sons are all obedient to him and he has no grief. However, he is not content with this, but wishes to increase his power. He has sent me here to invite you and your brothers to Hastinápura, to behold his newly erected assembly hall and to say whether it is equal to your own. When you are there, he will ask you to sit down to a friendly match at dice; then you will see the cheats and gamblers that he has brought there for the game! For this purpose, O King, he sent me hither."

"O learned one," said Yudíshtira, "if we sit down to a match at dice, we may quarrel. What man, knowing this, can be willing to gamble? What shall we do? We always obey your counsel."

"Gambling is the root of misery," answered Vídura. "I tried to prevent the King from doing this; however, he sent me to you. Do as you think best!"

"Besides the sons of Kuru," Yudíshtira asked, "what other dishonest gamblers will be there? Tell us, Vídura, who are they with whom we shall have to play, staking all our possessions?"

"Shákuni, the King of Gandára, an expert at dice, a desperate gambler with great skill of hand, will be there," answered Vídura.

"It seems, then," said Yudíshtira, "that there will be foul play. The whole universe, however, is at the will of its Maker; it is not free. I have no desire to gamble; I will not do so if Shákuni does not challenge me in the assembly hall; but if he does, I cannot refuse."

Yudíshtira ordered his attendants to prepare for his journey without delay. The next day, with his brothers and the Brahman who was their family priest, taking with him also the women of his household, with Dráupadi and her children in their midst, he set out for the capital of Kuru. Riding upon his splendid chariot, attired in royal robes, he arrived in Hastinápura, summoned by his uncle and impelled by fate. Entering the palace, he met Bishma and Drona, Karna and Ashvattáman and he embraced them all. He went to Duryódana and saluted him and all his brothers, as well as Shákuni and other kings who had come to behold the match. Then he entered the apartments of the old king to greet him and the revered Gandári; the blind king caressed Yudíshtira and his brothers, welcoming them with joy.

The next morning, wakened by sweet music, they rose at dawn; after their morning worship they entered the assembly hall and greeted those who were already there for the gambling. When they had taken their seats, Shákuni, the King of Gandára, said to Yudíshtira, "O King, the assembly is full; we have all been waiting for you. Now let us fix the stakes, and let the game begin without delay!" "Gambling is a sinful thing," Yudíshtira said. "There is no valor in it and no virtue. To wage war without crookedness or cunning is the sport of honest men, for even enemies should not be vanquished by deceitful means. We use our wealth for virtuous purposes, O Shákuni, and give it to the Brahmans. Do not win it from us by fixing desperate stakes or by deceitful means!"

"O Yudíshtira," Shákuni answered, "in any sort of contest men play with the desire to win: whether it is a contest of arms or a contest of learning, the purpose is victory, O King! So also a man skilled in dice plays with another who is not so skilled, with the desire to win. The purpose may not be a high one, but it is not dishonest. But if you think my intentions are not honest, if you are afraid, then do not play!" "I never refuse a challenge, O King," said Yudíshtira. "With whom in this assembly am I to play? Who is here who can stake as much as I?"

Then Duryódana spoke: "I shall supply jewels and every kind of wealth for my uncle, Shákuni, who is playing for me." "Gambling through the agency of another person," Yudíshtira said, "seems to me contrary to the rules, as you, O learned one, must admit. If you are bent upon it, however, let the play begin!"

When the match began, all the kings who were present, with Kuru at their head, took their seats in the assembly, while Bishma and Drona and the high-souled Vídura sat behind them with heavy hearts. The mansion looked splendid with these assembled kings, like heaven itself with a conclave of the gods.

Yudíshtira said to Duryódana, "O King, this excellent wreath of pearls, set in gold, is my stake. What is yours?" Duryódana replied, "I have many jewels, but I am not vain of them. I stake them all against your wreath. Win them if you like." Then Shákuni, well skilled at play, took up the dice and cast them deceitfully. He said to Yudíshtira, "Lo, I have won!"

"You have won this stake of me by unfair means," Yudíshtira answered, "but do not be proud, Shákuni! Let us stake thousands upon thousands. I have many beautiful jars full of jewels in my treasury, inexhaustible gold, and much silver. This wealth, O King, I will stake against what I have lost." Casting the dice again, Shákuni said to the eldest of the sons of Pandu, King Yudíshtira of undying glory, "Lo, I have won!"

"I have thousands of serving girls," Yudíshtira said, "adorned with garlands and rich robes, with golden bracelets on their wrists and arms, and jewels round their necks. They are well skilled in the four and sixty arts, especially in dancing and singing; they serve at my command the gods, Brahmans, and kings. This wealth is my stake, O King." At these words, Shákuni, skillful with the dice and using unfair means, said, "Lo, I have won!"

"I have thousands of serving men," said Yudíshtira, "attired in silken robes, self-controlled and wise in spite of their youth, who feed my guests night and day with golden dishes in their hands. This wealth, O King, is my stake." And Shákuni, casting the dice, said, "Lo, I have won!"

"I have, O son of Súvala," Yudíshtira said, "thousands of elephants with golden girdles, decked with ornaments, with fine white tusks as long and thick as plowshares. They are worthy of carrying kings on their backs; they can bear every kind of noise on the field of battle, and each possesses eight female elephants. This wealth, O King, I will stake with you." Unto Yudíshtira, when he had spoken thus, Shákuni laughing said, "Lo, I have won it!"

"I have as many chariots as I have elephants," said Yudíshtira, "all furnished with golden poles and flagstaffs, all drawn by well-trained horses and manned by warriors. I have also sixty thousand broad-chested warriors, who drink milk and eat rice. This is the wealth, O King, that I stake." The wretched Shákuni, pledged to enmity and using deceitful means, said, "Lo, I have won it!"

During the course of this gambling that was bringing ruin upon Yudíshtira, Vídura spoke to Kuru: "O great king, listen to what I say, although my words may be disagreeable to you, as medicine is to one who is ill unto death! When this Duryódana of sinful mind was born and immediately began to bray like an ass, it was well known that he would bring destruction to the Báratas. Know, O King, that he will be the death of you all. Men who collect honey in the mountains, climbing to dangerous heights, do not see that they are about to fall, for they are intent on the sweetness that they seek. Duryódana, maddened by the play at dice, does not see that if he makes enemies of these great warriors he will surely fall.

"O King, give up Duryódana and make the Pándavas your heirs! Exchange this crow, your son, and buy these peacocks, the Pándavas! Exchange this jackal and buy these tigers! O King, do not persecute the sons of Pandu for their wealth! What will you gain by winning it from them? Win these Pándavas themselves, for they will be more to you than all their wealth!"

Duryódana heard these words and said, "O Vídura, you are always boasting of the fame of our enemies and belittling the sons of Kuru. We know, O traitor, whom you really love. We have cherished you like a serpent in our laps; like a cat, you wish ill to him who feeds you. Go, then, away from us! Why should we give shelter to the friends of our foes?"

"O monarch," said Vídura, turning to his brother, "what do you think of one who abandons his minister for giving him good advice? After this, if you wish to hear agreeable words about everything you do, ask women and idiots and cripples for their counsel. A man who speaks the truth when it is bitter and one who listens to it are both rare."

Shákuni said, "You have lost much of your wealth, Yudíshtira. Tell me, have you anything that has not been won by us, O son of Kunti?" Yudíshtira replied, "I have, O son of Súvala, numberless cattle and horses, milch cows with calves, goats and sheep in the country that extends to the eastern bank of the Indus. With this wealth, O King, I will play." Shákuni, throwing the dice, said to the son of Kunti, "Lo, I have won!"

"I have my city," Yudíshtira said, "my land, the wealth of everyone who dwells therein, except that of the Brahmans, and all those people themselves, except the Brahmans. My kingdom still remains to me; with that, O King, I will play!" Skillful with the dice, and playing unfairly, Shákuni said to him, "Lo, I have won!"

Then Yudíshtira, maddened by the game, said, "This Nákula of mighty arms and neck like a lion's is now my one stake. He is my wealth." Shákuni cast the dice and said, "Lo, he has been won by us! O King Yudíshtira, Prince Nákula is dear to you and is now subject to us. With whom will you play next?"

"This Sahadéva," answered Yudíshtira, "administers justice and is renowned for his learning. He does not deserve to be staked in play, yet even such a dear thing as this I will stake with you,

89

against all that I have lost." Shákuni, throwing the dice, said, "Lo, I have won! O King, the sons of Madri, both dear to you, have been won by me, but Bima and Arjuna remain to you."

"Wretch!" cried Yudíshtira. "It is sinful of you to divide us, who are all of one heart." "One who is drunk falls into a pit and lies there unable to move," Shákuni said. "You know, O bull of the Báratas, that gamesters, while excited with play, do things that they would never dream of doing at any other time."

"Arjuna, like a boat," said Yudíshtira, "carries us from one shore of the sea of battle to the other shore. He is ever victorious over foes, the hero above all other heroes in the world. Arjuna does not deserve to be staked, but he is all my wealth; with him I will play!" Shákuni, casting the dice, said, "Lo, I have won! This foremost of all wielders of the bow, this son of Pandu who uses both his hands with equal skill, has now been won. Play with the wealth that is left to you, even with Bima, your dear brother, as your stake, O son of Kunti!"

"O King," Yudíshtira said, "though he does not deserve to be staked at play, I will stake Bima, that prince who is our leader, the foremost in fight, the high-souled one with a lion's neck and arched eyebrows, who cannot put up with an insult, who has no equal in strength or in the wielding of the mace." Hearing this, Shákuni, skillful with the dice, using foul means, said, "Lo, I have won! You have lost, O son of Kunti, wealth and horses and elephants, your kingdom, and your brothers. Tell us if there is anything that you have not lost."

"I alone, the eldest of all my brothers and dear to them, have not been lost," said Yudíshtira. "If you win me, I will do whatever he who is won must do." Shákuni, casting the dice, said, "Lo, I have won! It is sinful of you, O King, to have lost yourself, for there is still one stake dear to you that has not been won. Stake Dráupadi, the princess of Panchála, and with her win back all that you have lost!"

"With Dráupadi as stake I will now play with you," Yudíshtira said. "She is a woman whom a man might dream of as a wife, for her heart is tender, she is beautiful and virtuous and sweet of speech. Her waist is slender as a wasp's, her hair is long and curling, her lips are red, and her eyes are like the leaves of the autumn lotus. O King, making the slender-waisted Dráupadi my stake, I will play with you."

When the King had spoken, the older people in the assembly said, "Shame! Shame!" The whole concourse was troubled and the kings who were present gave way to grief. Bishma and Drona wiped the sweat from their brows; Vídura sat with his head between his hands, like one bereft of reason. But Kuru could not hide his joy, asking again and again, "Has the stake been won? Has the stake been won?" Karna and Dushásana laughed aloud, while many wept.

Shákuni, proud of his success, in a flurry of excitement, kept saying, "There is still one stake—there is still one stake—" Then, playing with skillful hands, he cried, "Lo, I have won!" and picked up the dice.

The Insult to Dráupadi

"Come, Vídura," cried Duryódana," bring hither Dráupadi, the beloved wife of the sons of Pandu! Let her sweep the rooms and dwell among our serving women!"

"O wretch," Vídura answered, "do you not know that you are tying yourself fast with cords? Do you not understand that you are hanging on the edge of a precipice, that you are like a deer who provokes tigers to rage? In my judgment, Dráupadi has not been won, since she was staked by the King after he had lost himself and was no longer his own master."

Drunk with pride, Duryódana said. "Fie upon Vídura!" He commanded an attendant: "Go and bring Dráupadi hither! You need not heed the words of Vídura nor fear the sons of Pandu."

The attendant went with haste to the apartments of the Pándavas, entering there like a dog in a lion's den. He approached the Queen and said, "Yudíshtira, maddened by the dice, has lost you to Duryódana, O Dráupadi. Come now, and I will put you to some servant's task." "How can you speak thus?" Dráupadi cried. "What king has ever gambled, staking his wife? Maddened he must have been if he could find no other stake." "When he had nothing else to lose," the attendant said, "then he staked you, O Queen. He lost first his brothers, then himself, and lastly you." "O son of the Suta caste," said Dráupadi, "go and ask that gambler which he lost first, himself or me. Then come and take me with you."

The messenger came back to the assembly and said to Yudíshtira, "Dráupadi asks you, 'Whose lord were you at the time you lost me in play? Did you lose yourself first or me?'" But Yudíshtira sat there like one who had lost his mind and gave no answer to the Suta's son. Then Duryódana, looking triumphantly at Yudíshtira, said to the messenger, "Let the princess of Panchála come hither to put her question to him. Bring her hither at once!" The messenger, afraid to face the anger of the Queen, asked, "What shall I say to the princess of Panchála?" Duryódana turned impatiently to his brother: "Dushásana, this stupid fellow is afraid of Bima. Go yourself and bring Dráupadi by force!"

At his brother's command, Dushásana rose with blood-red eyes. Entering the apartments of the Pándavas, he said to the Queen: "Come, come, Dráupadi, princess of Panchála, you have been won by us. Put aside your modesty, come and behold Duryódana and accept the sons of Kuru as your lords!"

Dráupadi, rising up in great distress, covered her face with her hands and ran to the place where the ladies of Kuru's household were sitting. Dushásana, roaring with anger, ran after her. Seizing her by her long curling locks, those locks that had been sprinkled with holy water in the Rajasúya Sacrifice, he dragged her, trembling like a tree in a storm, into the assembly. Helpless, with bent body, she faintly cried, "Wretch! It is not fitting to take me before the assembly, for I am not properly dressed and have but one garment on." But Dushásana, dragging her forcibly, said, "It does not matter whether you have one garment or none. You have been won at dice; you are our slave and must live among our serving women."

With hair disheveled, her garment loosened, the modest Dráupadi, burning with anger, cried, "O wretch! O cruel one! Do not drag me so! Do not uncover me so in the presence of the elders! The sons of Pandu are bound now by honor, but they will never pardon you for this, even if Indra were your ally. O shame! Does no one here rebuke you? Surely the Báratas have forgotten the Kshatria usage! Surely Drona and Vídura have lost their virtue, and so have the high-souled Bishma and the King. Else, why do the Bárata elders look silently on at this great crime?" Thus did the slender-waisted Dráupadi cry in distress in that assembly. Looking at her enraged lords, she angered them still further, for they were not so much distressed at losing their jewels, their wealth, and their kingdom as they were at that look of hers, so full of shame and anger. But Dushásana laughed aloud, as did Karna, while Shákuni applauded Dushásana's act. Everyone, except these three and Duryódana, was filled with sorrow.

Beholding Dráupadi thus dragged into the assembly, Bishma said, "O blessed one, the way of virtue is subtle; I cannot decide the question that you have asked. The son of Kunti played willingly with Shákuni, staking you in the game, for wives are ever at the disposal of their lords. Yudíshtira will give up a world of wealth, but he will never give up honor. I cannot decide whether you were won or not."

Then Vikarna, the son of Kuru, rose and said, "You kings, answer now the question that has been asked by the blessed daughter of Panchála and declare which side each of you upholds." But the kings, from fear of Duryódana, answered him not a word. Then Vikarna wrung his hands, sighing, and said, "You kings of the earth and you Báratas, whether you answer or not I shall say what seems to me just and right. It has been said that hunting, drinking, and gambling are the vices of kings. This son of Pandu, deeply indulging in one of these vices, made Dráupadi a stake; besides, he did so after he had already lost himself. Considering these things, I do not think that she was lost."

An uproar arose in the assembly at these words, for many men applauded them. But Karna, beside himself with anger, said, "O

93

DRAUPADI IS WON AT DICE

younger brother of Duryódana, you speak like a fool, while your elders here do not speak a word, because they all believe that Dráupadi was justly won. How can you consider her not won, when here in this assembly the eldest of the Pándavas staked all he had? Is Dráupadi not included in the possessions of her lord? If anyone think it improper to bring her here attired in one garment, are her robes not also ours? Dushásana, take their robes off the Pándavas and this garment off Dráupadi!"

The Pándavas, hearing these words, took off their upper garments and threw them down, while Dushásana, seizing Dráupadi's robe, began to pull it off. Then Dráupadi, resplendent still in her beauty, covered her face, crying aloud, "O Darma, lord of justice, protector of the virtuous, save me, who am suffering here in the midst of the Báratas!" And the illustrious Darma heard her and covered her with beautiful garments of many colors. As one garment was pulled from her body, another appeared, covering her, until many robes of different colors were heaped up in that assembly and Dushásana, tired and ashamed, sat down.

All that were in the hall cried, "Shame!" And Bima, wringing his hands with rage, swore a loud oath in the midst of all those kings. "Hear these words of mine, you Kshatrias of the world! I shall tear open in battle the breast of this wretch, this wicked-minded scoundrel, and drink his lifeblood. If I do not do so, may I never follow the path of my ancestors!"

These terrible words made the listeners' hair stand on end; all those who were present applauded him and blamed the son of Kuru. But Karna said to Dushásana, "Take away this serving woman, Dráupadi, to the inner apartments."

"Wait a little, you wicked-minded Dushásana, worst of men!" Dráupadi cried. She knelt upon the ground and, weeping piteously, addressed those who were present, saying, "Alas! I was beheld once before, at my swayámvara, by the assembled kings in the amphitheater, but never since that time. She, whom even the sun never beheld in her palace, is dragged today before the assembly and exposed to the gaze of the crowd! Alas! She whom the sons of Pandu would not suffer even the winds to touch, is seized today and dragged here by this wretch! Alas! These elders of the Báratas allow their daughter and their daughter-in-law to be so treated before their eyes! I can bear it no longer. You kings, I am the wedded wife of the just king Yudíshtira; I come from the same caste to which he belongs. Tell me now, whether I am a serving woman or not, whether I am won or unwon at dice. I will cheerfully accept your answer, whatever it be."

The kings sitting in that assembly uttered not a word, for good or ill. Beholding this, Duryódana smiled a little and said to Dráupadi, "O daughter of Panchála, let your husbands decide this question themselves. If Bima and Arjuna, Nákula and Sahadéva, will here declare that Yudíshtira is not their lord, if he himself declares that he is not your lord, you shall be free from slavery." Everyone in the assembly approved these words, for all were curious to know what Arjuna, who was never defeated in battle, what Bima and the twins would say.

When the hum of many voices was stilled, Bima rose and said, "If this high-souled king Yudíshtira, our eldest brother, had not been our lord, who is there, among creatures touching the earth with their feet, that would have escaped from me with his life after touching the hair of the princess of Panchála?" Then Karna said to Dráupadi, "O beautiful one, Bima has spoken; you are now a slave. Go to the inner apartments, therefore, and serve the King's family. The sons of Kuru are now your masters; choose another husband from among them—one who will not make you a slave by gambling."

Bima sat, breathing heavily, hardly able to control his fury at these words, while Duryódana, in order to encourage Karna and to insult Bima, bared his left thigh before the very eyes of Dráupadi. Seeing this, Bima with blazing eyes said to the son of Kuru, "May I never touch those regions where my ancestors dwell if I do not break that thigh of yours in the great battle!"

Paying no heed to him, Duryódana said, "I am still willing to abide by the words of Arjuna and the twins. Let them say that Yudíshtira is not their master and Dráupadi shall be freed."

"The noble son of Kunti, the just king Yudíshtira," Arjuna

said, "surely was our master before he staked himself. But after he had lost himself, whose master could he be?"

Just then a jackal howled loudly in the sacrificial room of the King's palace; asses brayed in response, and terrible birds answered with their cries. Vídura, who understood all signs, and Gandári, who also knew the meaning of these sounds, came quickly to the King and told him that those frightful omens boded ill to him and all his people. The King, filled with fear, listened to their counsel and said to his son, "O wicked-minded Duryódana! Behold, ruin has already overtaken you for insulting these bulls among the Báratas and their wedded wife, Dráupadi!" He then began to comfort the princess of Panchála, saying, "Ask any boon of me, O lovely one! Chaste and virtuous, you are the best of all my daughters-in-law."

"If you will grant me a boon, O foremost of kings," Dráupadi said, "let the handsome and dutiful Yudíshtira be freed from slavery. Do not let my child, his son, who has been a prince, cherished by kings, be called the child of a slave."

"O excellent one," said Kuru, "let it be as you say. Now ask another boon, for my heart is inclined to grant you a second one."

"I ask, O King," said Dráupadi, "that Bima and Arjuna and the twins, with their chariots and their weapons, regain their liberty."

"Let is be as you wish, O blessed daughter," replied the King. "Ask now a third boon, for you deserve more than two."

"O first of kings, O noble one!" Dráupadi said. "One who is greedy loses all virtue. I do not deserve a third boon and dare not ask for more. These my husbands, freed from bondage, will be able to achieve whatever more they need."

Then Bima said, rising and stretching his mighty arms, "Shall I, O Yudíshtira, slay here and now all these our enemies, or shall I destroy them by the roots outside this palace? Let me slay them even now, so that you may rule the whole earth without a rival." And the mighty-armed hero began to burn with the fire of his fury until sparks and smoke came from his ears and nostrils and his face was as terrible to behold as that of Yama himself.

But Arjuna, with pleading eyes, soothed his elder brother and

Yudíshtira forbade the mighty hero, embracing him and saying, "Be not so angry! Let there be silence and peace!" And having pacified his brother, he approached King Kuru with his hands joined.

"O King," he said, "you are our father and we are obedient to you. Tell us what we shall do."

"May you be blessed, O righteous one," replied Kuru. "Go in peace and safety, and rule your kingdom with all its wealth. And take to heart, my child, this advice of an old man. You know the subtle path of virtue. You are wise and you are also humble; you honor those who are old. Therefore follow the counsels of peace. Do not remember the harshness of Duryódana, but look upon me who am old and blind; look upon Gandári and remember only what is good. Return to Indra Prasta. Let there be brotherly love between you and your cousins, and let your heart be ever fixed on virtue."

Thus blessed by his uncle, Yudíshtira took his leave of everyone with the utmost courtesy. Then he and his brothers, with Dráupadi, mounted their chariots and with cheerful hearts set out for Indra Prasta.

Exile

When the Pándavas had gone, Dushásana hurried to Duryódana; finding him with his counselors, he said to them all, "You mighty warriors, the old man has thrown away all that we won with so much trouble. What now, O bulls of the Báratas?"

Stung by his words, Duryódana, Karna, and Shákuni, guided by vanity and jealousy, consulted together. Going privately to King Kuru, they spoke these smooth and artful words: "O slayer of foes, the angry sons of Pandu, like wrathful and poisonous snakes, will now surely destroy us. Even now they are whipping their horses in order to return quickly to their capital and assemble their armies. Even now Arjuna is driving his chariot, lifting his mighty bow and casting angry glances round him; Bima is whirling his heavy mace; the twins have their swords in their hands and their shields on their arms. They cannot forgive the injuries we have done them. Who is there among them that can forgive the insults that Dráupadi suffered?

"Let us gamble again and let this be the stake: those who lose at dice must be exiled to the forest for twelve years and must spend a thirteenth year in some inhabited place, unrecognized. If they are recognized, they must go into exile for another twelve years. The Pándavas will surely lose, for Shákuni knows the whole science of dice. During the thirteen years of their exile we shall, with their wealth, ally ourselves with all the kings of the earth and assemble a vast, invincible host. Thus we can defeat them if they reappear, and bring them under our sway. Let the sons of Pandu play once more, casting the dice!"

"Let it be as you desire," Kuru said. "Bring back the Pándavas, even if they have gone a great way. Let them come once again to cast the dice!"

Then Drona and Bishma, Vídura and the virtuous Gandári all entreated the King: "Let not the play begin again! Let there be peace!" But Kuru, partial to his sons, paid no attention to the counsels of his wise friends and his wife, but summoned the sons of Pandu.

The royal messenger overtook Yudíshtira, who had gone a long way, and said, "Hear the words of your uncle, O King: 'The assembly is ready! O son of Pandu, O Yudíshtira, come back and cast the dice!'"

"Good and evil come at the Creator's will, whether I play or not," said Yudíshtira. "This is a challenge and is, besides, the command of the old King. I cannot refuse, although I know that it will injure me." Therefore, turning his chariot, he retraced his way, along with his brothers and Dráupadi. Knowing full well the deceitful ways of Shákuni, the mighty warriors entered the assembly, where, amid their sorrowing friends, they sat down to gamble.

Shákuni said, "The old king has given you back your wealth, O son of Pandu. That is well; but there is still a stake of great value to be won. Those who are defeated at dice shall dress in deerskins, and entering the great forest, live there for twelve years. The thirteenth year they shall spend in some inhabited place, unrecognized. If they should be recognized, they must spend another twelve years' exile in the woods. But if these conditions be fulfilled, their kingdom shall be restored to those who lost, after the thirteen years are past. Either you five sons of Pandu, with Dráupadi your wife, shall suffer this, or we. Therefore play with us, Yudíshtira, and cast the dice."

At these words, all who were in the assembly, raising their hands in great distress, cried, "Alas! Fie upon the friends of Duryódana, that they do not warn him of his danger!"

Yudíshtira, knowing well what would happen, answered Shákuni: "O monarch, how can a king like me, always obedient to the usage of his caste, refuse a challenge to dice? Therefore I will play with you." And Shákuni, taking up the dice, cast them and said, "Lo, I have won!"

Then the vanquished sons of Kunti prepared for their exile into the forest, one after another casting off their royal robes and dressing themselves in deerskins. Dushásana, beholding them thus, shamelessly danced around them; Duryódana also, unable to restrain his joy, mimicked the lionlike step of Bima as he left the assembly. Beholding this insult, suppressing his rising rage, the mighty and proud Bima spoke to him: "O fool, I shall slay you with all your brothers, reminding you of this! Arjuna will slay Karna and Sahadéva will slay Shákuni, that gambler with dice. Hear these proud words, for the gods will make them good if ever we fight with the sons of Kuru!"

"On the fourteenth year from this day, O Bima," Arjuna said, "if Duryódana does not return to us our kingdom, your words shall come true. I vow that I will slay in battle this Karna and all those other kings who from foolishness fight against me. May the Himálayas be removed from where they stand, may the maker of the day lose his heat and the moon his coolness, if this vow of mine be not fulfilled!"

Sahadéva said, raising his strong arms, "O Shákuni, you disgrace of the line of Gandára! Those dice of yours are sharp-pointed arrows whose wounds you will receive in battle. I shall surely slay you in battle if you stay in the fight."

The handsome Nákula spoke: "I shall send to the abode of Yama all those who spoke harsh and insulting words to the daughter of Panchála at the gambling match."

Then those tigers among men, having pledged themselves so, approached King Kuru. Yudíshtira said, "I bid farewell to the Báratas, to my old grandsire Bishma, to Drona and Vídura, to Kuru and his sons, and to his courtiers. I shall see you all again when I return." Those who were present were so overcome with shame that they could not say a word to Yudíshtira, but in their hearts they prayed for his welfare.

Only Vídura spoke to him, saying, "O child, one who is vanquished by sinful means need never be downcast by his defeat. Go hence with our leave and with our blessings! You love each other and delight in each other's presence; your enemies cannot separate you. Who is there that will not envy you? It will be good for you to be away from the world for a time; for after this experience, no enemy in the world will be able to stand against you. Learn from the moon the power of giving joy; learn from the water the power of nourishing all things; learn forbearance from the earth, energy from the sun, and strength from the winds! I hope to see you return in safety, crowned with success."

"So be it!" Yudíshtira said, and bowing low to Vídura, Bishma, and Drona, he went away.

When Dráupadi was ready to go, she took her leave of the noble Kunti and the other ladies of the household, embracing each one of them, while a wail of sorrow arose in the inner apartments. Kunti, sorrowing deeply, said in a voice choked with grief, "O child, go safely, blessed by my prayers. I need not teach you your duties to your lords. They are fortunate that they have not been scorched with your anger. In the woods, watch over my son Sahadéva, who is the dearest of all my children—dearer than life itself. See that his heart does not sink under this misfortune." Sorrowfully she followed Dráupadi and came upon her sons, shorn of their robes and ornaments, clad in deerskins and hanging their heads in shame.

Weeping and lamenting their misfortune, she said farewell to them, while they consoled her as best they could. Then, with their hearts plunged in grief, followed by their children and their servants in their chariots, they set out for the woods. The sorrowing citizens followed them past the gates, blessing them as they went.

When the Pándavas had departed, Vídura sought out Kunti and, as sorrowful as she, led her slowly to his house, for she no longer wished to live in Kuru's palace. The ladies of the royal household wept, blaming the sons of Kuru; then they sat silent for a long time, covering their lotuslike faces with their fair hands.

King Kuru, too, thinking of the dangers that threatened his sons, was anxious and had no peace of mind. He sent for Vídura and asked him fearfully, "How did Yudíshtira go away? How did Bima and Arjuna go, and the twin sons of Madri? What did their priest do, and the illustrious Dráupadi? Tell me everything, O Vídura, that they did."

"Yudíshtira, the son of Kunti, went away covering his face with his cloak," Vídura replied; "Bima went, O King, looking at his mighty arms; Arjuna followed his brothers, scattering grains of sand upon the ground; Sahadéva smeared his face; and Nákula, handsomest of men, stained himself with dust. The large-eyed Dráupadi covered her face with her disheveled hair, following in the wake of the King and weeping. And their priest, O King, walked along the road before them, with kusha grass in his hand, chanting the awful verses that relate to death."

"Tell me, Vídura," asked the King, "why is it that the sons of Pandu leave Hastinápura in these different ways?"

Vídura replied, "Though persecuted by your sons and robbed of his kingdom by foul means, King Yudíshtira is always kind, O monarch, to your children. He is filled with anger but he will not show his face because he thinks, 'I must not scorch the people by looking at them with angry eyes.' Listen to me as I tell you why

Bima looks at his mighty arms: he thinks, 'There is none equal to me in strength,' and he longs to do to his enemies deeds worthy of his strength. Arjuna follows the footsteps of his brothers, thinking that he will shower arrows upon his enemies as easily as now he scatters grains of sand. Sahadéva smears his face, thinking, 'None shall recognize me in this day of trouble!' Nákula stains himself with dust, thinking, 'I must not steal the hearts of the ladies that look at me.' And Dráupadi, disheveled and weeping, thinks, 'The wives of those who have brought me to such a plight shall, fourteen years from now, be weeping and disheveled, as I am now, for those whom they have lost.'

"The learned priest, O King, holding the sacred grass in his hand, singing the hymns that relate to death, is thinking, 'When the Kúravas are slain in battle, their priests and teachers will be singing these hymns, as I am doing now.' The citizens cry out in their grief, 'Alas! Alas! Our masters are leaving us. Shame upon the Kúravas for acting like foolish children, banishing the sons of Pandu out of greed! Now we shall have no masters, for how can we love the wicked and jealous sons of Kuru?'

"When the Pándavas left the city, lightning appeared in the cloudless sky; the earth began to tremble; meteors fell to the left of the city and birds shrieked from the temples of the gods and from the tops of the sacred trees. These evil omens were seen and heard, O King; they are a warning of the doom that will follow your wicked counsels."

BOOK VIII

IN THE FOREST

The Kámyaka Forest

THUS the sons of Kunti, defeated at dice, with anger in their hearts, set out from the city called after the elephant, Dráupadi and her five sons and Subádra, with Abimányu, going with them. When they had passed beyond the gates, they mounted their chariots, while their servants, carrying their bows and bow-strings and their other splendid weapons, and the maidservants, carrying Dráupadi's robes and jewels, rode in carts behind them. Many Brahmans walked beside them, and the citizens of the town followed them for a long way, wailing aloud in their sorrow.

At sunset they reached the banks of the Ganges, where a mighty banyan tree stood. After purifying themselves by touching the sacred water, they spent the night there, taking nothing but water for their food. In the twilight hour, that is both beautiful and terrible, the Brahmans lit their holy fires and chanted the Vedas, comforting Yudíshtira, that best of kings.

The next day they set out for the forest of Kámyaka, which lay to the west, on the banks of the Sarasváti River. As they entered that forest, they were overtaken by several of their friends and kinsmen: Krishna, who had been at war when the gambling match occured, Dráupadi's brother, Dyumna, and other kings and Kshatrias who had heard of their exile with sorrow and anger. "Alas!" said Krishna, "If I had been at Hastinápura, O best of kings, this evil would not have befallen you, for I should have prevented the game, either by persuasion or by force. The earth shall drink the blood of Duryódana and Karna, of Dushásana and Shákuni, for the wicked deserve to be slain." And Dyumna said, comforting Dráupadi, "O sister, I will slay Drona and our brother Shikándin will slay the grandsire. With Krishna's help we are invincible even by the gods—and what are the sons of Kuru?"

When they had talked together for a long while and the visitors were taking their leave, Yudíshtira said, "O Krishna, take back with you the delicate Subádra, your sister, and this Abimányu, Arjuna's son. Train him in the science of arms, in the study of the Vedas and the duties of the Kshatria order. And do you, O Dyumna, take these five sons of Dráupadi and care for them as if they were your own. They need not share the dangers and the hardships of our exile." The two heroic princes gladly did what Yudíshtira asked; mounting their shining chariots, they took the children and their nurses and set out for their own cities. The other kings and warriors, reverently saluting the Pándavas, returned to their kingdoms.

Then the sons of Pandu and Dráupadi went deeper into the forest, to find a pleasant place where they could spend the twelve years of their exile. It was late summer; they saw with delight the trees covered with flowers or fruits, hummed over by swarms of black bees, while on the topmost branches birds poured forth their songs. As they drew near the Sarasváti River, they came upon a hermitage where men of purified souls, clad in the bark of trees, were living. The King, his brothers, and their followers, descending from their cars, entered the hermitage with joined hands, and the holy men and forest dwellers came toward them, eager to behold that king devoted to truth. Saluting them, and saluted in return, Yudíshtira sat down in their midst at the foot of a mighty tree covered with flowers and creepers, as his father Pandu had done before him. Bima and Arjuna, the twins and Dráupadi, tired by the journey, sat down around him, making that mighty tree, bent down with the weight of creepers, look like a mountain with five great elephants resting on its side. There in that holy hermitage the Pándavas made their home.

They picked the forest fruits for their food, and the five brothers, each going in a different direction, went out every day with their bows in their hands to shoot the deer. They first gave a portion of the food to the Brahmans, eating the rest themselves; the faultless Dráupadi fed her husbands and the Brahmans as if she were their mother, taking her own food last of all. No one that lived with Yudíshtira was thin or ill or had anything to fear.

One evening the sons of Kunti, with their beloved wife, seated under that mighty tree, talked sadly together. The beautiful Dráupadi, dear to her lords and devoted unto them, said to Yudíshtira, "When I behold this bed of grass, remembering what you had before, I grieve, O King, for you who do not deserve any sorrow. What peace can my heart know, beholding you here? Alas, these brothers of yours were once dressed in rich apparel and fed by cooks with food of the sweetest savor; I grieve for them, who live now in the woods on what the woods may yield.

"Why does your anger not blaze up, O King, when you behold Bima living in sorrow in the woods, though he deserves every happiness? Why does your anger not blaze up at the sight of Arjuna in exile, who alone on his chariot has vanquished gods and men and serpents? How, O King, can you forgive our enemies when you behold Nákula in exile, so fair and young and strong, the foremost of all swordsmen? Why does your anger not blaze up at the sight of the brave and handsome Sahadéva in exile, who is so undeserving of grief? And how, O King, can you forgive our enemies when you see me in exile, who am the daughter of Panchála's king, the daughter-in-law of Pandu, and the devoted wife of heroes? Every Kshatria should be capable of anger, but you can have no anger if your heart is unmoved by the sight of your brothers and me in such distress.

"Forgiveness is not always admirable, O son of Kunti. He who always forgives is despised by his servants, by strangers, and by his enemies; mean-minded men take advantage of him and no one respects him. Forgiveness and force should both be used, each at the proper time. The wise say that one who has done you a service should be forgiven, even if he wrongs you deeply; those who offend from ignorance or folly should be forgiven, for it is not easy to become wise; and a first offense should always be forgiven. At all other times but these, force should be used against sinners. O King, these wicked and greedy sons of Kuru, who have injured us again and again, are not to be forgiven. You should use force against them.

"O Yudíshtira, there was a learned Brahman at my father's court. Sometimes, when I was a girl, I went out of the inner apartments and sat on my father's lap and listened to the wise words of that Brahman. He taught me these things."

"Anger is the slayer of men, O beautiful one," Yudíshtira said. "He who controls his anger conquers the world. There is no act that an angry man cannot commit, no word that an angry man may not utter. From anger a man may slay one who should not be slain and may reward one who deserves death. The angry man may even send his own soul to Yama's realm. How, then, can we indulge in anger?

"If, among men, there were not some who are as forgiving as the earth, there would be no peace at all. If everyone returned evil for evil, if everyone who was punished wanted to punish in return, there would be nothing but sin in the world, and all creatures would perish. Creatures are born because there is peace, O Dráupadi; they enjoy life and happiness because there are men in the world who are as forgiving as the earth. Therefore, O beautiful one, we should forgive every injury. Forgiveness is virtue; forgiveness is truth; forgiveness is sacrifice and holiness; forgiveness is the power of the strong; forgiveness is peace of mind; by forgiveness the universe is held together. Whoever knows this can forgive anything. The forgiving man is always victorious, for the world belongs to him. Therefore do not give way to anger, Dráupadi!"

"I cannot see," Dráupadi said, "that victory or happiness are won by virtue of forgiveness. Everyone knows that you are virtuous, yet this unbearable misfortune has befallen you. I do believe

that you would give up Bima and Arjuna and these twin sons of
Madri along with myself before you would give up virtue; yet
virtue does not protect you. Therefore surely you should act, O
son of Kunti, to remove this evil that has come upon us."

Then Bima, breathing hard with anger, spoke to Yudíshtira.
"O King, what do we gain by living here like holy men, unable
to accomplish any of the three purposes of life—duty, pleasure or
profit? Why, just for the sake of keeping a promise, should we
submit to this banishment? Only cowards would do it, and that is
what the people believe us to be. This grieves me more than death
in battle. We cannot live by begging, as Brahmans do; we are
forbidden to do so. A Kshatria must win his wealth by strength
and energy. Awake, O King, and understand the duties of the
caste into which you were born! Kill your enemies and destroy
the power of Kuru's sons! There is no man that can bear the touch
of Arjuna's arrows, winged with vulture's feathers. There is no
warrior or horse or elephant that can stand the stroke of my
mace in battle. Why then, should we not wrest our rightful kingdom from our enemies, with the help of Krishna, Dráupadi's
father and brothers, and our many friends?"

Yudíshtira, after a few moments, patiently answered his
brother: "I cannot blame you, O Bima, for piercing me with your
arrowy words. This misfortune has befallen you all because of
my folly. You know well, however, that when we were challenged to play the second time, Shákuni, in the presence of all the
court, told me the stake that we were playing for, and that I replied, 'So be it!' Having made that agreement in the presence of
those good men, how could I dare to break it, even for the sake
of a kingdom? Wait, O Bima, for the return of better days, as
the sower waits for the harvest!"

"If we wait for thirteen years, O King," said Bima, "we shall
only be so much nearer death. Life is uncertain; we should try
to regain our kingdom before we die. During the last year of our
exile we must live, unrecognized, in some inhabited place. O son
of Kunti, everyone in the world has known us, ever since we
were boys. How can we live unrecognized? And if our enemies,

through their spies, discover us, we must live in exile for another twelve years. O King, anger is hard to control. I burn with it day and night and cannot sleep. Arjuna also burns with grief, though he lives here like a lion in its den, desiring to please you. The twins do not speak, but all of us long for battle. Why, then, do you not act, O tiger among men, and slay your enemies? There is no higher duty for a Kshatria than a righteous battle."

Yudíshtira sighed deeply, thinking to himself, "I hear a great deal about the duties of kings and Kshatrias, yet I know the path of virtue, and I must follow it." Then he said to Bima, "O best of speakers, courage is not enough to accomplish what you desire. There must be well-laid plans. Our enemies are skilled in fighting and always ready for battle. Many kings whom we have injured will fight for them. Bishma and Drona love us as well as our cousins, but because of the wealth and favor they enjoy, they will have to fight for Kuru's sons. They cannot be vanquished even by the gods. And there is also that mighty warrior Karna, fierce and angry, master of all weapons. How can we slay Duryódana, while he is protected by these tigers among men? O Bima, I cannot sleep at night when I think of Karna's lightness of hand, for I think he is the foremost of all wielders of the bow."

At these words, Bima was silent, and sat there, thinking. While they talked thus together, the holy Vyasa came to them, and they rose to worship him. He said to Yudíshtira, "O slayer of all foes, I knew what was passing in your heart. I can dispel this fear of yours, concerning Bishma and Drona and Karna, the Suta's son." Taking Yudíshtira's hand, he led him aside and said to him, "The time will come, O best of kings, when Arjuna will slay all your foes in battle. For this he will need better weapons than those he now has. He must go to Shiva and to Indra to learn from them the use of heavenly weapons. He is pure and brave enough to behold them and to win their favor. When he receives these divine weapons no one will be able to stand against him." Then, bidding him farewell, Vyasa vanished.

Yudíshtira called Arjuna to him. Taking both his hands and looking lovingly at him, he said, "The whole science of arms,

Arjuna, is known to Bishma, to Drona, and to Karna. The earth, besides, with all its towns and villages, its seas and woods and mines, is now under the sway of Duryódana. You are the only one who can win this back for us; you are our one support. Let me tell you, O slayer of foes, what Vyasa said unto me: you must go to Indra and learn from him all his weapons. O child, devote yourself fiercely to discipline so that you may obtain his favor. Take your bow and sword, put on your mail, and go northward this very day, without giving way to anyone, until you find Indra."

Arjuna's Sojourn in Heaven

At the command of Yudíshtira, the strong-armed Arjuna, taking up his bow and his quivers, wearing his mail and his finger protectors made of lizard skin, said farewell to his brothers and Dráupadi and set out on his journey. He strode through the forests and over the mountains and all the creatures fled out of the path that he took. Walking day and night without wearying, he crossed the Himálayas, passing many fearful and dangerous places, until he reached the mountain of Indra.

As he climbed its slope, a voice said to him, "Stop!" Looking round him he saw a holy man, ablaze with spiritual light, sitting under a tree. The holy one said to him, "Why do you come here armed and dressed in mail? There is no need of weapons here, for there are no quarrels in this place. You have reached a pure state of life by coming here; therefore, O child, throw away that great bow of yours, and tell me in what region of bliss you desire to dwell."

"I cannot dwell yet in any region of bliss," replied Arjuna, "for I have left my brothers behind me in the forest and I have enemies on whom I must be revenged."

The holy one then smiled and said to him, "O slayer of foes, may you be blessed! I am Indra. Ask whatever boon you desire."

The heroic Arjuna bent his head and joined his hands, saying to the god of a thousand eyes, "O illustrious one, grant me this boon! Let me learn from you all your weapons!"

With gentle words the god replied, "When you are able to behold Shiva, the lord of all creatures, who has a third eye in his brow, who carries the trident, then I will give you all the heavenly weapons. Open the eyes of your soul, O child; strive to behold the highest of the gods, for when you have seen him you will obtain all your wishes."

Arjuna stayed in that delightful place, by the bank of a rushing stream where swans and cranes abounded. With fierce energy he devoted himself to mastering his body and his mind so that the eyes of his soul might be opened. Dressed in rags, seated on a black deerskin, he ate the withered leaves that fell upon the ground. During the first month he ate these with some fruits every third night; the second month he ate every sixth night and the third month he ate once in a fortnight. When the fourth month came he lived on air alone, and trained himself to stand on tiptoe, with his arms upraised, for days at a time. The light of his soul began to shine through his body.

The great sages, beholding his fierce discipline, went together to Shiva to tell him what Arjuna was doing; but Shiva, smiling, said, "Do not grieve because of Arjuna! I know what is in his heart; I shall give him this very day what he desires." And the sages, glad at heart, returned to their dwellings.

Then the illustrious Shiva, the cleanser of all sins, the wielder of the great bow, took on the form of a hunter of huge and stalwart body, carrying a handsome bow and arrows, and came down upon the mountain breast where Arjuna sat. His wife, Uma, in the guise of a huntress, came with him, and a crowd of merry spirits. The whole mountainside suddenly blazed with beauty, because the god of gods had come there; the birds stopped singing, even the brooks and springs were silent, awed by his presence.

At this moment Arjuna saw a mighty boar rushing upon him to kill him. He sprang up and strung his bow, breaking the silence with the thunderous twang of its string. As he aimed at the animal, Shiva cried, "Stop! This boar is my prey, for I aimed at it first." Paying no heed to these words, Arjuna let fly his arrow; Shiva, in the form of a hunter, shot at the same moment, both arrows striking the heart of the boar, which fell and yielded up its life.

Then Arjuna turned and saw the hunter, splendid as a golden tree, and asked him, "Who are you that wander in this solitary wood? Why did you shoot the boar that was my prey? You have not obeyed the customs of the chase; therefore I must kill you."

Smiling, Shiva answered, "I aimed first at the boar; my arrow killed him. You were at fault and therefore shall not escape me. Now shoot your sharpest arrows and do your best to kill me."

This angered Arjuna, who engaged the hunter in a fierce battle. The son of Kunti poured forth hundreds of arrows, blazing like the rays of the sun, but the illustrious creator of the worlds, the bearer of the trident, stood unwounded, like a mountain under a shower of stones. Arjuna wondered, thinking to himself, "Well done! Well done! This mountaineer bears, without wavering, all my shafts. Is he Shiva himself, or some other god or demon?" When he had shot all his arrows he lifted his bow and struck the hunter with the end of it, but Shiva snatched the heavenly bow out of his hands. Arjuna drew his sword and with the whole might of his arm struck at the hunter's head; but that best of swords, at the moment of striking, broke in a hundred pieces. Then the son of Pandu, his mouth smoking with anger, fell upon the invincible god with his clenched fists, striking him blows like thunderbolts, which the hunter returned. At last Arjuna closed with him, pressing him against his breast, and then the god, putting forth his might, crushed Arjuna's breath out of his body, ending the fight. Bruised and breathless, the son of Kunti fell down on the earth as if he were dead, while Shiva stood above him, laughing.

The god, seeing how thin Arjuna's body was because of his fasting, wondered at his strength and, looking down at him, spoke in a voice as deep as thunder: "O Arjuna, I am pleased with what you have done. There is no Kshatria equal to you in courage and patience. O sinless one, I will allow you to see me in my true form and I will grant you any boon that you desire."

Then Arjuna beheld the very god and worshiped him, saying, "O god of gods, O cause of all causes, O pure one, rainer of boons, I bow down to you and worship you. Forgive this rashness of mine, this fight that I waged, in ignorance, with you. I came to this mountain only to behold you, for I seek your protection. Therefore forgive me for what I have done."

Shiva raised him and took his hands, saying, "I have forgiven you. Now ask of me the boon that you desire."

Arjuna said, "O lord of all created things, I ask of you that fierce celestial weapon that you wield, the weapon that, hurled forth with incantations, sends out thousands of darts and arrows like poisonous snakes, the weapon with which, at the end of the world, you will destroy the universe. With its help I shall be able to vanquish Karna, Bishma, and Drona in the terrible conflict that must take place between us. My great desire is to be victorious in that fight."

Shiva replied, "I will give you that weapon, O powerful one, for you are worthy to hold and hurl and withdraw it. It may be hurled by the mind, by the eye, by words, or by the bow; but, O son of Kunti, beware of using it! If it were hurled at a foe of little strength, it might destroy the universe. Only when all your other weapons have failed, may you use it."

Arjuna purified himself, and returning, stood before Shiva with rapt attention, while the god taught him the use of that mighty weapon and the mysteries of hurling and withdrawing it. After that the weapon waited upon Arjuna as it did upon Shiva; the gods and demons saw it at his side. Arjuna, with joined palms, worshiped the god, who forthwith left that blessed mountain with its caves, its valleys, and its snowy peaks; he disappeared before the very eyes of the gazing son of Pandu as the sun sets in the sight of the world.

Arjuna spent the night and the next day in that spot, rejoicing that he had obtained that wonderful weapon and had beheld the great god. In the evening a pure, refreshing breeze began to blow, new and fragrant flowers blossomed around him, and on all sides he heard the chanting of hymns to Indra. The lord of heaven, with his queen, seated on the back of a celestial elephant, alighted on a mountain peak, like a second sun, and spoke to him, saying, "O child, prepare now to ascend to heaven. Soon I shall send my chariot to take you to that blessed region where I will give you my divine weapons and teach you how to use them."

After Indra had returned to heaven, Arjuna purified himself by a bath in the river, worshiping the gods with sacrifices of water. Even as he wondered what manner of chariot Indra would send for him, it appeared to him, dividing the clouds and filling the sky with blazing light and the thunder of its wheels. It was drawn by ten golden horses swift as the wind, driven by a charioteer adorned with gold who, descending from the chariot, bowed before Kunti's son and invited him to mount it.

Arjuna first bade farewell to the mountain on whose breast he had lived, saying, "O king of mountains, you who give shelter to holy and heaven-seeking sages! As a child sleeps happily on his father's lap, so have I lived on your heights, eating your savory fruits, drinking the sweet water that flows from your body. Every day I have spent here has been happy; now, leaving you, I bid you farewell."

Then he mounted the chariot and with a glad heart soared upward through the sky, drawn by those steeds that had the speed of thought. When they had gone so far that they could no longer see the earth, they entered the region of the gods, where the sun and the moon do not shine, for it shines with its own brilliant light. He saw the stars, which look as small as lamps from the earth, blaze with splendor and beauty, and on the stars he saw royal sages, heroes who had died in battle, and saints by hundreds and hundreds. Wondering much, he asked the charioteer who these might be. "These, O son of Kunti," the charioteer replied, "are men who have attained the blessed regions through their virtue. They are called stars on earth." Thousands of other chariots moved through those regions; the Gandárvas and Apsaras sang and rejoiced there.

As they drew near to Indra's city, at whose gate the four-tusked celestial elephant stood, Arjuna beheld gardens and sacred trees that seemed to welcome him among them, while all around he heard the sound of drums and conchs. There was no heat or cold, no poverty or sorrow or fatigue in that celestial city. No one could behold it who had not purified himself under difficult vows; no one could approach it who did not know the Vedas and had not performed sacrifices and made gifts. As he drove through it, gods and sages and Gandárvas greeted him cheerfully, blessing him as he saluted them. Then at last he arrived at the hall of Indra, which the sage Nárada had described to him and to his brothers, and alighted there.

The lord of heaven, his father Indra, was seated under a white canopy held up by a golden staff, surrounded by bards and singers and Brahmans chanting the Vedic hymns. Arjuna approached and saluted him, bending his head to the ground; and Indra raised his son, took his hand, and seated him at his side upon the throne, caressing him and looking at him with delight.

Arjuna lived then in his father's palace, learning all the while the use of divine weapons and the means of withdrawing them. Indra gave him his own favorite missiles—the thunderbolt and the lightning, which come when the heavy clouds appear and the peacocks dance; he also gave him other weapons belonging to Agni and Vayu, to the demons and the storm gods, for all were entrusted to Indra. Arjuna became the friend of the chief of the Gandárvas, who taught him the music, singing, and dancing that those heavenly minstrels practice. So, surrounded by every joy and comfort, the son of Pandu lived full five years in heaven; but his mind was never at peace, for he always remembered his brothers and the unfair game at dice and thought with rage of Shákuni and Karna and Dushásana.

After five years had passed, Indra said to him, "O son, the time has come for you to return to earth; your brothers are sorrowing for you. With the heavenly weapons that are now at your command you can overpower every foe: neither Bishma nor Drona, Karna nor Shákuni nor any other Kshatria shall ever be able to defeat you." He set on Arjuna's head a golden diadem, girded him with a coat of mail that no shaft could pierce, gave him rare, unearthly garments and jewels, and a mighty conch to blow in battle. Then Arjuna, having bowed down to Indra and walked round him thrice, mounted the blazing chariot of the god, which sped like a meteor through the skies. The charioteer guided the golden horses to a peak of the Gandamádana Mountains, where Arjuna alighted.

On that mountain peak his brothers and Dráupadi awaited him; for during his sojourn in heaven he had sent messages to them, by those holy sages who wander at will through the three worlds, and asked them to meet him there.

The Pilgrimage

After the high-souled Arjuna had left them, his brothers and Dráupadi were filled with sorrow; they were like pearls loosed from their string, or like birds whose wings had been clipped. They often spoke of him, remembering how he could use his bow with his right or his left hand equally well, recalling his amazing deeds in battle, his sweet speech and forgiving temper, his high honor, and his mercy to a fallen foe.

One day, while they were talking thus, a great and holy hermit came before them. When he was seated and refreshed, Yudíshtira said to him sadly, "O holy one, I have been robbed of my wealth and my kingdom by cunning gamblers who exiled me to this great forest with my brothers and my wife, who is dearer to me than my own life. I cannot sleep at night when I remember our misfortunes. Even when I have regained my kingdom, I may be challenged again to gamble and I may again lose all, for I am not skilled in play nor can I stoop to deceit. Now besides, I have lost the company of the largehearted Arjuna, that wielder of the bow on whom our lives depend. When will he return to us, having mastered the heavenly weapons? Alas, I am the most wretched man on earth!"

"Be comforted, O King; do not yield to grief," said the hermit. "I have heard from certain holy pilgrims that Arjuna is living on a peak of the Himálayas, engaged in fierce discipline of mind and body. He lives on air and speaks to no man; surely he will soon attain all his desires. You need not fear to be challenged again to gamble, for I know the whole science of dice, which I will gladly teach you."

Then he taught the science of dice to the high-souled son of Pandu, who learned it with a glad heart, knowing that he need never again fear a gambling match.

Many holy men and hermits lived within the Kámyaka forest and many others came there from various parts of the country, or passed through it when they went on pilgrimages. One day one of the great sages, who shone with spiritual light, came to the forest, where the Pándavas and the Brahmans received him reverently, sitting round him as the gods sit round Indra. Yudíshtira asked him whence he had come and the great sage delighted the Pándavas with his answer.

"A short time ago," he said, "I went to Indra's palace, where I saw your heroic brother, who wields the bow with either hand, sitting on the very throne of Indra. Listen carefully, O King, for he sent this message to you: 'Tell my brother Yudíshtira to devote himself to virtue and to discipline, for they will bring him victory. Persuade him to make pilgrimages to the sacred bathing places, with his brothers and Dráupadi, that their souls may be cleansed of any evil. And tell him that in five years I will come to that king of mountains, the Sveta Peak in the Gandamádana Mountains, where I will meet him.' He also asked me to go with you, to show you the way to distant and difficult places and to protect you from the mighty demons whom you will encounter there. I have twice made the pilgrimage, O son of Kunti, and will gladly make it the third time in your company."

"My heart is so full of joy, O sinless one," Yudíshtira answered, "that I can hardly find words to answer you. Who could be more fortunate than I, who have Arjuna for my brother and you for my guide? Let us start our pilgrimage on the first favorable day."

On the day following the next full moon those heroes, with Dráupadi, set out in their chariots, accompanied by the high-souled sage and the Brahmans who had lived with them in the forest, and followed by their cooks and other servants in fifteen carts.

They first turned their faces toward the east till they came to the sea where the river Ganges falls into it. There the Pándavas bathed in the holy waters; then turning southward along the seashore, they visited the sacred bathing places, one after another, plunging into the waters that cleansed their hearts of sin. They purified themselves also by fasting and by long days of thought and meditation. Passing through various countries, they visited the shrines of all the gods, worshiping each one with offerings of flowers and water. After they had bathed in the waters of the Godávari and Nerbáda rivers, the Indus, the Jumna, and the Sarasváti, they turned northward; for four years had passed and the time for Arjuna's return drew near.

When they reached the slopes of the Himálayas, they saw with delight a kingdom abounding in horses and elephants, inhabited by huntsmen and horsemen. The King received them gladly at the borders of his land, and they lived in comfort with him until the sun rode high in the heavens and they were ready to start their journey into the mountains.

Then Yudíshtira said to Bima, "Dráupadi always looks to you for protection, even when Arjuna is with us, O Bima. Therefore, stay with her here, keeping Sahadéva with you, while Nákula and I, carrying only our bows and swords, go forward on foot with the holy one."

"O tiger among men," Bima replied, "this blessed princess has suffered much hardship and sorrow, but she will gladly go forward if she hopes to meet Arjuna. You, who miss him so much, will be still more unhappy if Sahadéva and I are not with you, and we cannot let you go alone through these steep and dangerous mountains. Let the Brahmans stay with our chariots and servants, but let us all go together to meet Arjuna. Do not be anxious; I will carry Panchála's daughter if her strength fails her." Dráupadi smiling, said, "Do not fear. I shall be able to go with you." And Yudíshtira consented to their going.

Leaving with the king of that country their chariots and servants, they set out on foot for the mountains, holding their bows strung at full stretch, keeping their quivers full of arrows, and their lizard-skin gloves on their hands. As they walked along the mountain paths their hearts were filled with delight, for the slopes were covered with blossoming trees, looking like garlands hung upon the mountain, and the birds, mad with joy, filled the air with their songs. Herds of elephants moved like clouds among the trees, and deer lifted their heads, holding the grass in their mouths, to watch the wayfarers. They walked beside lakes covered with lotuses whose buds were like joined hands greeting them. The air was filled with the sweet hum of bees covered with yellow pollen and drowsy with the heady honey of the lotus. Peacocks danced and spread their gorgeous tails; high in the branches their feathers were like crowns upon the trees. The Pándavas and Dráupadi, wide-eyed with wonder, went deeper into the forest, exceedingly delighted at heart.

When they reached the Gandamádana Mountains, the way became steep and rocky; it passed through mighty forests filled with tigers, boars, and monkeys. One day a violent storm arose, raising clouds of dust and dry leaves; trees fell and crashed around them, and they could neither see nor hear one another. Thunder roared, hail beat down upon them, and then a torrent of rain. Dráupadi, unused to walking and worn out by the storm, sank down to the ground, faint and trembling. They all ran to her; Yudíshtira took her on his lap, comforting her, while the twins took her rosy-soled feet and rubbed them gently with their strong hands, scarred by the bowstring, till she gradually regained her senses. Then Bima said, "Do not despair, O king of kings. I will carry her now over all the mountains that lie before us." So saying, he lifted her in his mighty arms and they went quickly on. Before many days had passed, they saw, on the side of a great mountain, a pleasant hermitage, well swept, fragrant with flowers, and echoing with the chanting of the Vedas. Many mighty sages lived there, dressed in black deerskins, feeding on fruits and roots and wild honey; these holy ones received the travelers joyfully, offering them fresh water, flowers and fruit. So they rested there for seven days before going on their way.

When they were rested, they took the mountain path again, ever traveling toward the north. They climbed with ease the steep and fearful rocks, passing deep caves and towering cliffs, and neither the Pándavas nor their guide, the holy sage, ever grew tired. Suddenly one day they beheld the peak that they sought and their hair stood erect at the sight: for the great mountain, dazzling in its brightness, with clouds stretching out at its sides, seemed to be dancing with outspread wings. Its forests were more beautiful than any they had seen; its rocks gleamed with brilliant minerals, and streams, like strings of pearls, rushed down its sides.

High on its slopes they came upon a solitary hermit, sitting like a skeleton bound together with naked muscles, for he had worn away his flesh with discipline. As they stopped to greet him, he said to Yudíshtira, "O best of the Báratas, do not go beyond this place, for the summits of these mountains are the playgrounds of the gods and no mortal may set his foot on them. Even here you may hear the drums and conchs of the Apsaras and the Gandárvas and the sweet notes of their songs. O child, stay here until you meet with Arjuna; live on the fruits and honey of this mountain and do not venture farther."

They spent a month in that high hermitage, beholding many marvels, watching the rising and the setting of the sun, performing the daily sacrifices, and reciting the Vedas. All the time they thought and talked about Arjuna and every day seemed to them as long as a year, for they had known no joy since their high-souled brother left them in the Kámyaka forest.

One day the sky was suddenly lightened; looking up, they beheld the chariot of Indra, like a smokeless fire or a blazing meteor, drawn by horses bright and swift as lightning. Quicker than thought it alighted on the mountain and Arjuna, radiant with beauty, decked with fresh garlands and bright jewels, leaped to the ground. He bowed down first to the sage, then to Yudíshtira and Bima, touching their feet, while the twins bowed down to him, touching his feet. Then he greeted his beloved wife, presenting to her the rare unearthly jewels and the garments that Indra had given him. They were exceedingly happy as Arjuna, sitting in the midst of his brothers, his wife, and the holy one, began to tell them all that had happened. "Thus I have learned the weapons of Shiva and Indra and all the other gods," he said. "Indra himself set on my head this diadem, gave me this mighty roaring shell, and this celestial mail; I have lived delightfully these five years in his high abode."

When he had told them briefly about his sojourn in heaven, promising to tell them all on the following days, Arjuna of the spotless deeds lay down and sweetly slept that night beside the two sons of Madri.

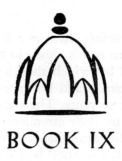

BOOK IX

IN THE FOREST

The Visit of Krishna and His Wife

WHEN Arjuna, that prince among heroes, had returned from the abode of Indra, the Pándavas sported in the forests of that beautiful mountain, caring nothing for wealth or fame. Now that they were together, their lives passed so happily that they spent four years there as if a single night had gone by. These four years, with the six that had passed before Arjuna's return, made ten years that they had spent in the forest.

One day Bima, the fierce son of the Wind God, with Arjuna and the heroic twins, seated himself before Yudíshtira and earnestly said, "It is only for the sake of your honor and good name, O King, that we have not left the forest and slain Duryódana with all his followers. This is the eleventh year that we have ranged the woods, deprived of our kingdom. Our enemies no longer fear us, so we shall be able easily to live out the thirteenth year undiscovered. Then we shall have our revenge on that meanest of men, Duryódana, when we slay him and regain our kingdom. Now, O just king, let us return to the world, for if we live much longer in this place that is so like heaven, we shall forget our sorrows and your fame will vanish from the earth, as a fragrant flower withers."

Yudíshtira listened to his brothers and did as they desired. They left that splendid peak and sought out the path by which they had come. As they started down, the holy sage bade them farewell, counseling them as a father does his sons; then he left them, to return to his abode in heaven. Those heroes, following the same road by which they had come, reached at last the kingdom of huntsmen and horsemen where they had left their chariots and their servants. There they were welcomed joyfully by the King and by their attendants.

Mounting their chariots, they drove back to the Kámyaka forest, where they had dwelt before Arjuna left them, and stayed there for a year, spending their days in hunting.

They passed the hot season in those cool woods; then the rainy season came, which ends the heat and is delightful to all living things. Hundreds of black clouds, like domes built up into the sky, thundered and poured down rain, day and night without ceasing; the sun disappeared, and the stainless lightning took its place. The earth was washed with rain and overgrown with grass; the rivers flooded, hissing like serpents. Boars and stags, birds and insects, excited frogs and snakes all welcomed with joy that happy season of rain.

Then the autumn came, thronged with geese and cranes; the river water turned clear and was covered with lilies and lotuses. The nights were free of dust, cool with clouds, and beautiful with myriads of stars, the planets, and the moon. The season was joyous and pleasant for the sons of Pandu, who roved by the rivers and in the woods, wielding their powerful bows.

During that autumn season, Krishna and his beloved wife came to see them. Alighting from their chariot, they saluted the Pándavas and were joyfully welcomed. Krishna, when he saw at last his beloved friend Arjuna, after such a long absence, clasped him in his arms again and again, while his wife embraced the princess of Panchála. While Krishna and the sons of Pandu talked together, Dráupadi and her friend, seated at their ease in the hermitage, laughed merrily together and talked about all that had happened in both their families.

"O Dráupadi," said the beloved wife of Krishna, "have no anxiety and no grief! Do not lie sleepless at night, for you will surely rule the earth again with your godlike husbands. Your brave sons are well and have become skillful in arms; they are living with us, and Subádra cares for them as if they were her own sons. She makes no difference between them and Abimányu, delighting in them all, grieving in their griefs, and rejoicing in their joys. They are beloved by everyone and take the greatest delight in the science of arms and in horsemanship.

"Tell me now, O daughter of Panchála, how is it that you rule the sons of Pandu, those heroes who are as strong and beautiful as gods? How is it that they are so obedient to you, so anxious to do your bidding, and are never angry with you? Do you use spells or drugs to keep their love, or is it because you always look so young and beautiful? Tell me how I, too, may keep Krishna ever obedient to me."

The chaste and blessed princess of Panchála replied to her, "How can I answer such a question, noble lady? Only a wicked woman uses spells or drugs to keep her husband's love. When a man knows that a wife uses such means, he fears her as he would a serpent ensconced in his bedchamber. How can a man who is troubled with fear have peace, or how can one who has no peace be happy?

"Hear now, O beautiful one, how I behave toward the high-souled sons of Pandu, those heroes who can slay their foes with a glance. My heart desires no others, whether they be gods, men, or Gandárvas. With deep devotion and humility I serve the sons of Kunti: I never bathe or eat or sleep until my husbands have bathed or eaten or slept, until, indeed, our servants also have bathed, eaten, and slept; I rise and greet each of my husbands when he returns from the field, the forest, or the town, offering him a seat and water to wash his feet; I keep the house and all household articles and food well ordered and clean, and serve the food at the proper time. I never speak angrily or fretfully; I am never idle; I do not laugh without cause; and I never linger at the door of the house.

"Formerly, O lady, thousands of Brahmans lived in Yudíshtira's palace, in Indra Prasta; all these Brahmans I honored daily with food, drink, and clothing taken from the storehouses. There were thousands of maidservants, adorned with jewels and gold, skilled in singing and dancing; I knew the names and faces of all those girls, what they ate, and what they wore, and what they did. The son of Kunti had thousands of serving men who daily used to feed his guests with plates of gold in their hands; he had thousands of horses and elephants that followed in his train while he ruled the earth. But it was I, O lady, who knew their number, ordered their lives, and listened to all complaints about them. Indeed, I knew everything that all the attendants of the palace did, down to the shepherds and cowherds. I alone knew the income and the expenses of the kingdom and the extent of its wealth. While my husbands were busy with their duties, I took charge of their treasury, as inexhaustible as the ocean. This burden, so heavy for any-one of evil heart, I bore day and night, sacrificing my ease. I awoke first and went last to bed, devotedly serving the sons of Kunti.

"This, O lovely one, has been the charm that has kept my husbands obedient to me; this is the art that I have always known and practiced in order to keep their love!"

Hearing these excellent words, Krishna's wife touched the feet of Dráupadi and said, "O princess of Panchála, forgive me for my light words. I spoke in joke, as one friend to another."

"Adore your husband, Krishna," said Dráupadi, smiling, "with friendship and love and sacrifice, so that he may think, 'She loves me truly with all her heart.' Serve him: even when he commands a serving maid to do a thing, rise up and do it yourself. And make yourself beautiful for him, decking yourself with fresh garlands and jewels, anointing yourself with fragrant perfumes."

The Sage's Stories

After their friends had left them, there came to the hermitage a great saint who had lived for many thousand years, yet his life was so holy that he looked like a young man twenty-five years old. As he sat among them in a friendly way, Yudíshtira said to him, "O deathless one, all of us who are assembled here long to hear your most excellent words. You have seen thousands of ages pass away, having seen with your own eyes the acts of creation. You have beheld God Himself with the eyes of your soul, having first opened your pure and lotuslike heart to Him. Therefore, you are deathless. When the sun and moon and earth pass away and God sleeps, you will still be there to worship Him. Tell us stories of bygone times and teach us how kings and saints and women should behave."

The saint stayed for many months in the hermitage, delighting the hearts of the sons of Pandu with stories of gods and heroes and sages. He comforted them for their own misfortunes, telling them the story of Rama, the heroic King of Ayódya, who was also banished to the forest for fourteen years and then returned victorious to his kingdom. He gave them wise counsel about the duties of kings and warriors and told them the following story:

"There was once a king so wise and virtuous that Indra and Agni decided that they would go down to earth to test his goodness. So Agni took the form of a pigeon, while Indra pursued him in the form of a hawk, and that pigeon fell upon the lap of the King as he sat on his throne. The pigeon said to him, 'O King, do not yield me up to the hawk! The protection of his subjects is the highest duty of a king. Therefore save my life!'

"Then the hawk, clinging to the royal throne, said, 'It is not right, O King, for you to keep from me the food that God has given me. If I have no food I shall surely die and then my wife and children will perish. Therefore by protecting this pigeon you destroy many lives. This is not virtue, O King.'

" 'Has any man ever heard birds speak like this?' the King said, wondering. 'How can we act rightly, having heard them both? He who gives up an affrighted creature that seeks protection will never live in heaven. On the other hand, he who refuses food to the hungry is also doomed. O hawk, let a bull cooked with rice be placed before you instead of this pigeon, and let abundant food be carried to the place where you live!'

" 'O great king, I do not desire a bull,' said the hawk, 'or any other food except this pigeon, whom God today gave me for my prey.' 'O ranger of the skies,' answered the King, 'I will bestow on you a rich province in my kingdom, or any other thing that you desire, except this one pigeon that has come to me for protection. Tell me what I can give in exchange for him.'

"The hawk said, 'If you care so much for this bird, O great ruler of men, cut off a piece of your own flesh and weigh it in a balance against the pigeon. When you give me a piece of your flesh that is equal in weight to the pigeon, I shall be satisfied.' 'Your request is a favor to myself,' answered the King.

"Then the good king, cutting off a piece of his own flesh, placed it on one of the scales of a balance, putting the pigeon on the other scale. That piece, however, did not equal the weight of the bird. So he cut off another piece and still another and another, but the pigeon still was heavier. At last, the King himself mounted the balance cheerfully, willing to sacrifice himself to save the frightened bird. When the hawk saw this he cried, 'Stay O virtuous king! I am Indra, the wielder of the thunderbolt, and the pigeon is Agni, the smoke-bannered God of Fire. We came to test you. Behold, these gashes in your body, where you cut off your flesh, shall be made the color of gold and shall emit a sweet fragrance. Your glory shall be resplendent, O King; you shall dwell in the holy regions after your death!' Saying this, Indra, with Agni, ascended into heaven, and the King, after filling heaven and earth with his good deeds, went to the blessed regions."

He told them also the following tale:

"O King, foremost of men, there was once a powerful saint named Manu, who practiced severe and rigid discipline for many thousands of years, in a forest by the side of a river. One day a fish, approaching the bank of the river, said to him, 'Worshipful sir, I am a helpless little fish and am very much afraid of the big fish, for it is a custom among us for the large ones to prey upon the small. I hope, O holy one, that you will find it worth your while to protect me. I will reward you for your kindness.' On hearing these words, Manu was filled with pity. He took the fish, whose body gleamed like a moonbeam, and put it in a water jug. He tended it carefully, as if it were a child, and it soon grew so big that there was no room for it in the jug. So he took it out and put it in a pool and the fish lived there for a year, until it became so large that it could no longer play about in that pool.

"Seeing Manu one day, it said to him, 'O holy and adorable father, pray take me to the Ganges, that favorite wife of the Ocean, so that I may live there.' And Manu took it and put it into the river with his own hands; and there, O conqueror of wealth, it grew still more, and seeing Manu again, it said to him, 'O lord, I can no longer move about in the Ganges because of my great body. Please take me quickly to the sea!'

"Then Manu took it out of the river, and in spite of its great bulk, he carried it easily and threw it into the sea. Turning to him, it said with a smile, 'O sinless one, listen now to me. The time for the cleansing of this world is at hand. A fearful flood will overwhelm the earth and all creatures moving and immovable will be destroyed. You must build a strong and massive boat and furnish it with a long rope. You must get into it and take with you all the different seeds that grow on the earth and preserve them carefully. Then wait for me, O adorable one, for without my help you cannot escape death. I shall appear to you with horns and thus you shall recognize me.' And Manu said, 'I believe all that you say, O mighty one, and shall obey you.'

"So Manu built the boat and collected all the seeds. When the waters began to rise he entered his boat and set sail on the surging sea. Then he remembered the fish, who, knowing his thoughts, appeared before him with horns on its head. Seeing that horned creature rise up like a rock in the midst of the ocean, Manu tied the rope into a noose and threw it round the head of the fish, who towed the boat with great strength through the roaring, tossing sea. Nothing but water could be seen; the boat reeled like a drunken man while the fish, for many days, towed it diligently toward the highest peak of the Himálayas.

"There the fish told Manu to tie his boat to that peak (which is still called the Harbor) and Manu obeyed. Then it said to him, 'I am the Creator of all things: there is none greater than I. I took this form to save you from the flood. Now you must create again all beings—gods, demons, and men—and plant again all the seeds that you have brought with you. With my blessing and your own spiritual power you can accomplish this.' So saying, the fish vanished; and there, upon that mountain peak, Manu set about the work of creating all things in their proper order.

"This is the Legend of the Fish and he who meditates upon it may be cleansed of all his sin."

So with many tales and much wise talk the Pándavas spent their last year in the forest.

The Riddles of the Crane

One day, toward the end of that year, a deer wandered into the clearing where the hermitage stood; while it was butting about there it chanced to catch in its antlers two sticks with which a Brahman made his fire, by rubbing them together until a spark appeared. Thereupon the deer bounded swiftly away, carrying the sticks with it. The Brahman, who offered his daily sacrifice to Agni, God of Fire, with those two sticks, ran to the Pándavas and told them what had happened, begging them to follow the deer and bring back his sticks so that his sacrifice might not be hindered.

Taking up their bows they started out at once, and seeing the deer at no great distance, they shot barbed arrows and javelins at it, but could not pierce it. They pursued it deep into the woods and at last lost sight of it. Tired and disappointed, hungry and thirsty, they sat down in the cool shade of a banyan tree, wondering why such mighty hunters and bowmen as they were should have failed to track down and kill this one deer.

Yudíshtira said to Nákula, "O son of Madri, climb this tree and see whether there is any water near us, for all your brothers are tired and suffer from thirst."

Nákula speedily climbed the tree and said, "I see trees that grow on watery ground and I hear the cries of cranes. Therefore water must be near."

"O amiable one," Yudíshtira said, "fetch water for us in our quivers."

Running off, Nákula soon came to a crystal lake, where cranes abounded. He stooped to drink the water when a voice said to him, "O child, do not be rash. This lake is mine. Answer my questions first; then drink and take all the water that you desire." But Nákula, who was very thirsty, paid no heed to these words and drank the cool water. No sooner had he drunk it than he fell down dead.

When Nákula did not return, Yudíshtira sent Sahadéva to find him and to bring the water, and Sahadéva, coming to the lake, found his brother lying dead on the ground. Horrified at the sight and suffering with thirst, he stooped to drink, when he heard the same voice saying, "O son of Madri, do not be rash. This lake is mine. First answer my questions; then drink and take the water." But Sahadéva, too, paid no attention to the voice; he drank the water and fell dead beside his brother.

Then Yudíshtira sent Arjuna to find his younger brothers, and Arjuna, with his bow in one hand and his naked sword in the other, ran to the lake, where he found his two brothers lying dead. Filled with grief and rage, he raised his bow, looking around the wood, but saw no one. He thought, "I shall surely have to fight today; therefore I must quench my thirst." And, stooping to drink the water, he heard the same words that had been addressed to his brothers. Leaping up, Arjuna said, "Show me who it is that forbids me to drink! When you are pierced by my arrows you will not speak so insolently!" And he shot his invincible shafts in all directions, showering them even into the sky.

The voice said, "Why take so much trouble, O son of Kunti? Answer my questions and then drink, for if you drink first you shall surely die." But Arjuna, like the others, paid no heed to the words: he drank and fell down dead.

Then the mighty Bíma came to find them and suffered the same fate, falling beside his brothers.

Yudíshtira waited for them a long time, his heart deeply troubled. He rose up and entered the forest, listening for some human sound, but he heard nothing but the hum of the black bees and the songs of warblers. He went on until he came to that beautiful lake, overgrown with lilies and lotuses, where he found his brothers, as glorious as gods, lying dead, with their bows and arrows strewn on the ground. Overwhelmed with grief, he wept and lamented for them, wondering greatly what could have killed them. "Alas," he said, "why do these unvanquished ones lie here on the earth, their bodies unwounded? There are no marks of weapons here, no footprints on the earth. Some powerful being must have killed them, for each of them was like a mighty cataract. Who could have overthrown these four great mountains; who but Yama himself, who in due time brings about the end of all creatures?"

He stepped down to the water in order to purify himself from the sight of death, and as he did so he heard a voice saying, "I am a crane that lives on tiny fish. It was I who sent your brothers to Yama's realm, because they drank of this water after I forbade them to do so. If you, O prince, do not answer my questions before you drink, you will be the fifth to die. This lake is mine. Do not be rash, O son of Kunti!"

"I do not desire what belongs to you, O worshipful one!" Yudíshtira said. "Exceedingly wonderful is the deed that you have done, for you have slain those whom neither gods nor demons could endure in battle. I do not know what your purpose is or who you are, but great curiosity and also fear have taken hold on me. I shall answer your questions as best I can; therefore ask me now!"

The crane then said, "What does not close its eyes when it sleeps? What does not move after it is born? What has no heart? What grows as it moves?"

"A fish does not close its eyes when it sleeps," Yudíshtira answered. "An egg does not move after it is born. A stone has no heart. A river grows as it moves."

The crane asked, "What always travels alone? What is reborn after its birth? What god is the guest of man? What is swifter than the wind?"

Yudíshtira answered, "The sun always travels alone. The moon is reborn after its birth. Agni, God of Fire, is the guest of man. The mind is swifter than the wind."

THE CRANE ASKED-WHAT IS THE HIGHEST DUTY?

The crane asked, "What, O King, is true knowledge? What is ignorance? What is mercy and what is the highest duty?"

"True knowledge is the knowledge of God," Yudíshtira replied. "Ignorance is not knowing one's duty. Mercy consists in wishing happiness to everyone. The highest duty is not to hurt any living creature."

"You have, O king of men," said the crane, "truly answered all my questions. Therefore let one of your brothers, whichever one you choose, regain his life."

"Let this one who is tall as a tree, who is broad-chested and long-armed, let Nákula regain his life!" Yudíshtira answered.

"How can you," rejoined the crane, "forsake Bima, who is as strong as a thousand elephants, and wish Nákula to live? How can you forsake Arjuna, on whom all the sons of Pandu depend, and wish Nákula to live? Bima and Arjuna are dear to you. Why do you want a stepbrother to regain his life?"

"He who sacrifices virtue sacrifices himself also," Yudíshtira said. "He who cherishes virtue is cherished by it in return. Therefore I always cherish virtue and never sacrifice it, lest we ourselves be sacrificed. My father had two wives, Kunti and Madri. There is no difference between them in my eyes and no difference between my brothers. In me Kunti has a living son, but there is no one now to make offerings to Madri's spirit. Therefore let Nákula regain his life!"

"Since you know the true meaning of knowledge, duty, and mercy, O bull of the Báratas," said the crane, "let all your brothers live!" At these words, the four brothers rose up, refreshed, their thirst and hunger gone, and they all embraced each other with great joy.

Then Yudíshtira said, "O you who stand on one leg in this lake, what god are you, for surely you are no bird, O unconquerable one? Are you the lord of the gods, the wielder of the thunderbolt? Each of my brothers can slay ten thousand warriors; I know no man or god or demon who can slay them all. They are refreshed as if they had just been wakened from sweet sleep. Are you a friend of ours, or perhaps my father himself?"

The crane vanished; in its place the mighty Darma, God of Justice, appeared before them, saying, "O child, I am your father, the lord of justice. I came here to test you and I am well pleased with you. Now ask what you will of me, O foremost of kings, for I will grant whatever you desire. Those who honor me never come to harm."

Yudíshtira answered, "A deer carried away a Brahman's fire sticks. Let us find them, O exalted one, so that the Brahman's adorations of Agni may not be interrupted. This is the first boon I ask."

"It was I, O son of Kunti," the lord of justice said, "who, in the form of a deer, carried away the fire sticks so that I might test you. Behold them here! Now ask another boon!"

"We have spent twelve years," said his noble son, "in the forest, and the thirteenth year has come. May no one recognize us during that year! That is my second boon."

The worshipful one replied, "I grant this second boon. You will spend this thirteenth year, secretly and unrecognized, in Viráta's kingdom. Ask a third boon, O King!"

"It is enough that I have beheld you with my eyes, O god of gods," said Yudíshtira, worshiping him. "May I conquer greed and folly and anger; may my mind be ever devoted to truth and kindness!"

"These qualities you have by nature, O sinless one," answered the god. "May you attain all that you desire!"

With these words he vanished from their sight. The Pándavas lay down and slept sweetly; when they awoke they returned to the hermitage and gave the Brahman his fire sticks.

They Plan the Thirteenth Year

Shortly after that Yudíshtira called his younger brothers together and said to them, "Twelve years of our exile have now passed and the thirteenth year, hardest of all to spend, has come; we must choose some pleasant region where we may live in se-

crecy, free of fear. The aged Viráta, King of the Matsyas, is virtuous, powerful, and generous. Let us spend this year in his city,
serving him even as the adorable God of Justice has commanded
us. Tell me, O sons of the Báratas, how each of you can serve the
King and how you will present yourselves to him."

"O god among men, what service will you take in Viráta's kingdom?" Arjuna asked. "It is hard for a king to bear trouble as an
ordinary person does. O righteous one, how will you live unrecognized?"

"I shall present myself as a Brahman, skilled in dice and fond of
gambling," Yudíshtira replied. "In the court of that high-souled
king I shall entertain him and his friends, moving ivory men on
boards of gold and silver, or throwing jeweled dice. I shall call
myself by another name, and if the monarch asks me who I am,
I shall say, 'Formerly I was the intimate friend of King Yudíshtira.' What service will you perform, O Bima?"

"I shall present myself to the King of the Matsyas as a cook,"
said Bima. "I am a skillful cook and I shall make better curries for
him than he has ever tasted, and carry mighty loads of wood for
the fires. The King will be so pleased with me that he will give
me charge of all his kitchens. I shall also break powerful elephants
and bulls, and if any wrestlers come to the court I will fight them,
thereby entertaining the King. If he asks me who I am, I shall say,
'Formerly I was the cook and wrestler of King Yudíshtira.'"

"What task," Yudíshtira said, "will be performed by Arjuna,
who lived for five years in the shining halls of heaven, learning the
use of all the heavenly weapons; who is among warriors what the
Himálayas are among mountains, what the ocean is among waters,
and what the tiger is among beasts?"

"O lord of the earth," answered Arjuna, "it is hard to hide the
scars of the bowstring on my arms. Therefore I shall cover my
arms with bangles, put brilliant rings in my ears, braid my hair,
and call myself a eunuch who can teach singing and dancing to
the ladies of Viráta's palace. In the inner apartments I will entertain the King and the ladies by reciting stories. If anyone asks me
whence I come, I will say, 'I taught music and dancing in Yudísh-

tira's palace.' Thus, O King, as fire is hidden in ashes, I will pass my days unrecognized in Viráta's palace."

"O Nákula," Yudíshtira said, "you are tender and graceful and worthy of every luxury. Tell me what you will do in the kingdom of the Matsyas."

"I shall become the keeper of King Viráta's horses," answered Nákula. "Horses are ever dear to me, as they are to you, O King of the Báratas. I am skillful in training and tending them; even wild colts and mares become gentle under my hands and let me break them for riding and for drawing chariots. If anyone asks about me I shall say, 'Formerly I was employed by King Yudíshtira and took charge of his horses.' So I shall spend my time delightfully in Viráta's city and no one will recognize me."

"How will you, O Sahadéva," asked Yudíshtira, "present yourself before the king? What will you do in order to live in secrecy?"

"I shall offer myself as a cowherd," answered Sahadéva, "and take charge of all the King's cattle. O lord of earth, I often watched over your herds; I have a particular knowledge of cattle and can tame the unruly ones. I am skilled in milking and keeping count of cows and take delight in working with them. I shall say that I used to serve you."

"This beloved wife of ours," said Yudíshtira, "dearer to us than our lives, is not used to any kind of work, for she has enjoyed, ever since her birth, garlands and perfumes, ornaments and costly robes. What service can she perform, who is so delicate and young?"

"I shall offer myself to the Queen as a serving woman skilled in dressing hair," Dráupadi replied, "saying that I served Dráupadi in Yudíshtira's household. I will please her and she will cherish me; therefore do not grieve, O King."

After they had talked together thus and made their plans, they sought the advice of their priest. They decided that he should return to Panchála, taking the holy fire with him so that he could continue their daily sacrifices; the maidservants and the cooks were to go with him, while the empty chariots were to be taken to Krishna, and all of the servants were to say, "We do not know where the Pándavas have gone. They left us in the Kámyaka forest." Then the priest blessed them, performing the ceremonies of departure; they saluted him and the other Brahmans in the hermitage, respectfully taking their leave of all. Girding on their swords and their lizard-skin gloves, carrying their various weapons, they set out for the kingdom of the Matsyas, Dráupadi walking before them.

They left the forest where they had lived so long and came into open country where there were footpaths and fields where the grain was growing. They passed Dráupadi's home, the land of the Panchálas, and entered the kingdom of the Matsyas, calling themselves hunters.

When they came in sight of the city, Yudíshtira said to Arjuna, "Where shall we leave our weapons, before we enter the city? If we carry them with us, the citizens will surely be alarmed and wonder who we are; besides, your great bow, Gandíva, is well known to all men and would betray you. Remember that if even one of us is discovered, we shall have to pass another twelve years in the forest."

"Near yonder cemetery there is a mighty tree with many branches that are hard to climb," Arjuna said. "No one will see us if we leave our weapons there; no one will find them in that dreary place, so full of snakes and wild beasts. Let us put them in that tree, O son of Kunti, before we go on to the city."

Arjuna loosened the string of the dreadful Gandíva, whose twang was like thunder, and his brothers unstrung those bows with which they had gone into the four directions and conquered all the earth. With their bows they put their long and flashing swords, their precious quivers, and their arrows sharp as razors. Nákula, climbing the tree, tied the weapons fast on those branches that he thought could never break, where the rain could not reach them. Then they entered the great city where they meant to remain undiscovered for the thirteenth year of their exile.

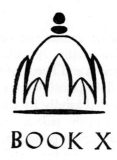

BOOK X

IN VIRATA'S KINGDOM

Kíchaka's Insolence

KING VIRATA was seated on his throne when Yudísh-tira, looking like the moon hid in clouds or a fire covered with ashes, came before him. The King said to his counselors and Brahmans, "Find out who it is that has just entered my court. He looks like a king of kings, a lord of earth, for he shines like Indra himself."

As he was speaking, Yudíshtira came to him and addressed him: "O great monarch, I am a Brahman who has lost all his possessions and comes to you for support. I am skilled in casting dice and can entertain your friends by gaming with them."

"I will grant you any boon that you desire," Viráta replied, "for you look as if you deserved a kingdom. You shall have plenty of food and drink and clothing; you shall be my friend and ride in my chariot; all my doors shall be open to you. You need have no fear as long as you live with me." So Yudíshtira began to live happily in Viráta's palace, highly honored by all men.

In the same manner the other sons of Pandu presented them-selves, one by one, to the King who, marveling at their strength and beauty, gave to each one the place that he desired. Bima was put in charge of all the kitchens, while Arjuna, wearing bracelets and large earrings, his thick hair braided, was sent into the maidens' apartments, where he taught the King's daughter, her friends, and waiting maids the melodies and dances that he had learned in Indra's halls. Nákula took charge of all the King's stables and chariots and herds of horses, while Sahadéva was made chief cowherd, responsible for a hundred thousand kine and all their keepers. Treated kindly by the King, they made themselves dear to all that were in the palace and no one suspected who they were.

Dráupadi bound her soft, black, curling hair into a long braid, hiding it under the single robe that she wore. Then she wandered through the streets, looking deeply distressed. The Queen chanced to look down from her terrace as Dráupadi passed and called to her, saying, "O beautiful one, who are you and what are you seeking?"

"I am a royal hairdresser, seeking employment, O Queen," Dráupadi answered. "I know how to dress the hair, how to pound sweet herbs for perfume, and how to make beautiful garlands of jasmine and lotus and blue lilies. Yudíshtira's queen, Dráupadi, called me the maker of garlands."

"I fear that the King will forsake me when he sees your beauty," the Queen said, "for see, all my maids are looking at you now, and how could any man resist you?"

"O fair lady," Dráupadi replied, "no man may make love to me, for I have five young husbands who are Gandárvas. They always protect me so well that any man who troubles me meets death that very day."

"If that is true," said the Queen, "I will take you into my household, O delighter of hearts."

So Dráupadi, ever devoted to her lords, lived in the Queen's palace and no one suspected who she really was.

Those lords of the earth, the Pándavas, true to their promise, spent their days with perfect self-control, although they often suffered because of the false positions they were in. Yudíshtira, who was now very skillful at dice, entertained the King and his sons and courtiers so well that they sat in the gaming hall like a row of birds bound on a string, playing according to his pleasure. Unknown to the King, he shared with his brothers the wealth that he won at gambling. Bima, on his part, brought them the food and sweetmeats that were given to him in the kitchen, while Arjuna divided with his brothers the money that he got by selling the cast-off garments that the ladies gave him. Nákula brought milk, curds, and butter to the others, and Sahadéva shared the wealth that the King freely gave him because of his excellent management of the horses. And Dráupadi, though she herself was waiting on the Queen, secretly looked after the welfare of all the brothers. Thus, taking care of one another, they lived for ten months in the capital of the Matsyas as safely hidden as if they were once more in their mothers' wombs.

When the year was nearly spent, the mighty Kíchaka, the commander of the King's army, chanced to see Dráupadi, for he was the brother of the Queen and often came to her apartments. Beholding his sister's hairdresser treading the earth like a goddess, Kíchaka was smitten by the shafts of the God of Love. He approached her as a jackal might approach a lioness, speaking to her in a winning voice: "Who are you, O beautiful one? Never before in this world have I beheld beauty like yours. But alas, blessed lady, your loveliness is now unused, like a graceful garland that lies unworn. I pray you, sweet damsel, to marry me and live with every luxury and joy. I will forsake all my wives and make them your slaves. I, too, will be your slave, ever obedient to you."

"It would be unworthy of you to marry a lowborn servant," Dráupadi replied. "Besides, your behavior is unseemly, for I am the wife of others. You must not bend your heart to sin, or misfortune will overtake you."

Then Kíchaka, maddened by desire, said to her, "You do ill, O beautiful one, to scorn me, and you will repent it. I am the real lord of this kingdom, for all its people depend on me. I will make you the mistress of it and you can enjoy all the power and wealth that you desire. How can you choose to remain a servant?"

Hearing these accursed words, Dráupadi answered him reproachfully, "O Kíchaka, do not throw away your life. I have five Gandárvas for my husbands who will slay you in their anger. You could not escape them even if you were able to enter the earth or soar into the sky. Why then do you desire me, like a baby lying on its mother's lap, crying for the moon? Be warned and save your own life."

Kíchaka went to the Queen, lamenting because Dráupadi had refused him and begging for his sister's help. That gentle lady, touched with pity, said to him, "I will send the damsel to you, pretending that I need some wine. Then you can see her alone and perhaps she may incline her heart to you."

She called Dráupadi and told her to go to Kíchaka's house for wine, but Dráupadi fell down before her weeping and said, "O Princess, do not send me to Kíchaka's palace. You yourself know how shameless he is. You have many maids, O gentle lady. I pray you to send one of them and not me, for I know that Kíchaka will insult me." "He will not harm you," said the Queen, "when you come from me. Now take this golden bowl and bring the wine."

Weeping and filled with dread, Dráupadi went toward Kícha-ka's palace, praying to the gods and thinking to herself, "I have never cared for any man except my husbands. Let that truth protect me from any harm at Kíchaka's hands." When that wicked man saw her coming toward him like a frightened doe, he rose up joyfully to welcome her, but Dráupadi said, "I have been sent by the Queen to get some wine. Give it to me quickly, for she is very thirsty."

"Others will take, O lovely one, what the Queen wants," Kíchaka said, and he caught hold of her arm. When she turned to run away, he seized her garment and Dráupadi, trembling with anger and unable to bear any more, threw him on the ground. Then she ran to the King's court, followed by Kíchaka, who seized her long hair and struck her in the very presence of the King. Both Bima and Yudíshtira were seated there, but Dráupadi, not wishing to betray them, made her complaint to the King, reproaching him for allowing her to be so insulted in his presence.

Yudíshtira and Bima found it hard to control their fury and the sweat stood on their foreheads. Bima's eyes began to smoke, his eyelashes stood on end, and he gnashed his teeth with rage. He was about to rise, looking at Kíchaka as an elephant looks at a tree it is about to uproot, when Yudíshtira restrained him, saying, "Are you looking for fuel for your fires, cook? If you want fagots, go out and fell some trees." Then he spoke to his beloved wife, saying, "Do not stay here, O maker of garlands! Go to the Queen's apartments. Wives of heroes bear great suffering for their husbands' sakes. Your Gandárva husbands, I am sure, will take the life of him who has wronged you, in their own good time. Meanwhile you are interrupting the play in the King's court."

"My husbands are indeed very kind!" Dráupadi replied. "Since the eldest of them has a weakness for gambling, they are not in a position to help me." With these words, her eyes red with anger, she ran to the Queen's rooms.

That night, as she lay weeping on her bed, she said to herself, "No one but Bima can help me now." She rose and went swiftly to his room in the kitchens; putting her arms around him, she waked him, crying, "Arise, arise, Bima! How can you sleep while the wretched Kíchaka lives?" Bima sat up, surprised. "Why have you come here in such a hurry?" he asked. "Tell me quickly what you want, for you know that I will always save you from any danger. Then return to your bed before anyone wakes and sees you." Dráupadi hid her face on Bima's breast and began to weep.

"How can you ask me what I want," she said, "you who know all my sorrows? Who but Dráupadi could go on living after suffering such grief? I must behold Yudíshtira—who used to be followed by ten thousand elephants adorned with golden garlands—supporting himself by casting dice. I must see you, O bull of the Báratas, engaged in the ignoble work of a cook and when the King makes you fight with lions and elephants in the arena, I must look on, nearly swooning with fear, while the ladies and maidservants look sideways at me and believe that I must have a secret love for you. Alas, I must see Arjuna, the terror of his foes, teaching dancing to King Viráta's daughter, living among women and despised of men. When I behold Sahadéva, who is Kunti's favorite child, tending the kine and sleeping at night on calfskins, how can I bear to live? And Nákula, before whom hostile armies fled, now trains horses to display them before the King. But I have even greater griefs than these.

"You know, O Bima, what happiness was mine. Alas, I, whom the whole earth with its belt of seas obeyed, must now obey the Queen and stand in fear of her. This I can bear because the time of our exile draws to its end. But now the wicked Kíchaka asks me every day to be his wife and strikes me in the presence of the King. This, O slayer of foes, I cannot bear and my heart is bursting like a fruit ripened in its season. O Bima, slay this wretch who has insulted me, as you would dash an earthen pot against a stone! If tomorrow's sun sheds its rays upon him, I shall surely drink poison, for I shall never yield to him."

Bima, embracing her, comforted her and wiped the tears from her face. "I will do as you say, O lovely one," he said. "I will slay him and all his friends. Arrange a meeting with him tomorrow evening in the dancing hall, when the dancers have gone home for the night. But do it secretly, that no one else may know." Then they took leave of one another and waited impatiently for the day.

In the morning Kíchaka went at once to Dráupadi, begging her again to marry him. She, pretending to yield to him, asked him to meet her in the dancing hall that night, and the stupid Kíchaka went home in great delight. He adorned himself with garlands, jewels, and fragrant perfume, and his beauty flamed up, like the wick of a lamp that is just going out. The day seemed endless to him. Entering the dancing hall at the appointed hour, he saw through the darkness a figure sitting in the corner. He approached it as an insect approaches a flaming fire and began to speak, when suddenly the figure rose and the mighty Bima, laughing, seized him by the hair.

Kíchaka freed his hair and the two great warriors grappled with each other in the dark in that lonely place. Locked in each other's arms, they fought like two powerful bulls or like two elephants in spring. At last Kíchaka grew tired and began to tremble. Then Bima threw him down, seized his throat, and placing his knee upon Kíchaka's chest, strangled him as he would a beast. Calling Dráupadi, he lighted a torch, showed her the body of her enemy, and

quickly returned to the kitchen. Dráupadi, with the greatest delight, woke the keepers of the dancing hall, saying to them, "Come
and see what has befallen that wicked man who desired other
men's wives! There he lies, slain by my Gandárva husbands."

They looked at him in amazement; then ran to tell his kinsmen,
who came and stood, surrounding his body and wailing for his
death. When they were carrying him out, in order to prepare his
funeral, they saw Dráupadi leaning against a pillar. "There is the
wicked woman for whom he lost his life!" they cried. "Let us
burn her with him!" And they seized her, bound her with cords,
and placed her upon the bier of Kíchaka, to be burned with him.
Dráupadi, terrified, screamed for help and Bima heard her. Leaving the palace by another gate, he ran toward the place where the
funeral pyre was being raised and leaped over the wall. Near it
was a tree; he uprooted it and, carrying it on his shoulders, he
rushed like an angry lion upon the family of Kíchaka.

When they beheld him they said, "Lo, the powerful Gandárva
is attacking us! Set the woman free!" And they unbound Dráupadi
and ran away toward the city, but Bima pursued them, killing
many of them. The rest of them went to the King and told him
what had happened, saying, "When this woman returns, O King,
send her away from your kingdom, or it will be destroyed entirely."

So when Dráupadi returned to the city the people hid their eyes
from her, fleeing from her in all directions, and when she came
before the Queen, that lady said, "O beautiful one, the King is
filled with fear at what the powerful Gandárvas have done. Go
now wherever you choose to go and good betide you."

"Suffer me to stay here just thirteen days more," said Dráupadi. "Then my Gandárva husbands will carry me away. They
will be so pleased, if you do this, that they will grant many boons
to King Viráta." She said this because in thirteen days the year of
secrecy would be over.

The Kúravas Steal the Cattle

During the course of this thirteenth year Duryódana had sent his spies far and wide, through the villages and towns and cities of every country to search for the Pándavas. When they had completed their work, they returned to Hastinápura and said to their master, "O lord of men, we have searched through the solitary wilderness abounding with deer and overgrown with trees and creepers; we have searched on the mountaintops and on the plains, in many kingdoms, provinces, and cities, but we have found no trace of the sons of Pandu. It seems that they have perished without leaving a mark behind. Yet we have discovered one piece of news, O monarch, that you will be glad to hear. The commander of King Viráta's armies, Kíchaka of the wicked soul, who has often defeated your friends and allies, now lies slain with all his kinsmen. He was killed by invisible Gandárvas during the hours of darkness, O king of unfading glory!"

The mighty King of the Trigartas, a friend and ally of Duryódana, was sitting beside him as he received this news. He spoke at once, saying, "My kingdom has many a time been invaded by the Matsyas, led by the King's general, Kíchaka, a crooked and wrathful man, yet famous the world over for his might. If Kíchaka is dead, I believe that Viráta will lose his courage and his pride. Let us therefore, O tiger among kings, invade his kingdom, carry off his excellent cattle and his wealth, and then divide the kingdom among ourselves."

Karna agreed, saying, "Let us forget the sons of Pandu, who are either dead or have disappeared for good, and go at once into Viráta's kingdom."

Duryódana also agreed; turning to his brother Dushásana he said, "Consult with the elders and then array our forces without delay! Let the Trigartas march first toward the city of Viráta and seize his immense herds of cattle. Then, when all the Matsyas have gone out to fight them, let us secretly invade the kingdom from another quarter and drive off all the cattle we desire."

Therefore, the Trigartas, on the seventh day of the dark fort-night of the moon, with their chariots and infantry, marched off to the southeast to invade the Matsya kingdom.

As soon as they began to drive off the cattle, one of Viráta's herdsmen ran to the city, entered the court where the King sat surrounded by his counselors and the sons of Pandu, and bowed down before him saying, "O foremost of kings, the Trigartas are seizing your cattle by hundreds and by thousands! Oh, rescue them quickly, that they be not lost!"

The King immediately arrayed for battle the Matsya army with its chariots and elephants, cavalry and foot soldiers. The King and princes put on their shining and beautiful armor, yoked to their chariots their white horses encased in mail, and raised their gold-decked banners of various shapes and devices. Viráta said, "Let the dice player and the cook, the keeper of my stables and the chief herdsman fight with us! Give them chariots and coats of mail, banners and weapons, for I am sure that they are Kshatrias." But he never thought of Arjuna, who spent his days in singing and dancing. The four sons of Pandu put on with glad hearts the coats of mail and mounted the chariots yoked with good steeds, for it was at the very end of the thirteenth year of their exile that the Trigartas invaded the kingdom of the Matsyas, and they no longer feared to be known.

The army of Viráta, looking very splendid with its elephants, chariots, and horses, marched out of the city to the place whence the cattle had been stolen. Following the hoofprints of the herds, they caught up with the army of the Trigartas in the afternoon. Both the Matsyas and the Trigartas, fighting for the possession of the cattle, sent up loud roars and the encounter between them made the hair stand on end. Chariots clashed against chariots, foot soldiers fought against foot soldiers, horsemen against horse-men, and elephants against mighty elephants, fighting with great fury, neither side overcoming the other. The battle raged so furi-ously, such clouds of dust arose that the warriors could hardly tell friend from foe.

Then the King of the Trigartas and his brother rushed toward

King Viráta, with their maces in their hands. They killed his charioteer and his two horses, as well as the soldiers who protected him,
and took him captive, carrying him off the field in a chariot.
The Matsyas, seeing their king a captive, began to fly in fear in
all directions, but Yudíshtira, perceiving what had happened, said
to Bima, "King Viráta is a prisoner. Rescue him, O mighty-armed
one! We have lived happily in his city; let us now pay our debt
to him."

Bima turned his chariot and rushed furiously after the King of
the Trigartas, the twins driving on each side of him to protect his
wheels. They destroyed all the chariots that tried to stop them;
elephants, horsemen, and fierce bowmen were overthrown by
Bima as he rushed on. The Matsya warriors, seeing the Pándavas
advancing, returned to the fight and charged upon the enemy,
driving them back and sending thousands of them to the realm
of Yama. Bima overtook the King's chariot, slew the horses and
threw the driver upon the ground. Leaping from his own chariot,
he seized the hair of the King of the Trigartas and dashed him
senseless on the ground. The whole Trigarta army was panic-
stricken, fleeing in all directions. King Viráta was rescued and all
his cattle were regained. Bima lifted up the King of the Trigartas,
brought him before Viráta, and made him say, "I am your slave."
Viráta freed the vanquished king, who, hanging his head with
shame, saluted his victorious enemy and returned to his own
kingdom.

Then Viráta turned to the sons of Pandu, saying, "O smiters of
foes, I owe to you my kingdom and my wealth. It belongs now
as much to you as it does to me. Live here with me always; I will
bestow upon you all that you can desire." He sent messengers to
the city to proclaim the victory at sunrise the next morning; then
all those mighty warriors lay down and slept happily on the field
of battle.

Meanwhile, after the King of the Matsyas had led his whole
army against the Trigartas, Duryódana invaded the kingdom from
another quarter. With his brothers and Bishma, Drona, Karna, and

Ashvattáman, he drove away the cowherds and seized sixty thousand of King Viráta's cattle.

The chief cowherd, terrified, mounted a chariot and drove to the city for help; but only the youngest of the King's sons was there, for all the other princes and warriors had gone forth with the army of the King. This prince, whose name was Uttar, boasted loudly in the presence of the cowherd, saying, "I would set out this very day in pursuit of the cattle if only I had a charioteer. If anyone can be found who is fit to drive my chariot I will fight with all the Kúravas until they say, 'Can it be Arjuna who is fighting against us?' "

Arjuna heard him say this and sought out Dráupadi, saying to her privately, "O beautiful one, go quickly to Uttar. Tell him that I was formerly the charioteer of Arjuna and that I will hold his horses' reins today." Dráupadi, stepping bashfully out from among the women, gave this message to the prince, who quickly summoned Arjuna, ordering him to put on a coat of mail and mount the chariot. The little princess and her waiting maids crowded around Arjuna, who pretended not to know how to put on the armor and made them laugh by trying to step into it. The princess said, "Bring us some rich, bright-colored cloths from the field of battle so that we can make some dresses for our dolls." Smiling, Arjuna promised that he would; then he mounted the prince's chariot and drove him swiftly out of the city, along the very same road that the Pándavas had taken when they first came into the kingdom.

Before they had gone very far they saw in the distance the army of Duryódana, looking, with all its banners, like a vast forest and sending great clouds of dust into the sky. At the sight of it, Uttar cried, "Stop, O charioteer! I dare not fight with the Kúravas. See, my hair is standing on end and I am faint with fear! My father has left me alone and I am only a boy, unskilled in war. Turn back!"

"You ordered me to take you to battle with the Kúravas," Arjuna answered. "I must certainly take you there, where those innumerable flags are flying. If you return now, after all your boasting, everyone will laugh at you. As for me, I cannot return without rescuing the cattle."

"Let the cattle perish!" cried Uttar. "Let the Kúravas have all our wealth and the city become a desert! Let everyone laugh at me! I will not fight!"

Saying this, he leaped from the chariot and began to run away, throwing aside his bow and arrows. Arjuna ran after him, laughing, caught him by the hair and pulled him back, while the prince, wailing, offered him all sorts of gifts if he would set him free. "If you do not dare to fight with the foe, O tiger among men," said Arjuna, "come and hold the horses' reins while I fight them and recover the cattle." And he lifted the fainting prince into the chariot, giving him the reins.

They were close to that cemetery and to that great tree where the Pándavas had hidden their weapons. Arjuna said to Uttar, "Climb that tree, O prince of the Matsyas, and bring me some bows that you will find there. These bows of yours cannot bear my strength or the stretch of my arms." Unwillingly Uttar got out of the chariot and climbed the tree, while Arjuna, holding the horses' reins, directed him. He found the weapons and cut the wrappings and the ropes that bound them to the branches.

Then he beheld Arjuna's bow, Gandíva, with four others, shining with splendor as the planets do when they rise. Holding the bows, his hair standing on end with awe, he said to Arjuna, "To what famous warrior does this excellent bow belong, that has a hundred golden bosses and such shining ends? Whose is this bow, with golden elephants gleaming on its back? Whose is this splendid one, adorned with threescore golden insects, and whose is this with the three suns that blaze so brilliantly? Whose is this beautiful bow inlaid with gold and jewels? What great warrior owns these thousand arrows with golden heads, encased in golden quivers? Whose are these thick, long shafts of iron, sharp pointed, well tempered, winged with vulture's feathers? Whose is this black quiver bearing five images of tigers and holding boar-eared arrows? Whose are these seven hundred arrows with heads shaped like the crescent moon, and whose are these gold-crested ones, winged with parrot feathers?

"Whose is this excellent and terrible sword that bears the image of a toad; and whose is this, its blade inlaid with gold, in a sheath of tigerskin, all set with tinkling bells? Whose is this handsome scimitar with polished blade and golden hilt, sheathed in a cow-skin scabbard? Whose is this long and beautiful sword, with the sky-blue blade, mounted in gold, well tempered, sheathed in goat-skin? Who owns this broad and heavy blade—just longer than the breadth of thirty fingers—polished by the clash of other weapons, in a sheath of gold as bright as fire? Whose is this scimitar covered with golden bosses, the touch of whose blade is as sharp as that of a venomous snake? Answer me truly, for I am filled with wonder!"

Arjuna answered: "These are the bows, the arrows, and the swords of the heroic sons of Pandu, of Yudíshtira and Bima, Arjuna and the twins. The largest of them all is that powerful bow of Arjuna's, Gandíva, equal to a thousand other bows, handsome and smooth, and stiff enough to bear the heaviest weight."

"Indeed, these weapons are exceedingly beautiful," Uttar said. "But where then are the high-souled Pándavas, who have not been heard of since they lost their kingdom at dice? And where is Dráupadi, that jewel among women, who followed the sons of Pandu to the forest?"

"I am Arjuna," answered his charioteer. "Your father's dice player is Yudíshtira and his cook is Bima; the groom of horses is Nákula and Sahadéva keeps the cows. That waiting woman for whom Kíchaka was slain is no other than Dráupadi, the beloved wife of the Pándavas."

Hearing these words, Uttar climbed swiftly down from the tree, bringing the weapons. He saluted Arjuna, saying, "Welcome, O illustrious one! What good fortune is mine today! Command me now; my fear has vanished. I am a skillful driver and will hold the reins of these four horses that are equal to those of Krishna himself. Which part of the enemy's army do you wish to attack?"

"I am pleased with you, O mighty warrior," answered Arjuna.

"Have no fear, for I will rout your enemies in battle. Bind all these quivers to my chariot and take for yourself a polished sword adorned with gold."

Then Arjuna took the bracelets from his arms, drew on a pair of gloves adorned with gold, and wound a cloth around his curling hair. He turned toward the east, concentrating his mind on those celestial weapons he had obtained from the gods, and all the weapons came to him and said, "We are your servants, O son of Indra." Arjuna bowed down to them and took them gladly in his hands, replying to them, "Stay with me now." He took down Uttar's banner and thought of his own celestial one, bearing the figure of the gigantic ape with the lion's tail. No sooner had he thought of it than it seized upon his flagstaff, the ape glaring fiercely out, seeking his enemies. Arjuna strung his bow, Gandíva, and twanged it, and the sound of that bowstring was like the collision of two mountains.

"Stand firmly on the chariot," he said to Uttar. "Press your feet down hard and hold tight the reins, for I am going to blow my conch." Taking up the thundering shell that Indra had given him, he blew it so loudly that the sound seemed to split the mountains and shake the meteors from the sky. "Now drive at their best speed these white steeds decked with golden bridles," he said to Uttar, "for I wish to approach this crowd of Kuru lions."

When the Kúrava warriors heard the twang of Gandíva and the blare of the conch, and the thunder of the chariot wheels, their hearts sank. Drona said, "This mighty bowman who is approaching can be no other than Arjuna. Array the troops in order of battle, expecting a terrible slaughter, and guard well the kine! There is no one among us who can withstand him."

Karna said, "How you always praise Arjuna! He is not equal to a sixteenth part of Duryódana or of me!"

"If this be Arjuna," said Duryódana, "I shall indeed be happy, for then the Pándavas will have to wander in the woods for another twelve years. This was their pledge, and the thirteenth year of exile has not yet run its course."

Bishma said, "I have calculated the days and fortnights, the seasons and the years. The thirteenth year has run its course; the sons of Pandu have fulfilled all that they promised, for they are all high-souled and follow the path of virtue. That is Arjuna's banner, with its roaring ape; that is the sound of his chariot. See, two arrows have fallen at my feet, another passed my ear. The wise and beloved Arjuna, having completed the term of exile, salutes me and whispers in my ear. Let us withstand him, as the shore withstands the surging sea!"

As Bishma arrayed the army, Arjuna drove forward, announced himself by name, and covered the troops with countless arrows, thick as locusts. The soldiers, unable to see the earth or the sky, were so bewildered that they could not even run away. Arjuna blew his conch and twanged his great bow; the ape, high on his flagstaff, roared frightfully and King Viráta's cattle, terrified, turned and ran bellowing toward the city, their tails in the air. Seeing the army bewildered and the cattle lost, the Kúrava warriors rushed upon Arjuna in their chariots, with their banners waving over them.

Then that great warrior, burning with anger, began to destroy the host of chariots as a mighty fire destroys a forest. Carried by four swift steeds driven with great skill by the son of Viráta, Arjuna ranged the field in all directions, routing his foes, as the wind ranges at will in the autumn season, scattering the clouds and the masses of fallen leaves. He seemed to be dancing on the field of battle. Those brave bulls among men, wounded by that braver one, wavered and trembled, many falling on the ground like up-rooted trees. The heroic Karna, however, met Arjuna's arrows with numberless shafts of his own, pierced the four horses and the flagstaff, and wounded Uttar. Then Arjuna, like a lion awakened from sleep, took the keen, crescent-shaped arrows from his quiver, drew his bowstring to his ear, and pierced every part of his enemy's body until Karna, wounded and bleeding, left the fight and was carried in his chariot to the rear.

Those mighty warriors, Duryódana and Ashvattáman, Drona and Bishma, surrounded the son of Kunti, pouring arrows upon him. Not wishing to kill them, he took up a weapon that Indra had given him and sent forth a shower of its bright-winged shafts, which stupefied the senses of those warriors, causing them to stand motionless as if asleep; their horses, too, stopped and drooped their heads. Seeing them thus, their bows dropping from their hands, Arjuna remembered the little princess and said to Uttar, "O best of men, go among those warriors and bring me the white garment of Drona, the handsome yellow one that Bishma wears, and the blue cloak of Duryódana." Uttar, giving him the reins, leaped from the chariot and took the garments; then, returning, he drove Arjuna from the field.

When Duryódana recovered his senses, he saw Arjuna at a distance, standing on his chariot, looking like the chief of the gods or like the sun coming out of clouds. "Why have you let him escape?" he cried to Bishma. "Strike him down before it is too late!" Bishma said, smiling, "Where was all your might when he escaped? You were unconscious, with your bow and arrows dropping from your hand. Arjuna might have slain us all then, but he cannot commit a dishonorable deed. We owe our lives to his honor; therefore turn back, O King, to your own city and let Arjuna depart with the cattle." Duryódana drew a deep sigh and was silent; the other warriors also heeded the words of Bishma and left the field, returning slowly to Hastinápura.

Arjuna followed them for a while, saluting each one of them with a beautiful arrow. With one last arrow he broke to pieces the jeweled crown that Duryódana wore. Then he filled the three worlds with the twang of his Gandíva, and blowing his great conch, pierced the hearts of the departing host. Seeing them disappear, like clouds scattered by a violent wind, he said to Viráta's son, "Turn back the horses, for the cattle are recovered and the enemy routed. Now let us return to the city. You are the only one, my child, who knows that the sons of Pandu are living with your father. Do not praise me when we enter the city, but proclaim this deed as your own."

"What you have done is far beyond my power to achieve," Uttar said. "I cannot call the deed my own, but I will not discover you to my father until you tell me to do so." He sent the cowherds

to the city to proclaim the victory, while he and Arjuna returned
to the cemetery to replace the weapons of those mighty bowmen
on the branches of the tree. The terrible ape on Arjuna's banner
leaped like fire into the sky and they set Uttar's banner on the
pole again. Arjuna, binding his hair into a braid, drove Uttar into
his father's city.

There the prince entered King Viráta's court, to tell him all that
had happened, while Arjuna went to the inner apartments and
presented to the princess the cloth that he had brought her for
her dolls. She and her companions were delighted with the rich,
bright garments and clapped their hands for joy.

The Thirteen Years Are Over

King Viráta, having vanquished the Trigartas in battle and
recovered all his cattle, returned to his city with a glad heart,
accompanied by the four Pándavas. Seated on his throne, he received the worship of his subjects; then he looked for his son,
asking, "Where has Uttar gone?" The chief minister, who had
heard the news of Uttar's victory from the cowherds, told it all
to the King, who was so happy at the news that all the hair on
his body stood erect. "Make all the highways gay with flags, and
let us worship all the gods with offerings of flowers! Let the
bellman, riding swiftly on an elephant, proclaim the victory at
every crossroad, while princes and warriors, musicians, poets, and
dancers, receive my victorious son!"

When Uttar entered the court, he touched the feet of his father,
who raised him joyfully and said, "O joy of your father's heart,
I have no other son who is your equal! How could you, my child,
encounter Bishma, who cannot be conquered by men or demons?
How could you vanquish in battle Drona and his son Ashvattáman,
and Duryódana, who can pierce a mountain with his arrows? How
did you rout those mighty warriors and snatch my cattle from
them, like one who takes a tiger's prey from between its claws?"

"The foe was never vanquished by me, nor were the cattle recovered," Uttar replied. "It was all done by the son of a god who, mounted on my chariot, pierced with his arrows the Kúrava army and, having vanquished them, laughed at them and robbed them of their clothes. All the great chariot warriors of the Kúravas were defeated by him alone, as a herd of cattle is scattered by one enraged tiger."

"Where is that mighty and godlike hero," asked the King, "who has saved both you and my cattle?"

"He disappeared immediately after the battle," Uttar said, "but I believe that he will reveal himself to us tomorrow or the next day."

On the third day after the victory, the sons of Pandu bathed, put on white garments, and decked themselves with jewels; with Yudíshtira at their head, they entered the council hall of King Viráta and took their seats on thrones reserved for kings, where they shone resplendent like the fires on a sacrificial altar. When Viráta entered and saw them sitting there, he was angered and said to Yudíshtira, "You were employed by me as a dice player. Why are you sitting on a royal throne, dressed in a king's robes?"

Arjuna answered, smiling, for his brother: "This person, O King, deserves to sit on a royal throne in the very hall of Indra, for he is no other than that bull of the Báratas, the just King Yudíshtira."

Viráta said, "If this, indeed, be the just King Yudíshtira, the son of Kunti, which among these is his brother Arjuna and which the mighty Bima? Which is Nákula and which Sahadéva and where is the matchless Dráupadi?"

"Even this one," Arjuna said, "who is your cook, he who killed tigers and bears here in your palace and slew the wicked-souled Kíchaka, is the mighty-armed Bima. The manager of your stables is that slayer of foes named Nákula, and Sahadéva is the keeper of your cattle. And even this lady with eyes like lotus petals, with the slender waist and the sweet smiles, your wife's hairdresser, is the princess of Panchála, for whom Kíchaka was slain. I am Arjuna, who am younger than Bima and older than the twins."

"That is he," cried Uttar, "that dark-skinned youth with shoulders broad as a lion's and a tread like a mighty elephant's, who vanquished the Kúravas and regained the cattle! That is Arjuna, the foremost of bowmen, who ranged through crowds of hostile chariots like a lion putting to flight a herd of deer! The deed was his, not mine."

Hearing these words, the King of the Matsyas said, "May you be blessed, with all your brothers, O Yudíshtira! It was Bima who rescued me from the King of the Trigartas; my cattle were recovered by Arjuna. By the might of your arms we have been victorious. O King, if we have ever, in ignorance, done or said anything to offend you, I pray you to forgive us."

He embraced the sons of Pandu again and again and never tired of looking at them. He made an alliance with Yudíshtira, offering him his army, his kingdom, his treasury, and himself. He also offered the hand of Uttara, his daughter, to Arjuna in marriage. But Arjuna said, "O monarch, let the princess be my daughter-in-law but not my wife. For a whole year I have lived in the inner apartments, teaching her singing and dancing, and she trusts me as a father; it is not fitting, after this, that I should marry her. But my son, the mighty Abimányu, skillful in war, beautiful as a god, the favorite nephew of Krishna, is worthy to be your son-in-law and the husband of your daughter. I welcome her as my daughter and rejoice in this alliance between us."

"Let it be as you say, O wise son of Kunti," answered Viráta. "He who marries his daughter to Arjuna's son is indeed happy."

Yudíshtira gave his consent to the marriage and invited all his friends and kinsmen to come to the wedding, as Viráta also did. Krishna came, decked in garlands of flowers, bringing with him Abimányu and his mother, Subádra; the mighty King of Panchála and Dyumna came, bringing the heroic sons of Dráupadi. Many other kings came from different parts of the country, followed by thousands of elephants and chariots, horsemen and foot soldiers; and Viráta received them all and entertained the troops and the servants, for he was greatly pleased to marry his daughter to the son of Arjuna.

When the wedding festival began, conchs and cymbals, drums

and stringed instruments resounded in Viráta's palace. Countless deer and smaller animals were slain, and excellent wines were brought to the palace. Poets and actors and singers waited upon the kings and sang their praises. The Matsya ladies, headed by the Queen, dressed in bright robes and adorned with many jewels, came to the place where the wedding was to be held, and among them all Dráupadi was the foremost in beauty and in splendor. They led forth the Princess Uttara, decked with every ornament and looking like a daughter of the gods. Arjuna welcomed her on behalf of his son; Yudíshtira also greeted her and caused the wedding ceremonies to be performed between her and Abimányu. Viráta gave him as dowry a thousand horses swift as the wind, two hundred fine elephants, and much wealth besides, while Krishna gave him chariots and horses and gave each one of the sons of Pandu jewels and robes and male and female servants.

As this marriage was celebrated that united the family of the King of the Matsyas with that of the Pándavas, the city of King Viráta, crowded with happy people, was one great festival.

BOOK XI

THE PREPARATIONS FOR WAR

The Council

AT sunrise on the day after the wedding of Abimányu, the Pándavas and those kings and warriors who were their friends met in the audience hall of King Viráta. On high thrones inlaid with jewels sat the Kings of Matsya and Panchála, with Krishna and Yudíshtira beside them. Behind them sat the sons of those kings with Bima and Arjuna, the sons of Madri and Abimányu. The five sons of Dráupadi, who rivaled their fathers in valor, strength, and grace, sat upon excellent seats inlaid with gold. Those mighty heroes adorned with shining ornaments and robes talked together for a while; then they remained silent and thoughtful, looking at Krishna and waiting for him to speak to them about the Pándavas.

Krishna said: "It is known to you all how Yudíshtira was unfairly defeated at dice by Shákuni, how he was robbed of his kingdom, and sent into exile in the forest. The sons of Pandu were true to their pledge, although they could have won back their kingdom by force. For six and seven years they have carried out the cruel task imposed upon them, spending the thirteenth year, the most difficult of all, in menial service here. It is for you to consider now what will be for the good of both Yudíshtira and Duryódana, and what will meet with the approval of all good men. These brave sons of Pandu ask only for what belongs to them and what they themselves won in battle from other kings. We do not know what Duryódana thinks or what he may do. Therefore, let a virtuous and honest ambassador be sent to ask him to give back the kingdom of Yudíshtira."

Then the brother of Krishna spoke, saying, "The son of Kuru should of course give back the kingdom of Yudíshtira; he should rejoice and be exceedingly happy that the quarrel he created can be so easily settled. He has, however, taken possession of the kingdom with a strong hand, and has ruled the whole realm of the Báratas for thirteen years. Let the ambassador, therefore, say nothing to provoke him, but let him speak words full of humility and address Duryódana in a friendly way. Do not seek war with the Kurus."

Another warrior, rising up angrily, condemned those words. "Yudíshtira has fulfilled to the utmost," he said, "the terms of the stake that he lost at dice. Why should he humble himself? I should ask for his kingdom not with words but with sharp arrows, with a strong hand forcing the Kúravas to prostrate themselves at the feet of the noble son of Kunti. Either Yudíshtira must regain his throne this very day or all his enemies must be slain!"

"O mighty one," said the King of Panchála, "you speak wisely. Duryódana will never give up the kingdom willingly and his father, who dotes on him, will do as he desires. He should never be addressed in mild words, for then the fool will think that he has won. Let us make preparations for war and send word to all our friends to raise their armies. Then let my priest, a learned Brahman, go to Duryódana and ask him to give back to the Pándavas the throne that is theirs by right of birth."

"These words are worthy of the chief of the Panchálas," Krishna said. "This, surely, is our best course. It is fitting that you should send a messenger to the Kúravas, for you are the foremost of kings, both in age and in learning. If they will make peace on just terms, all will be well, but if the wicked Duryódana haughtily and foolishly refuses, he will pronounce his own doom."

Then Krishna and the assembled kings returned, each to his own kingdom, while Yudíshtira and his friends began to prepare for war. Viráta and his kinsmen sent word to all their friends, asking for their support; the King of Panchála did likewise, for it was the custom among Kshatrias to grant the request of the person who was the first to ask, and therefore they made haste before the Kúravas could hear what they had done. At the request of the Pándavas and the two Kings of Matsya and Panchála, many lords of earth, with mighty armies, came together with cheerful hearts. When the sons of Kuru heard of this, they too assembled their friends and allies, until the whole land was thronged with the armies of those heroes who were marching to fight for the Pándavas or for the Kúravas. From all sides the horsemen and the chariots, the elephants and the foot soldiers poured in, until the earth with its mountains and forests trembled beneath their tread.

After they had sent messengers to the kings of various countries, Arjuna himself set out for Dváraka, the city of Krishna. Duryódana knew, through his spies, all that the Pándavas were doing; when he heard that Arjuna had gone to see Krishna, he too, driven by fine horses as swift as the wind, set out for Dváraka. Those two tigers among men arrived on the very same day and entered the palace together to seek out Krishna. Duryódana was the first to enter the room where he found Krishna sleeping. He sat down at the head of the bed and shortly afterward Arjuna entered and stood at the foot of the bed with joined hands. When Krishna woke, therefore, his eyes fell first upon Arjuna. He greeted them both, asking them why they had come.

Duryódana said, "I have come to ask for your help in the war that is coming. Arjuna and I are both your friends and are both related to you, but I was the first to come to you. All virtuous men grant the request of him who comes first: therefore, I ask you, who are the most virtuous of men, to follow this rule of conduct."

"I do not doubt," answered Krishna, "that you came first, O King, but the son of Kunti was seen first by me. Therefore it seems to me that I must help you both. I have a large army of cowherds, of mighty strength, all of whom are able to fight in battle. These soldiers shall be sent to one of you, while I alone, not fighting, will serve the other. You, O son of Kunti, may have the first choice, for it is the custom for the younger of two people to choose first."

Arjuna chose Krishna, even though he was not going to fight; while Duryódana took the great army of cowherds and was exceedingly delighted, although he knew that Krishna was not on his side. After he had departed, Krishna said to Arjuna, "Why did you choose me, who am not going to fight?"

"O best of men," answered Arjuna, "I alone am able to slay all the Kúravas. But you are a wise and illustrious person and your fame and wisdom will be with me. I have always longed to have you drive my chariot; I beg of you to fulfill this desire."

"I will be your charioteer," answered Krishna. "Your wish is fulfilled." The two friends, with glad hearts, accompanied by many of the finest warriors of the Yadus, came back to Yudíshtira.

At this same time Shalya, the King of Madra, accompanied by his sons and his army, was traveling from his kingdom to join the Pándavas. He was their uncle, for he was the brother of Madri, the mother of the twins. His encampment covered a square mile, so large was his army, and he traveled by slow marches, giving rest to his troops. Duryódana, hearing that he was on his way, had pavilions built at different places along his route, and filled them with food and drink, flowers and entertainment, and pools of fresh water. Shalya went from one to another of these pavilions, waited upon like a god by the servants of Duryódana, until he thought himself equal to Indra himself. Exceedingly well pleased, he asked the servants, "Where are those men of Yudíshtira's, who have prepared these pleasant places of refreshment? Bring them to me, for I wish to reward them."

Seeing the King so flattered that he was ready to grant any boon, Duryódana, who had been hiding, came forward and showed himself to Shalya, telling him that he, and not Yudíshtira, had taken all this trouble to entertain him. Shalya embraced the son of Kuru, saying, "Tell me what you desire."

Thereupon Duryódana said, "O gracious one, fulfill what you have just said and grant me a boon. Be the leader of my army!"

"So be it!" Shalya said. "How can I do otherwise? Return now to your own city. I must pay a visit to that best of men, Yudíshtira, but I shall speedily rejoin you." Those two kings embraced each other; then Duryódana returned joyfully to Hastinápura, while Shalya went on in order to tell the sons of Pandu what he had done.

When he arrived at their encampment, the Pándavas received him with the usual gifts of honor and he embraced with great delight the sons of Kunti and the twin sons of his sister Madri. Then he told them of his meeting with Duryódana and of the boon that he had granted. Yudíshtira said, "O brave king, you were right to grant the boon that you promised to Duryódana when you were pleased at heart, but I ask you to do one thing for my sake. At some time in the battle there will be a single combat between Arjuna and Karna, and I am sure that you will be asked to drive Karna's chariot, for you are equal to Krishna on the field of battle. When that happens, O my Uncle, you must do all that you can to discourage Karna and to protect Arjuna, so that the victory may be ours. This is not a proper thing to do, but still you must do it, O best of men, for my sake."

"I shall do just as you ask me to do, my son," answered Shalya. "I shall speak to that vile son of a Suta in such a way that he will be discouraged and dispirited and can be easily slain. And I shall do anything else for you that I am able to do." Then he bade farewell to the sons of Pandu and went with his army to Duryódana.

Other kings came to fight for the Pándavas; their great armies, splendid with battle-axes and spears, lances and clubs, swords and arrows, were absorbed into the army of Yudíshtira, like small rivers entering the sea. The army of Panchála, filled with brave soldiers from various lands, led by the king's mighty sons, and the army of Viráta, accompanied by the kings of the hilly regions, came to Pandu's sons. Thus from many lands and many directions, seven armies with waving banners assembled to fight against the Kúravas, gladdening the hearts of the high-souled sons of Pandu.

In the same way many kings from many lands, bringing

mighty armies, like clouds driven by the wind, came to Duryódana, eager to fight against the sons of Kunti. Eleven armies
assembled under the banner of Kuru's son: there was not room
enough in Hastinápura even for the leaders of his host; therefore
the whole of his kingdom, abundant with food and wealth, was
overspread by the warriors of the Kúravas, until the creatures of
the earth were frightened and the earth itself trembled under
their tread.

At this time the sons of Pandu sent the priest of Panchála to
Hastinápura, to carry their message to the court of Kuru.

The Pándavas Claim Their Kingdom

"O learned one," said Yudíshtira to that Brahman, "go now to
Hastinápura to the court of King Kuru and in the presence of all
the Báratas and their friends and kinsmen say these words: 'You
Báratas, the sons of Pandu greet each one of you according to
your ages. They salute the ladies of the household and embrace
the sons and daughters that have been born to you. They greet
the manservants and the maidservants and all those among them
who are lame or blind, dwarfed or imbecile, and ask about the
welfare of each one.'

"Salute the mighty Kuru in our name, touching his feet and
saying, 'O King, we wish to live united. Do not let yourself be
vanquished by enemies!' Again, O holy one, bending your head
in our name, salute the grandsire of the Báratas, saying, 'O Sire,
let your grandsons all live in friendship with one another!' Address
Vídura, that wise counselor of Kuru, saying, 'Counsel peace, O
amiable one, for Yudíshtira's sake!'

"Then speak to that unforbearing prince, Duryódana, and say,
'The insults you offered to the innocent and helpless Dráupadi,
when she was dragged into the assembly, we will quietly bear,
because we do not wish to see the Báratas slain. The other injuries,
before and after that, we will quietly bear, although we are able
to avenge them. You had us exiled, dressed in deerskins; that

GREAT ARMIES CAME LIKE RIVERS ENTERING The SEA

also will be forgiven, because we do not wish to see the Báratas slain. We do not desire war; but, O consumer of your foes, we must have our just share of the kingdom. Turn your covetous heart from what belongs to others. Give back what should be given, according to the agreement at the gambling match! Give me back my own Indra Prasta, and let us end our quarrel! O Duryódana, let the Pándavas and the Kúravas meet with laughter, and with cheerful hearts let us make peace!' "

Then Arjuna, asking the permission of his eldest brother, rose and addressed the priest. Fearless and eager to fight, his eyes red with anger, he said, "Speak these words to Kuru's son, in the presence of all the Báratas and of that foul-mouthed Karna, who wants so much to fight with me, and in the hearing of those kings who have assembled to fight against the Pándavas; see that my words are well heard by them all: 'The sons of Kuru, if they fight, will surely die! My bow Gandíva yawns without being handled; my bowstring trembles without being touched; my arrows leap from their quiver, longing to fly; my sword comes out of its sheath by itself, like a snake quitting its skin, and on the top of my flag-staff terrible voices cry, "When will your chariot be yoked, O Arjuna?" As a blazing fire consumes a forest, I will leave no remnant of those that come to the field of battle.' Tell them this, O holy one," he added gently, "but let it not be so! Let the counsel of Bishma and Drona and the wise Vídura be followed, and may the Kúravas live long and happily!"

The priest of Panchála was honorably received at Kuru's court, where all the kings and chiefs had assembled, anxious to hear the message of the sons of Pandu. When the Brahman had spoken, Bishma, the eldest of the Báratas, replied to him, "I rejoice that the Pándavas are well and that they desire peace with their cousins. Truly they have suffered long and truly they deserve to have their kingdom returned to them."

Karna interrupted him angrily and insolently, saying, "Every-one, O Brahman, knows all that you have told us. What is the use of repeating these things again and again? Yudíshtira went into the woods according to an agreement that he made; now let him return and live, safe and sound, under Duryódana's protection. If, however, he wishes to leave the path of virtue and go to war, let him remember the might that will be arrayed against him!"

"How foolishly you talk, O Suta's son," Bishma said. "Do you not remember how Arjuna, singlehanded, overpowered us all in battle in Viráta's kingdom?"

Kuru, after pacifying Bishma and rebuking Karna, said, "What Bishma has said is best for us and best for the Pándavas also. O Duryódana, give up this enmity. Half the realm is quite enough for you and all your followers. Give back to the sons of Pandu their own share! I do not want war, nor does Bishma, nor Drona, nor Vídura; indeed, these warriors assembled here do not desire war. My child, let peace be acceptable to you!"

"I shall challenge the Pándavas to battle," Duryódana answered, "without depending on you or Bishma or Drona or others who think as you do. O Sire, Karna and I alone are prepared to celebrate the sacrifice of battle, making Yudíshtira the victim. Three of us, O King, Karna and my brother Dushásana and I, will slay the Pándavas in battle. Either I, slaying them, shall rule the earth or they, having slain me, will enjoy this earth. O king of unfading glory, I had rather lose my wealth, my kingdom, and my very life than share them with the sons of Pandu!"

Then Kuru said, "I now abandon Duryódana. I grieve for you all, you kings, if you follow this fool to the realm of Yama. The sons of Pandu will smite your leaders, like tigers among a herd of deer. When you see your host of chariots, horses, and elephants leveled on the ground like a forest torn up by the roots, you will remember what I have said."

At these words, his passionate son, inflamed with anger, cried, "You think the Pándavas, having the gods for their allies, cannot be vanquished. Do not fear! They with all their followers will die as they approach me, like rivers entering the ocean. My power, my intelligence, my knowledge, and my possessions are all greater than those of the Pándavas."

Karna spoke to Duryódana, cheering with his words the spirit of the assembled kings: "I alone will slay within the twinkling of an eye the Pándavas, with the Panchálas, the Matsyas, and all their other allies, and bestow on you all the lands won by my weapons. Let Bishma and Drona and all the kings stay with you, while I go forth alone with my army and slay all our enemies!"

"Your mind is clouded, Karna," answered Bishma scornfully. "You speak mad words. Every weapon of yours will be consumed to ashes by the god-given weapons of Arjuna. Besides, Krishna, who has slain foes better than you, protects him."

"That may be so," said Karna, "but I will bear no longer the grandsire's cruel words. I now lay down my arms. Not until his voice is silenced shall the rulers of the world behold me in battle."

With that he left the court, while Bishma laughed aloud, saying, "Behold how the Suta's son keeps his promise! Having boasted that he alone would slay the foe, he now lays down his arms." When Karna left the court, the rest were silent; then the assembled kings rose up and retired, each to his own apartments. Kuru said to the priest of Panchála, "I shall send my own messenger to the sons of Pandu. Therefore, do not wait, but return to them this very day."

Then he summoned a man whom he trusted, Sánjaya, his friend and charioteer. "O Sánjaya," the King said, "go speedily now in a chariot to the encampment of the son of Kunti. Address him lovingly, telling him that Kuru desires only peace. Thus the hearts of the Pándavas will be softened, for they are righteous and kind. I have examined their conduct and never have I been able to find a fault for which they could be blamed. No one hates them except this vile, dull-witted son of mine and the mean and insolent Karna. It is childish of Duryódana to think that he can rob them of their just share of the kingdom or beat them in battle. Who can withstand those mighty warriors and their friends? My heart trembles with fear when I hear that Krishna and Arjuna will be seated in the same chariot. Yet I do not fear Arjuna or Bima, Krishna or the twins so much as I fear the just anger of Yudíshtira. Say anything to him, O Sánjaya, that will avert war!"

Sánjaya drove swiftly to the capital city of Panchála, where he found the Pándavas and those kings who were their allies. In the presence of them all he made obeisance to Yudíshtira and gave him King Kuru's message, pleading for peace but saying nothing about the return of the kingdom. "Why should you think, Sánjaya," said Kunti's eldest son, "that I desire war? What man is so cursed by the gods that he could wish to fight when peace is possible? Return now, and in the presence of all the Báratas say these words to Kuru's son: 'O Duryódana, we desire only peace. Give us even one province of the kingdom; give to your five brothers at least five villages, and this shall end the quarrel!' "

Krishna Pleads for Peace

After Sánjaya had departed, Yudíshtira, deeply troubled, pondered the message that he had brought. He summoned Krishna, saying, "O friend, only you can save us now. You heard what Sánjaya said in the name of Kuru and his son: they seek to make peace with us, keeping our kingdom for themselves. We have truthfully kept our pledge, expecting them to keep theirs, but now the covetous king has broken his word, forgetting his honor as a Kshatria. We cannot give up what justly belongs to us; Kshatrias must have both land and wealth, for duty as well as pleasure depends on wealth. For us poverty is worse than death, for what can be more sorrowful than this, O Krishna, that I cannot support my mother and my brothers and my friends? And yet, what good can there be in battle? Even if we win, we shall kill those whom we love. O friend, how can we be both just and virtuous? Only you can counsel us, who are so dear to us and know the ways of truth."

"I myself will go to the Kúravas," answered Krishna, "for your sake and for theirs, and do my best to make peace without giving up what rightly belongs to you. If I can do this, I shall have saved the whole earth from the meshes of death."

The King and his brothers rejoiced at his words and each of

them added a message to what Yudíshtira already had said. Only Sahadéva did not counsel peace. "Speak, O slayer of foes," he said to Krishna, "for war! Since Dráupadi was dragged by her hair into the assembly, my wrath has never ceased to burn within me and it will never be appeased until Duryódana is slain. If all my brothers are disposed to peace, I alone will fight Duryódana to the death!"

Then Dráupadi, her eyes full of tears, approached Krishna; taking in her hand her long black hair, bound into a soft, perfumed braid, she said, "Remember, O Krishna, how this hair of mine was seized by Dushásana's rude hands. If Bima and Arjuna have fallen so low as to desire peace, my aged father and his sons will avenge me, and my five sons will fight the Kúravas, with Abimányu leading them. Thirteen long years have I spent in the hope of better days, hiding my anger in my heart like burning fire. And now my heart breaks to hear this talk of peace."

She wept aloud and Krishna comforted her, saying, "Dry your tears, O Dráupadi. I swear to you that, if they do not listen to my words, the sons of Kuru shall become the food of jackals and their wives shall weep, as you do now."

The next morning Krishna mounted his splendid chariot; his swift steeds devoured the sky and drank up the road, bearing him to Hastinápura. The sun shone clear and fragrant breezes blew; flocks of cranes flew above his head; the fields were rich with grain, for the season was late autumn. He was received with honor at Kuru's court and lingered there, talking and laughing with his friends and kinsmen; then he went to the house of Vídura and talked with him far into the starlit night.

At sunrise the next morning a messenger summoned him to the court, where Kuru awaited him with all the assembled kings. Krishna entered and took his seat there, dressed in yellow robes, looking like some dark jewel set in gold. When the assembly was silent, he spoke to them, repeating all that had been said before, warning them against the terrible slaughter that would follow if they refused the just demands of Pandu's sons, reminding them that Yudíshtira had asked for only five villages out of Kuru's great domain. All the kings that were there praised his speech in their hearts, but none dared to speak aloud in the presence of Duryódana.

Duryódana turned to him and said, "O Krishna, harshly and unreasonably you find fault with me alone. Indeed, my father, Drona, Bishma, and Vídura all blame me and never anyone else, while I cannot find the least fault in myself. Is it my fault that in the match at dice, which they joyfully entered, the Pándavas were defeated and their kingdom won? Is it my fault that, again defeated, they went into the forest? What have I done to them that they should seek a quarrel with me? Listen, O Krishna! As long as I live, that share of the kingdom that was given by my father to the Pándavas shall never again be theirs! As long as I live, the Pándavas shall not have even as much of our land as can be covered with the sharp point of a needle!"

Reflecting for a moment, his eyes red with anger, Krishna said: "O dull of understanding, how can you say you have not injured them? You will not give them what they justly ask, but they will take it from you when you lie dead on the field of battle. O fool, who will not listen to the wise advice of your friends, you have spoken wickedly and shamefully."

Hearing these words, the proud Duryódana, breathing hard like a great snake, rose angrily from his seat and, paying no attention to his father and all the elders, left the court. His brothers, his counselors, and all the kings rose up and followed him. Seeing this, Bishma said, "I see, O Krishna, that the fate of all these Kshatrias is decided, for they have foolishly followed Duryódana." And Krishna answered, "You have all witnessed what has happened here. With your permission I will now return to Yudíshtira."

Before he left, Krishna sought out Karna. He took that fierce warrior up on his chariot and drove slowly out of the city. "O bull among men, you are the son of Kunti," Krishna said, "born in her maidenhood and begotten by Súrya himself. You are therefore by law the eldest son of Pandu. Come with me today and let

the Pándavas know that you are Kunti's son, born before Yudíshtira. Your five brothers will embrace your feet and, in the presence
of all the kings assembled for their cause, they will crown you lord
of the whole earth. Let Yudíshtira be your heir and ride on your
chariot, bearing the white fan, while the mighty Bima holds the
canopy over your head and Arjuna drives you. The twins and the
sons of Dráupadi and Abimányu, all the allied kings, and I myself
will walk behind you. Let there be a brotherly union between
you and the Pándavas today, O son of Kunti, and do you rule
the kingdom, surrounded by them, as the moon is surrounded by
the stars."

"I know already all that you have told me, O slayer of foes,"
said Karna. "I am the son of Kunti; therefore by law the eldest son
of Pandu. My mother, however, abandoned me as soon as I was
born, careless of my welfare. A Suta took me to his home and
performed for me the rites of infancy; he and his wife think of
me as their son, and my heart, also, is bound to them with all the
ties of love and gratitude. I cannot break those ties, O Krishna,
even for the sake of the whole earth or for heaps of gold. Besides,
because of my friendship with Duryódana, I have enjoyed for
many years the kingdom of Anga. He is counting on me to fight
Arjuna in single combat, and I cannot be false to him. I know, O
Krishna, that you have told me this for my own good and I believe that the Pándavas would do all that you have said. Keep this
talk of ours a secret from them, for they would not fight me if
they knew me for Kunti's firstborn son. O sinless one, if we come
out alive from this great battle, may we meet here again; otherwise
we shall certainly meet in heaven."

Karna embraced Krishna, pressing him tightly to his breast, and
then descended from his chariot, returning to the city. And the
horses of Krishna, fleet as hawks, carried him back to the encampment of the sons of Pandu.

After Krishna had gone, Kunti also sought for Karna. She went
to the bank of the Ganges, where she knew that he came each
morning to worship the sun. She heard his voice chanting the
Vedic hymns and saw him, facing the east with upraised arms.

Not wishing to interrupt his prayers, she stood behind him patiently, but soon she began to suffer from the heat of the sun; so she moved closer to him, standing in the shade of his broad shoulders. When Karna finished his prayers he turned and beheld her with great surprise. Saluting her courteously with joined palms, he said, "I am Karna, the Suta's son. Why have you come here, noble lady? What can I do for you?"

"You are my son!" she cried. "No Suta brought you forth. It is wrong that you should serve the sons of Kuru, not knowing your own brothers. Let the Kúravas behold today the union of Karna and Arjuna! If you two are united, what is there in the world that you cannot achieve? O Karna, do not let yourself be known as a Suta's son, but as a son of Kunti! The highest of all duties is to please one's father and one's mother; therefore listen to me, my child."

"Noble lady," answered Karna, "I cannot believe that it is my highest duty to please you. You cast me off and never sought my welfare; but now, for your own sake, you seek to lay your commands upon me. I cannot do what you ask, for the time has come when all those whom Duryódana has protected must stand by him and fight for him, and I shall fight for him against your sons to the best of my power. But I must not be hard, and your coming here shall not be fruitless. I promise you that I will fight with Arjuna alone and that no other son of yours shall be slain by me. The number of your sons shall always be five: if Arjuna is slain, I shall be the fifth; if I am slain, Arjuna still remains."

Kunti, trembling with grief, said, "Remember this your pledge! May you be blessed!" And they both departed, going their different ways.

The Field of Kuru Kshetra

When Krishna returned and the sons of Pandu heard all that had happened in Hastinápura, they gave up all hope of peace. Therefore they arrayed their troops for battle and Yudíshtira named the commanders of the seven armies. As the supreme commander of the host they all chose Dyumna, Dráupadi's brother, who had been born to slay Drona. A great shout of joy arose at this choice. The troops began to move about; the neighing of horses, the roars of elephants, the clatter of chariot wheels, and the sounds of drums and conchs made a tremendous din. The Pándavas and all the mighty kings and warriors who supported them put on their coats of mail, mounted their chariots, and set out with their unconquerable host for the plain of Kuru Kshetra.

In the front of that army marched Bima, Nákula, and Sahadéva, Abimányu, and the five sons of Dráupadi, with Dyumna at their head. Behind them came the army of the Panchálas. In the center marched Yudíshtira with the wagons carrying the food and fodder, the tents, the money chests, the weapons and machines of war, the skilled mechanics and the surgeons and physicians, furnished with every medicine and remedy they needed. In the rear marched the army of Viráta and his sons, and the remainder of the host, and with it rode Arjuna, driven by Krishna. The din made by that joyful, marching host was like the roar of the ocean when the tide is highest on the day of the new moon.

When they reached the field of Kuru Kshetra, the army encamped on a part of the field that was level and open, abounding with grass and fuel, beside the holy river Hiranwati, facing the east. Dyumna measured the ground for the encampment, where costly tents, by hundreds and thousands, soon rose for the kings and warriors. They looked like palaces and were filled with food and drink and fuel. To every tent Yudíshtira sent heaps of bows and bowstrings, coats of mail and weapons, honey and butter and water, fodder for cattle, chaff and coals. Each division had its thousands of elephants, cased in plates of steel, its tens of thousands of horses and foot soldiers, all camped upon that field.

Duryódana, when he heard that Yudíshtira was encamped on Kuru Kshetra and ready for battle, arrayed his own troops, appointing leaders for the eleven armies. Then, with all those leaders, he went to Bishma and stood before him with joined palms, saying, "Without a commander, even a mighty army is scattered like a swarm of ants. O wise grandsire, be our commander! March at our head as Indra leads the gods, and we shall follow you as calves follow a mighty bull!"

"So be it!" replied Bishma. "You know that the sons of Pandu are as dear to me as you are, but I will fight for you, as I have promised to do. Yet, listen to me, O son of Kuru, for there are things that you must understand if I am to command your host. First, I know that I am not able to kill the sons of Pandu. I shall, however, kill their warriors day by day and so, unless I am slain first, I shall destroy their host. There is another thing that you must understand, O lord of earth. Either Karna must fight first, or I, for the Suta's son so boastfully compares his might with mine that I will not fight by his side."

"As long as the grandsire lives, O King," Karna said quickly, "I shall not enter the battle. When he is slain, then I will fight Arjuna. So I vowed among the assembled kings, and so I shall do."

Then Bishma said, "This, too, I must tell you, O King. I shall encounter in battle all the lords of earth that may oppose me, but I shall not strike or slay Shikándin, the son of the King of Pan-chála, even if I behold him rushing upon me with upraised weapon."

"Why, O chief of Báratas, will you not slay Shikándin?"

"Listen to this story, O Duryódana," answered Bishma. "When I was young I took the vow that I should never marry or sit on my father's throne, but spend my life in study and meditation. I gained such power of soul that a boon was granted me that I should not die till I desired death. I crowned my younger brother king, and set my heart on finding him a beautiful and sweet-natured wife.

"I heard that the three daughters of the King of Kashi, who were all as beautiful as Apsaras, were about to choose their hus-bands at a swayámvara to which all the kings of earth had been invited. I went there alone and, desiring all those maidens for my brother, I took them by force upon my chariot, challenging all the other kings to rescue them, in accord with Kshatria usage.

175

Alone in my chariot, I drove back the other kings and brought the three fair damsels to my brother.

"The eldest one, however, had set her heart upon another suitor and was secretly betrothed to him, intending to choose him at the swayámvara. Therefore she asked me to permit her to marry him, and I sent her with an escort to his court. Her betrothed, however, no longer wanted her, since she had been taken away by me, and the unhappy maiden left his city, weeping bitterly and cursing me for causing her misfortune. She went to the forest and devoted herself to fierce discipline of mind and body that she might obtain a boon. After twelve years of fasting, prayer, and effort she obtained from Shiva the boon that she might be born a man, able to slay me in battle; then she built herself a funeral pyre and, setting it afire, laid herself thereon.

"It is she, O son of Kuru, who was born as Shikándin, and I have vowed that I will never strike a woman or one whom I know to have been a woman, or even one who bears a woman's name. Therefore even if Shikándin approach me, bow in hand, I will not slay or smite him, O lord of earth."

Duryódana pondered these words a moment, thinking them just and proper. "O mighty-armed one," he said, "in how many days can you destroy this host of Pandu's son, which abounds with elephants, men and horses, protected by many godlike warriors? In what time can our master, Drona, who takes delight in battle, destroy that host?"

Bishma answered, "When I am stationed in battle, shooting my great weapons that slay hundreds and thousands at a time, O foremost of the Kúravas, I can wipe out that host in a month."

Duryódana turned to Drona: "And you, O master?"

Drona smiled and said, "I am old, O chief of the Kúravas, but I, too, with the fire of my weapons, can consume the army of the Pándavas in a month's time."

The spies that Yudíshtira had placed in the Kúrava host told him all that had been said. The son of Kunti called his brothers together and spoke to them in private: "O Arjuna," he asked, "in how much time can you destroy our foes?"

Looking at Krishna, Arjuna of the curling hair replied, "Do not be anxious, O King! I can destroy all living creatures in the twinkling of an eye, with that terrible and mighty weapon that the lord Shiva gave me when I fought with him. It is not right, however, to use that weapon against men, and we shall fight fairly. With Krishna as my ally, I believe that in one day I can destroy our foes!"

The next morning, under a cloudless sky, the army of the Kúravas, led by Bishma, set out for Kuru Kshetra and encamped on the opposite side of the plain from the Pándavas. Duryódana made his camp look like another Hastinápura, graced with hundreds and thousands of tents, filled with provisions and weapons. He ordered excellent supplies to be sent to all those kings who came with him, for their elephants and horses and their foot soldiers; he provided also for the bards and the singers, the vendors and the traders, the spies and the people who came to witness the battle. The whole earth then seemed to be empty of men, of elephants and horses, for only old men and children were left at home. The forces that made up those two hosts came from the whole earth over which the sun shed its rays.

Thus these two great hosts were arrayed against each other, like two stormy oceans, on the east and the west sides of the plain of Kuru Kshetra. And beholding each other, the warriors, by thousands and tens of thousands, filled with joy and delighting in battle, beat their drums and blew their thundering conchs until the earth and sky resounded.

BOOK XII

BISHMA

Before the Battle

WHEN the night had passed away, the leaders of both armies arose and shouted, "Array yourselves for battle!" Then on all sides were heard the blare of conchs, the beat of drums, the clatter of wheels, the neighing of horses, the squeals of angry elephants, the shouts of men, and the clapping of armpits. As the sun arose, each of the splendid hosts could see the other, with its ranks of foot soldiers, horsemen, chariots, and elephants drawn up in their right places and armed with flashing weapons. Every warrior had his standard, bright colored and decked with gold and gems: these thousands of standards, blown by the wind, looked like fair ladies dancing.

The Pándavas, looking across the field, beheld ten armies led by ten tigers among men, while the eleventh great army, made up of the Kúravas and their troops, stood in advance of all the others, with Bishma at its head. Mounted on a chariot of silver yoked with white horses, with a white helmet and white mail and a white banner bearing the device of a gold palmyra and five stars, he looked like the full moon in the midst of clouds. They saw Drona, the teacher of almost all the kings assembled there, on a golden chariot yoked with red steeds, his banner bearing the device of a golden sacrificial altar, decked with a waterpot. His son, Ashvattá-man, stationed with Bishma at the head of the host, bore a standard with the device of a lion's tail. The King of Sind stood at the head of his army, his standard carrying the figure of a shining silver boar, decked with golden garlands. Shalya, King of Madra, at the head of his troops, had on his flag a golden plowshare, and the ruler of Mágada had on his the device of a golden bull. And the standard of Duryódana, on whom all the rest depended, bore the device of an elephant adorned with gems and was decked with gold and with a hundred tinkling bells.

The host of the Kúravas was arrayed in the form of a mighty bird: the kings in their chariots were its head, the elephants its body, and the horsemen its wings. Seeing that formation, the sons of Pandu arrayed their armies in the form called the thunderbolt, narrow and deep, for they had less men than their enemies. Bima and Dyumna and the twins led that host, while King Viráta, with his brothers and his sons, protected them at the rear. Behind Viráta came Shikándin, eager to slay Bishma and protected by Arjuna, who rode in his golden chariot, shining like the sun, tinkling with a hundred bells, yoked with white steeds, and driven by Krishna. In the center of the host Yudíshtira took his place, surrounded by huge and furious elephants looking like moving hills, while Dráupadi's father with his army stood behind him.

On the chariots of all the kings their banners waved, bright as the sun and the moon. Yudíshtira's bore the device of a golden moon, surrounded by the planets; on Bima's banner shone the figure of a gigantic silver lion; on the tall, fierce standard of Nákula a deer was portrayed, with a golden back; and Sahadéva's bore the silver figure of a swan and was decked with bells. The five sons of Dráupadi had placed on their flags the images of those gods who begot their fathers: Darma and Vayu, Indra and the twin Ashvins. On the chariot of young Abimányu waved a standard with the device of a peacock, as bright as heated gold. Over these and many others, adorned with gold and bells, belonging to noble warriors, rose the mighty ape with the lion's tail on Arjuna's flagstaff.

As both armies stood at the dawn of day, waiting for battle, a wind began to blow and a gust of rain fell; although there were no clouds, the roll of thunder was heard and the earth trembled. The banners shook in the wind and their bells rang.

Arjuna said to Krishna, "O sinless one, place my chariot between the two hosts so that I may see those with whom I have to fight, who are here to do the will of the evil-minded son of Kuru." Krishna drove the chariot out between the two armies, in the view of Bishma and Drona and all the kings of earth, saying, "Behold the Kúravas here assembled, O son of Kunti!" Standing there, Arjuna saw fathers and grandfathers, teachers and uncles, brothers and sons, grandsons, comrades, and dear friends in both the hosts.

Seeing these kinsmen opposed thus to each other, his heart was filled with pity and he said, "When I see these kinsmen, Krishna, ready to fight each other, my limbs become weak, my body trembles, I burn with fever, and my bow, Gandíva, slips from my hand. I do not want victory, O Krishna, or the kingdom with its pleasures. What use would the kingdom be to us, since those very ones with whom we wish to share its pleasures and its wealth are drawn up against us here in battle? I do not wish to kill these, even though they kill me, O lord of earth; not if the three worlds were offered to me, still less for a kingdom of this earth. Alas, we are about to commit a great sin! It would be better for me to lay down my arms and to let myself be slain by the keen weapons of Kuru's sons."

With these words Arjuna, his heart shaken with sorrow, cast aside his bow and arrows and sank down on the bench of his chariot.

To him Krishna said, "How has this faintheartedness come upon you, O Arjuna? It is inglorious and unmanly, unseemly for a Kshatria, O son of Kunti! Shake off this weakness and arise, O slayer of foes!"

"How can I loose my arrows against Bishma and Drona, who are worthy of all honor?" said Arjuna again. "It would be better to beg for my bread than to kill these men of great soul, who are my teachers. I cannot tell which is worse, to conquer them or to be conquered by them; for, conquering, we shall slay those without whom we shall not wish to live. My vision is darkened; I no longer know what is right. Teach me; I am your disciple."

"You grieve for those who need no grief," Krishna said. "The wise grieve neither for the dead nor for the living. There never was a time when you and I and all these princes were not living, and we shall never cease to live. These bodies of ours belong to the eternal lord of the body, the soul, which cannot be destroyed, O son of Bárata. It does not kill and it cannot be killed; it was never born and it cannot die. As a man throws away his worn-out clothes and puts on new ones, so the soul, casting aside the worn-out body, enters a new one. Weapons do not pierce it, nor is it burned by fire; waters do not wet it, nor the dry winds parch. This lord of the body dwells undying in each one of us. Knowing this, how can you grieve?

"Do not shrink from the duty of your caste, O conqueror of wealth! Nothing is better for a Kshatria than a righteous battle and this one has come to you unsought, like an open door to heaven. If you do not fight it, you will have failed in duty and honor; and for one who has stood high in honor, ill fame is worse than death. The warriors in their chariots will think that you have left the fight from fear and they will speak ill of you.

"Each man reaches perfection by doing his own duty; he worships God—from whom all beings come, by whom this universe was stretched forth—by doing his appointed work, with no desire for reward. If pleasure and pain, gain and loss, victory and defeat are the same to you, you may engage in battle without sin. If you act, dedicating your deeds to God, with no desire for reward, you will not be touched by sin, as a lotus leaf is not wet by water. God dwells in the heart of every creature, O son of Kunti, through His divine power moving them all. Take refuge in Him with your whole heart and you will find peace.

"Have you listened with singleness of heart, O conqueror of wealth? Has your weakness, caused by ignorance, been destroyed?"

"My weakness has gone, O sinless one," answered Arjuna. "I

remember all that you have said; my doubts have vanished and I will do your bidding."

Arjuna arose and took up his arrows and Gandíva, and all the mighty warriors of the Pándava host, seeing this, set up a shout and, filled with joy, blew their sea-born conchs. Drums were beaten and cow horns blown and there was a great uproar.

Then King Yudíshtira took off his coat of mail and laid his weapons down; alighting from his chariot, he went on foot, with joined hands, to the place where Bishma stood. Seeing him do this, Arjuna alighted also and followed him; so did his other brothers, amazed and anxious, asking him where he was going and what he meant to do. Yudíshtira answered not a word, but, walking through the hostile army bristling with arrows and javelins, he went to Bishma and bowed before him, holding the grandsire's feet in his two hands. Surrounded by his brothers, Yudíshtira said, "I salute you, unconquerable one! We must fight with you. Give us your permission and your blessing."

"If you had not come to me before this battle, O lord of earth," said Bishma, "I should have cursed you, and you would have been defeated. Now I am pleased with you, my son. Fight, and be victorious! A man is the slave of wealth, so I am bound to the Kúravas by the wealth they have given me. I must fight for your enemies, but, granted that, I will give you any boon that you desire."

"I bow to you, O grandsire," answered Yudíshtira, "and ask you this. How can we conquer you who are unconquerable? Tell us how you may be slain in battle."

Bishma said, "I do not know anyone, O King, who can vanquish me in battle. The time of my death has not yet arrived; therefore come to me again!"

Yudíshtira accepted Bishma's words and, once more bowing to him, went with his brothers to Drona's chariot, through the crowds of soldiers who were looking curiously at him. Saluting Drona, he asked, "Tell me, O unconquerable one, how I may fight without sin and how, with your permission, I may defeat my foes."

"I am pleased with you, O sinless one, and honored by you,"

Drona said. "Fight, and win the victory! I am bound to the Kúravas by the wealth they have given me, so I shall fight for them,
but I shall pray for you. You will without doubt defeat your enemies, for where righteousness is, there is victory. What do you
wish of me?"

"I ask you, O mighty-armed one," answered Yudíshtira, "how
we may vanquish you who are invincible?"

"As long as I fight, you cannot win, O King. Therefore try to
kill me as soon as may be."

"Alas, that I must ask this!" Yudíshtira said. "Tell me, then,
how you can be slain. O master, I salute you as I ask."

"While I am standing in battle," said Drona, "no one will be
able to slay me. Only when I am ready for death, withdrawn in
meditation, shall any man be able to slay me; but I shall not lay
down my arms or prepare for death till I am overwhelmed by
sorrow."

Then Yudíshtira saluted him once more and, with his brothers,
went to where their uncle, Shalya, the King of Madra, stood in his
chariot. Bowing to him, the son of Kunti asked his permission to
fight and reminded him of his promise to discourage Karna when
the great battle should come between Karna and Arjuna. And
Shalya blessed him, saying, "Go and fight, my son; I shall look
after your victory."

The Pándavas, coming out of that vast army, walked back to
their own side. Yudíshtira, filled with joy, put on his shining coat
of mail and those bulls among men mounted their chariots, taking
their places in the battle array. They caused the great drums and
cymbals to be sounded; trumpets and milk-white conchs were
blown. Krishna and Arjuna, standing in their chariot, blew their
conchs, called Fivefold and God-given; Bima blew the Reed-note
and Yudíshtira his conch called Eternal Victory; Nákula and
Sahadéva blew theirs called Sweet-sounding and Pearl-flowered,
and all the mighty warriors blew theirs, until the sound pierced
the hearts of the sons of Kuru and made the heavens and earth
resound.

The First Seven Days

On the morning of that awful day the battle began that caused the death of so many noble warriors. All the Kúrava host, reckless of their very lives, rushed with upraised standards against the Pándavas, and the Pándava host met them with cheerful hearts, Bima leading them. The mighty shouts, the twang of sounding bowstrings, the furious neigh of horses, the clash of weapons, the jingle of elephant bells, the uproar of conchs and trumpets made the hair stand on end and shook those vast armies as forests are shaken by the tempest. As the din arose, Bima began to roar like a bull till his shouts were heard above all other noises and struck fear into the hearts of the Kúravas.

Duryódana and his brothers, shaking their splendid bows, surrounded Bima, covering him with arrows like snakes that have just cast their skins. Then the five sons of Dráupadi, with Nákula and Sahadéva and Abimányu, rushed against the Kúravas, tearing them with whetted shafts as bolts of thunder shatter mountains. In that first encounter no warrior on either side turned back, and no difference could be seen between the two hosts. On both sides it was easy to see which warriors had been Drona's pupils, because of their lightness of hand and their sure aim. Bima and Duryódana fought fiercely, but neither prevailed over the other, for both were mighty warriors. On that first day Uttar, Viráta's son—he whose chariot Arjuna had driven—was struck down by the King of Madra.

Dushásana rushed against Nákula, striking him with many arrows, but the son of Madri, laughing, cut down with his arrows the standard and the bow of his enemy. Yudíshtira fought against Shalya, while Dyumna sought out Drona. The King of Panchála fought with the King of Sind and the battle between them was fierce and terrible. Thousands of single combats took place between chariots and elephants, horsemen and foot soldiers, for both sides fought as if possessed by demons. Chariot crashed against chariot, huge elephants with canopied seats and standards on their backs fought furiously against each other or, wounded and panic-stricken, dashed through the army, crushing chariots and horses under their feet. Many a young, heroic warrior fell from his car and lay prostrate on the ground; many a horseman was carried from the field, hanging dead from his saddle and still holding his bow. A thick dust arose, and the din was deafening. Over the field the palmyra banner of Bishma constantly waved, and the grandsire himself, on his great chariot, shone like the moon above a mountain peak.

On the second day the battle raged again, neither side prevailing over the other. On the third day Bishma arrayed his forces in the form of a great bird, and the army of the Pándavas was counter-arrayed in the shape of a half-moon, with Bima at the right horn, surrounded by many kings, Yudíshtira at the center, and Arjuna at the left horn. All that morning the warriors fought and none of them gave way.

In the afternoon, Bishma, with his bow constantly drawn to a circle, invoking celestial weapons, shot continuous lines of arrows in all directions and seemed to be everywhere at once. The Pándava warriors could not see him for the showers of arrows sent forth from his bow; they fell before his shafts like insects falling into a blazing fire. Even as he had said, the vast army began to tremble and give way, in spite of all the efforts of its leaders.

Then Krishna spoke to Arjuna, saying, "The hour is come, O tiger among men, when you must make good your promise to rout the Kúrava army and fight with Bishma himself. Behold, your army is being routed by him alone." And, with Arjuna's leave, he urged the white steeds to the place where Bishma's chariot stood.

Beholding him advancing, the Pándava host rallied, while Bishma, roaring like a lion, covered the onrushing chariot with his arrows. Arjuna, stretching Gandíva, cut the grandsire's bow in two, and the moment Bishma seized and strung another, he cut that one, too. Bishma praised his quickness, saying, "Well done, O mighty-armed one! I am pleased with you. Fight hard with me, my son!" With a third bow he sent forth showers of arrows. Krishna, with great skill, avoided many of these by driving in quick circles, but many struck their mark and he and Arjuna both looked like roaring bulls with the scratches of horns on their bodies. Krishna saw that Bishma's arrows were again driving back the Pándava army, while Arjuna was fighting only mildly, out of respect for the grandsire.

Therefore, afraid that Yudíshtira's army could not survive another attack, and very angry, Krishna dropped the reins, leaped from the chariot, and ran toward Bishma, whirling his discus, eager to slay him. But Arjuna also leaped to the ground, ran after him, and, throwing his arms round his friend, stopped him after he had run for ten steps. "Stop, O Krishna!" he cried. "Remember that you said you would not fight; do not let men say you are a liar. I swear, O slayer of foes, by my weapons, by the truth, by my own good deeds, that I will destroy our foes. The task is mine." Hearing this, Krishna, silent and angry still, mounted the car and took up the reins again.

Arjuna, drawing Gandíva with power, summoned a celestial weapon and with it filled every side of the field with sharp and blazing shafts, causing a river of blood to flow from the Kúrava host. Every other sound was silenced by the thundering twang of his bow; the Kúravas were struck with fear, while the Pándava army rallied to the attack. As the sun set the Kúravas withdrew, Bishma and Drona retreating with them, and the Pándavas sent up a triumphant shout. Then all the warriors, speaking of this great feat of Arjuna's, entered their tents, which were lighted without by flaming torches and beautified within by innumerable lamps.

Every day for eight days the armies were arrayed for battle in different formations, each trying to get the advantage over the other. Each day those mighty warriors, after their wounds had been tended by skillful surgeons, returned to the fight, slaughtering their enemies' troops, slaying brothers and sons, kings and warriors. Each day one of them gained added glory by his prowess in battle. Now it was Bima, careering over the field in his chariot with his lion banner flying, or seated on the neck of a mighty elephant, or on foot, whirling his great mace till he looked like a wheel of fire, felling elephants and cavalry and foot soldiers like

Death himself. Now it was Arjuna, in his chariot with its ape banner, the reins held by Krishna, Gandíva flashing like lightning, its shafts drinking the blood of countless heroes. Now it was Nákula and Sahadéva, fighting together against their uncle, Shalya, and driving him off the field, or falling upon the Kúrava cavalry, slaying so many of them that the rest broke and fled before them as a herd of deer flees before two tigers.

The five sons of Dráupadi, her brothers, and Viráta's sons were mighty warriors, while Abimányu, beautiful as a god, was the equal of his father Arjuna in lightness of hand, sureness of aim, knowledge of weapons, and bravery; for Arjuna had taught him all he knew. Always in the midst of the battle, he could fight with five or ten warriors at once, and made the Kúravas tremble, thinking that two Arjunas were on the field.

Every day Bima slew six or eight or ten of the sons of Kuru, for he had sworn after the gambling match that he would kill them all. Therefore his brothers and his nephews, though they often fought against their cousins and struck them from their chariots or drove them, wounded, from the field, never slew any of Kuru's sons, so that Bima might not be false to his promise. Several times he and Duryódana fought like two mad bulls, each longing to kill the other, but they were equal in might and neither prevailed in battle. But Duryódana, when he went each night to his tent, was overcome with grief, and wept for his brothers.

As the sun set each day, the field was strewn with gold-backed bows and winged arrows, broken swords with ivory handles and shields inlaid with gold, loosened from the grasp of the slain. Many a chariot warrior lay on the ground as if asleep, his weapons beside him; horses and elephants lay there dead, their blood staining the earth. Wheelless chariots and torn banners, embroidered blankets and elephants' housings, chains and ornaments and helmets scattered about made the plain of Kuru Kshetra look like the earth in spring when it is strewn with flowers or like the heavens adorned with stars.

Both armies ceased to fight when the darkness came. The warriors, after placing their sentries and caring for their troops, retired to their tents, praising one another's deeds. They plucked the arrows from their bodies, bathing their wounds and treating them with healing herbs. Brahmans performed the evening worship, poets sang the heroes' praises, and they enjoyed themselves for a while, not speaking of the battle, but listening to music and poetry. Then they slept deeply, and the two armies, with their sleeping warriors, elephants, and horses, were beautiful to behold.

Bishma Advises Yudíshtira

On the eighth day the army of the Pándavas gained the advantage, driving back the Kuru army with great slaughter. At night, after his troops, tired and defeated, had gone to rest, Duryódana and Shákuni, Dushásana and Karna met together to consider how the sons of Pandu could be vanquished. Duryódana said, "Neither Drona, Bishma, nor Shalya really fight against the Pándavas, and therefore my forces are being destroyed and my weapons will soon be exhausted. I am doubtful of victory."

"Do not grieve, O chief of the Kúravas!" Karna replied. "Let Bishma withdraw from the battle; as soon as he lays down his weapons, I will slay all the Pándavas before his eyes. Truly, he favors them every day. Go without delay to his tent and ask him to give up the command; then set your heart at rest, for I alone will vanquish your enemies."

"As soon as Bishma has consented," said Duryódana, "I will come to you, O chastiser of foes, and you will lead us to victory."

Then Duryódana, clad in clean robes, adorned with his royal crown and many jewels, mounted his horse and rode toward Bishma's tent, while all his brothers who were left alive and the leaders of his armies walked behind him, and servants lighted their way with golden lamps fed with fragrant oil. Arrived at Bishma's tent, he alighted and saluted the grandsire and sat down on a handsome seat covered with a rich carpet. With his hands joined and his eyes filled with tears, he said, "O slayer of foes, you promised that you would destroy all the armies of the Pándavas and therefore we entered into this mighty conflict. Make your words true, O mighty one! Or, if you are sparing our enemies because you love them or because you hate me, permit Karna to fight, for he can vanquish in battle the Pándavas themselves and all their friends and kinsmen."

Hearing these cruel words, the high-souled Bishma was filled with grief and, sighing deeply, was silent for a while. Then, raising his eyes, which blazed with anger, he said, "Why do you pierce me with such cruel words? I always try, with my utmost might, to achieve your victory, and am prepared to lose my life in battle. Arjuna alone vanquished every one of us in Viráta's kingdom and took away our clothes. That should prove to you that we cannot slay him and all his brothers. It is you who have provoked the Pándavas to battle; therefore fight them yourself, O King, and let us see you act like a man! As for me, I shall do as I have promised and slay their troops and their allies. Sleep happily, O son of Gandári, for tomorrow I shall fight so fierce a battle that men will speak of it as long as the world lasts!"

When the ninth day dawned, Duryódana called all the royal warriors, saying, "Draw up the forces! Today Bishma, filled with wrath, is going to slaughter our enemies. Our duty is to protect him, for even the lion can be slain by wolves if he is alone in the forest. If we protect him, our victory is certain."

Bishma arrayed his troops in a hollow square, taking his position in the center of the front, while all the Kúrava warriors, in chariots and on elephants, were ranged on each side of him, facing the Pándavas, whose host was arrayed in that prince of forms, the hawk. When the battle began the grandsire smote the Pándava host with blazing arrows; his shouts and the clapping of his palms struck terror to their hearts. He was like a fire in dry grass, blown by the wind. He struck off the heads of warriors as a man knocks ripe fruit off a tree with stones. He felled elephants and chariots or struck their riders from them, and many an empty chariot was dragged from the field by its runaway horses, many a noble warrior, advancing fearlessly against him, was sent to Yama's realm.

All day long this terrible battle went on, while Bishma took the

lives of warriors as the sun sucks up water in summer. As the Pándavas had been breaking the Kúrava ranks, so he broke theirs, and
the routed soldiers, hopeless and heartless, could not even look
at him, for he was like the midday sun, blazing with his own
splendor. Indeed, the sons of Pandu themselves looked at him with
awe because of the superhuman feats he was achieving, and their
troops, fleeing away in fear, found no protectors, but looked like
bulls running wild, no longer held by the yoke. Loud were their
cries of woe as they threw away their armor and fled with disheveled hair.

While he was still destroying the Pándava host, the sun, the
thousand-rayed maker of the day, reached the western hills; the
troops, tired out, withdrew to rest, and the night set in, which
steals away the senses of all creatures. In the fierce hours of darkness the Pándavas and their allies sat down in Yudíshtira's tent to
consider what they should do, for all were wounded by the shafts
of Bishma and all were thinking of his mighty deeds. "Behold,"
Yudíshtira said, "the high-souled Bishma is crushing my troops like
an elephant crushing a mass of reeds, like a raging fire in dry grass!
When I spoke to him before the battle he said to me, 'The time
of my death has not yet arrived; come to me again.' Therefore let
us all go to him again and ask him how we may vanquish him. He
will tell us, for he brought us up when we were children and
orphans. And now we seek to kill him! Shame upon the Kshatria
usage that forces us to slay the grandsire, our father's uncle!"

The others all applauded his decision, so Yudíshtira, his four
brothers, and Krishna put off their armor and went on foot to
Bishma's tent. He welcomed them all lovingly and asked them
what he could do for their pleasure. "Even if it be very difficult,"
he said, "yet I will do it with all my soul."

"O grandsire," answered Yudíshtira, "tell us how we may vanquish you in battle, how we may have victory, and how our army
may escape further destruction. How can we bear you in battle?
Tell us, O lord of earth, how we may compass your death, for
vanquished you can never be."

"It is true, O son of Pandu," said Bishma, "that even the gods cannot defeat me when I fight carefully in battle. But there are those with whom I will not fight, and through them I can be vanquished. In your army, O King, is Shikándin, a prince of Panchála who is brave and powerful. He was a woman once, later reborn to manhood, and with him I shall never fight. Let Arjuna, keeping Shikándin before him, pierce me with his shafts and cast me down from my chariot. Then your victory will be certain, for you can slay the rest when I am gone."

The Pándavas, saluting the grandsire, went back to their tents, and Arjuna, overwhelmed with grief and shame, said to Krishna, "How shall I fight the grandsire, the eldest of our family, whose lap I climbed upon when I was a child, all dusty from my play? How can I slay this wise and honored one?"

"Victory can never be yours unless you slay him, O conqueror of wealth," Krishna said. "And you have pledged yourself to victory. It has been said that one should slay even an aged person worthy of honor if he comes against one as an enemy. It is the eternal duty of a Kshatria to fight, to govern, and to sacrifice, but without hatred."

Bishma Falls

Toward the hour of sunrise, with beat of drums and cymbals and the blare of conchs, the Pándavas formed their troops into a terrible array and marched out for battle, putting Shikándin in the very front rank. Bima and Arjuna protected his wheels; behind him came the sons of Dráupadi and Abimányu; behind them marched Dyumna with the Panchála warriors, and behind him the royal lord Yudíshtira with the twins and all the armies of their allies. They marched directly against Bishma, scattering their arrows as they went.

That mighty warrior, the high-souled Bishma, having arrayed his troops, said to Duryódana, "Listen to what I say, O King! Today I shall either be slain myself or I shall slay the Pándavas. Today I shall free myself from the debt I owe you for the food and the wealth that you have given me, by casting away my life

at the head of your army." With those words, he attacked the
Pándava host, pouring upon them showers of long shafts, calf-
toothed or crescent-shaped, all sped with power and wrath, each
one like an angry and poisonous serpent. On that tenth day of
battle he shone resplendent as a fire without smoke, and the Pándavas could not look at him, for he was like the sun at the summer
solstice, scorching their troops with his arrows, taking the lives of
thousands, as the sun sucks moisture from the earth.

All the warriors of the Pándava army rushed against him while
the Kúrava warriors surrounded him to protect him, and a terrible
battle was waged around him, for in that game of battle Bishma
was the stake, on whom the victory of either side depended.
Shikándin attacked him joyfully, striking him with three shafts,
but these arrows caused him little pain, for he received them
laughingly; indeed, he received them as a person in the heat of
summer receives a shower of rain. Krishna, holding the reins of
Arjuna's white steeds, said to him, "O conqueror of wealth, put
forth all your strength now and slay the grandsire! See, he is
breaking our ranks. None but you can bear his arrows and none
but you can slay him."

Then the ape-bannered Arjuna, keeping behind Shikándin,
approached Bishma, cut his standard down with one arrow and
broke his bow with another. The grandsire took up another
stronger bow but Arjuna cut it into three pieces with two broad-
headed shafts. All the bows that Bishma took up, the son of Pandu
cut down, and then he pierced Bishma with ten arrows and then
another ten. And the grandsire, deeply pierced by the keen-
pointed shafts, said to Dushásana, who fought beside him, "These
arrows coming toward me in a line, whose touch is like the thunderbolt's—these are not Shikándin's. They cut me to the quick,
piercing my coat of mail, penetrating my vital organs—these are
not Shikándin's. Like angry poisonous snakes, like messengers of
death, they come; they are Arjuna's. No one can cause me pain
save the heroic wielder of Gandíva, the ape-bannered son of
Pandu." After that he no longer fought; but, although he was

sorely wounded, he did not leave the battle, but stood calmly in his chariot.

Then Arjuna, at the head of the Pándava troops, broke the center of the Kúrava army and the troops and many of the warriors fled from the field, abandoning Bishma. And the Pándavas, surrounding that mighty hero on all sides, drove off the Kúravas who protected him and covered him with their arrows, till there was not on his body a space of two fingers' breadth that was not pierced by them. He began to weaken, like an aged lion surrounded by the hunters. A little before sunset, in the sight of both armies, he reeled and fell down from his chariot, like a falling standard. Yet his body did not touch the ground, for it was held up by the many arrows piercing it. Even as he fell, he remembered that the sun was approaching the winter solstice; so he did not permit his life to depart, for it is not well to die at that season. He had been given the boon that he should die only when he so wished; therefore he held his life until the sun should move into the north, and lay, with his mind given to prayer, on his bed of arrows.

When Bishma fell, the hearts of all the Kúravas fell with him and cries of sorrow were heard, while the Pándavas, having won the victory, stood at the head of their ranks and blew their conchs and trumpets. Dushásana turned his chariot and drove quickly to Drona, who commanded an army in another part of the field, to tell him of Bishma's defeat and Drona, hearing the evil news, fell fainting from his chariot. Quickly recovering, he ordered the Kúravas to stop fighting. Beholding this, the Pándavas too, sending fleet messengers to all their troops, commanded them to cease, announcing Bishma's fall.

The kings of both armies and hundreds of other warriors put off their armor and came to where the eldest of the Báratas lay. Standing around him, they saluted him and Bishma said: "Welcome, you blessed ones! Welcome, you mighty warriors! I am pleased with you, for truly you are the equals of the gods." Then he said, "My head is hanging down. Pray give me a pillow." The kings ran to their tents and fetched many beautiful pillows, made of delicate soft fabrics, but the grandsire did not want these, say-ing, with a laugh, "These are not fitting for a hero's bed." Then, seeing that mightiest of all warriors, the ape-bannered son of Pandu, he spoke to him: "O Arjuna, my head hangs down. Give me such a pillow as you think fit, my son."

Arjuna, his eyes filled with tears, took up Gandíva and three straight shafts. Stretching the mighty bow, he drove the arrows deep into the earth, so that they supported Bishma's head. The grandsire was pleased that Arjuna had guessed his thought, and said, "Thus should a Kshatria sleep on the field of battle. I will lie on this bed till the sun turns to the north, and then I will yield my life as a friend bids farewell to a friend. With these arrows still in my body, let it be burned."

The kings of both armies were filled with wonder. With their armor and their weapons laid aside, they met as they had met in days of old and cheerfully talked together. Bishma, bearing his suffering with fortitude, sighed deeply and asked again for Arjuna, who came and stood before him with joined palms: "My body burns and my vital organs are in agony," said the grandsire. "Give me water, O Arjuna." Arjuna mounted on his chariot and stretched Gandíva, twanging its string with a sound like thun-der. Then he placed a blazing arrow on the string, speaking an incantation, and pierced the earth a little to the south of where Bishma lay; and lo, a jet of water rose, pure and cool and sweet, which he gave to Bishma to drink.

"This is not wonderful in you, O son of the Báratas," the grandsire said. "With Krishna as your friend, you will achieve many mighty feats that the gods themselves would not venture to achieve." Turning to Duryódana he said, "O King, forget your wrath! You have seen how Arjuna created a jet of cool, pure water. None but him, who knows the weapons of the gods, can do such deeds. Make peace with him, O King, and let this battle end with my death! Let this remnant of your brothers and of these warriors live! Let peace come with my death!"

But Duryódana said nothing, refusing this counsel as a dying man refuses medicine; and the kings and warriors returned to their abodes, after saluting Bishma reverently and placing guards about him to protect him.

When they had gone, Karna came to that place and, seeing the mighty hero lying with closed eyes on his arrowy bed, fell, weeping, at his feet, saying, "O chief of the Báratas, I am the Suta's son, on whom you have always looked with hate."

The aged leader, slowly raising his eyelids and telling the guards to stand aside, embraced Karna with one arm, saying with great love, as a father speaks to a son, "Come, come! You have been my adversary, one who always challenged me and compared himself with me. I tell you truly, my son, that I bear you no ill will. It was only to abate your pride that I spoke so harshly to you. I know your courage and your might, your generosity and your fairness in battle. You are not a Suta's son, but the son of Kunti, and the Pándavas are your brothers. O slayer of foes, if you wish to please me, join them today and let all the kings of the earth be free from danger."

"I know all this, O mighty one," Karna said, "but I cannot change now. This war must take its course. I have always offended the Pándavas and I cannot overcome my hatred of them. Therefore, cheerfully fulfilling the duties of my caste, I will fight with Arjuna. Grant me your permission, O hero, and forgive me for any harsh words I have uttered against you and for any rash and thoughtless act."

"If you truly cannot change, O Karna," Bishma said, "then I permit you to fight. Serve the King, without anger or pride, with no desire for revenge, with all your power and courage. For a long time I tried to make peace between you and your brothers, but I have failed. Do whatever you desire!"

Then Karna rose and, saluting Bishma, left him and went to the tent of Duryódana.

BOOK XIII

DRONA

Abimányu's Sacrifice

WHEN Karna returned to the spacious encampment of the Kúrava army, he spoke cheering words to the warriors and they, beholding him, were filled with joy and welcomed him with shouts, the twang of bowstrings, and the clapping of armpits. He and Duryódana agreed that Drona should be made commander of the host in Bishma's stead, and Drona was immediately installed by all the kings with ceremony, to the sound of conchs and drums, with hymns and the songs of bards and cries of "Victory!" With Karna and Drona to lead them, the warriors were freed from the grief of Bishma's fall.

Afterward, in the midst of all the troops, Drona said to the King, "Since you have honored me with the command of your host, what shall I do for you, O tiger among men? What boon do you desire?"

"This is the boon that I desire," Duryódana replied. "Bring Yudíshtira here to me, alive!"

"Why, O King, do you not desire his death?" asked Drona. "It would be truly wonderful if, after vanquishing him in battle, you made peace with him and gave him back his kingdom!"

"O master!" cried Duryódana. "Victory can never be mine if Yudíshtira be slain in battle, for Arjuna would never rest till he had slain us all. Nay, bring him here alive so that we may gamble

197

with him once again at dice and send the Pándavas again into the forest. Thus we shall gain a lasting victory."

After thinking a while about this crooked plan, Drona said, "As long as Arjuna protects him, Yudíshtira can never be taken even by the gods themselves. But if, O monarch, by any means Arjuna may be removed, I will bring the King to you before the day is over."

Hearing these words, the King of the Trigartas spoke: "We are always being humbled by him who wields Gandíva. We shall challenge him tomorrow and, taking him out of the field, surround him and slay him. I swear to do this now, before you all." And with his brothers and the leaders of his troops he took a solemn vow that all of them would die rather than return from the battle without slaying him of the white steeds.

Therefore, in the morning, they challenged Arjuna, summoning him to the southern part of the field. Before he went, Arjuna said to Yudíshtira, "These men, who have sworn to conquer or to die, have challenged me to a battle that I cannot refuse. Therefore let Satyajit, Dráupadi's brother, protect you in my place. As long as he lives, Drona can never seize you; but, O lord of earth, if this mighty Satyajit be slain, do not remain on the field, even if all our host surround you!" Yudíshtira gave him his promise, embracing him lovingly, and Arjuna went out against the Trigartas like a hungry lion longing to feast upon a herd of deer; while the Kúrava army, rejoicing in his absence, set their hearts on seizing Yudíshtira.

The Trigartas took their stand on a level field and formed an array in the shape of a half-moon. Seeing Arjuna, with his shining diadem, come toward them, they were filled with delight and shouted with joy, while Arjuna said to Krishna with a smile, "These men who are about to die in battle seem to be filled with joy, when they should be weeping." He took up his great conch called the God-given and blew it with such power that the Trigarta host stood still as if turned to stone, and their animals, with staring eyes, and necks and ears thrust out, were motionless. Quickly the warriors recovered and, placing their ranks in order,

ARJUNA SWIFTLY RETURNED WITH THUNDERING WHEELS·

shot their arrows all at once, which fell on the son of Pandu as bees fly to a flowering tree in the forest. He pierced them in return with many arrows, cut down their golden standards, and killed their leaders.

While Arjuna was fighting against these warriors in the southern part of the field, Drona arrayed his forces in the form of a great bird whose beak was himself, while the head was made up of Duryódana, his brothers, and Karna, who for the first time unfurled his shining banner that bore the device of an elephant's rope. Warriors eager to seize Yudíshtira started out from the wings and body of the bird like lightning flashing from the clouds in summer, and a sound arose in the Pándava army like the sound of a herd of elephants whose leader is attacked. Satyajit rushed at Drona and they fought like demons, for both were powerful. But Drona, taking a crescent-shaped arrow, cut Satyajit's head from his body and the great warrior fell from his chariot like a falling star. Then Drona rushed eagerly at Yudíshtira, but the son of Pandu, remembering Arjuna's words, turned his chariot and fled from the field. Bitterly disappointed, Drona attacked the Pándavas and their allies, and drove their troops back like frightened deer. The battle raged until, at sunset, Arjuna returned, having driven the Trigartas from the field. As his blazing banner with the shrieking ape drew near, the Kúrava army broke and there was great slaughter until the darkness came and both armies, broken and wounded, retired to their tents.

Since Yudíshtira had not been taken and the army had been routed by Arjuna, the Kúrava warriors were filled with sorrow and sat silent in their tents like men under a curse, while Drona was deeply ashamed because he had not kept his promise. In the morning he said to Duryódana, "I do my best to bring you victory, but no one can defeat the army that is protected by the diadem-decked Arjuna. I promise you, however, that today I will form an array that cannot be broken and that I will slay one of the foremost heroes of the Pándavas. If it is possible, take Arjuna out of the battle."

The Trigartas, therefore, still eager to slay Arjuna, challenged him again in the southern part of the field while Drona drew up his army in the great circular array. In the center of the circle was Duryódana, resplendent under his elephant banner, with Karna and Dushásana beside him. At the entrance of the circle Drona stood in his chariot; beside him was his son, Ashvattáman, and the mighty King of Sind, the gambler Shákuni, Shalya, King of Madra, and the thirty remaining brothers of Duryódana.

The Pándava warriors, headed by Bima, eager to fight and blazing with wrath, flung themselves against that immovable array but, like a mighty wave rushing against a rock, they were flung back by Drona. The strength of his arms was amazing and none could stand before the power of his weapons. Seeing that nothing prevailed against him, Yudíshtira called Abimányu, Arjuna's son, who was not yet of age, but who equaled his father in beauty, bravery, and knowledge. "O child," said the King, "we cannot break that circular array. Only Arjuna and Krishna and you know how to pierce it. O Abimányu, for our sakes and the sake of all these troops, take up this heavy burden; lead us through it so that Arjuna may praise us when he returns from battle."

"I will soon break that fierce array," said Abimányu, "for my father has taught me how to do it. But I do not know how to come out of it again if danger overtake me."

"Only break the array!" answered Yudíshtira. "Make a passage for us and all of us will follow and protect you."

"I will follow close after you," shouted Bima, "with Dyumna and the twins, once the array is broken."

Hearing these words, Arjuna's son ordered his charioteer to drive him swiftly toward Drona's army. "Are you sure," the charioteer questioned him, "that you can bear this heavy burden? You are not used to battle, while Drona is the master of all weapons."

Abimányu laughed. "Who is this Drona, O charioteer, and who are all these warriors? If my uncle Krishna and my father, if Indra himself came against me in battle, I should have no fear. Drive swiftly on!" And in his chariot with its gold-decked steeds, its

peacock banner flying, he sped toward the opposing army like a
young lion attacking a herd of elephants.

Beholding him coming toward them, with the Pándava host
following, the Kúrava warriors advanced against him joyfully and
a fearful battle raged around him, like the eddy made in the ocean
where the river Ganges meets it. Abimányu, with great lightness
of hand and a knowledge of the vital parts of the body, slew many
of the advancing warriors, and as he fought, he broke through the
array and entered the inner circle, where he careered through the
Kúrava army like a fire playing in dry grass. His bow, always
drawn to a circle, looked like the sun's disc, the twang of his bowstring and the clapping of his palms sounded like thunder.

Yudíshtira, Bima, and the twins, with all the warriors of their
army, followed close behind him, pressing in along the path that
he had opened. But the Kúrava warriors, turning from Abimányu,
opposed these mighty heroes with all their strength, led by the
King of Sind, who carried a silver boar on his banner. The King of
Sind, for a few moments, held back the Pándavas and the whole
army that followed them; in that time the path that Abimányu
had cut through the array was filled and blocked, and the son of
Arjuna was left alone within the circle.

Surrounded on all sides, Abimányu looked like Yama himself
destroying all creatures at the world's end. Showering arrows in
all directions, he strewed the ground with the bodies of his enemies and drove back mighty warriors. Shákuni said to Duryódana,
"Let us ask Drona how we may overcome him!"

Drona said to them, smiling, "Behold the lightness of hand and
the swift motion of this son of Arjuna! Can you see the least
weakness in him? I rejoice in him, even though his arrows wound
me sorely. You cannot pierce his coat of mail, for I taught his
father how to put on armor and he has taught his son. Therefore,
cut off his bow, kill his horses and his charioteer, and so make
him powerless."

Then Drona and Karna and Ashvattáman with three more great
warriors surrounded the boy and mercilessly slew his steeds and
his charioteer and cut his bow in pieces. Drona cut the hilt from

his sword and Karna destroyed his shield. Then Abimányu picked up a chariot wheel and lifting it high in his arms, rushed with a shout at Drona, but those warriors who surrounded him broke the wheel with their powerful shafts. He picked up a mace and with it slew the horses and charioteer of Ashvattáman and then those of Dushásana's son. The latter, taking up his mace, leaped from his chariot and the two cousins fought fiercely with their maces, each striking the other to the earth. The son of Dushásana rose up first, and while Abimányu was rising from the ground, struck him on the head with all his power. Arjuna's son fell dead, like a wild elephant slain by the hunters, like a tempest spent after destroying mountains, or like the setting sun. Thus one was slain by many.

The Kúrava warriors, beholding Abimányu prostrate on the earth, shouted with joy, but the Pándavas were filled with grief and wept, saying, "Alas, this one, fighting alone, was slain by six mighty chariot warriors, headed by Drona and Karna. This was not a righteous fight." The Pándava troops fled away and, since the end of the day had come, the warriors retired. Taking off their armor and laying aside their weapons, they sat round Yudíshtira, thinking of their great sorrow, their hearts fixed on Abimányu. And Yudíshtira, with a heavy heart, wept for him, thinking to himself, "What shall I say to Arjuna?"

Arjuna's Vow

In the hour of twilight Krishna and Arjuna, who had defeated the Trigartas again, turned their victorious chariot homeward. As they drew near to the encampment, Arjuna said, "Why does my heart sink, O Krishna, and my speech falter? The fear of disaster seizes my mind and I cannot shake it off. I wonder whether all is well with my brothers and their friends."

When they reached the camp they found it silent and joyless and Arjuna, with a heavy heart, again said, "No trumpet sounds the victory today. I hear no stringed instruments, no clapping of hands, no songs of praise, and these warriors whom we meet turn away from me, their heads hanging in grief. Alas, Subádra's son has not come out to meet me, smiling, as he always does. What evil thing has happened?" He entered Yudíshtira's tent and found his brothers and their sons sitting sorrowfully there.

"How pale your faces are!" Arjuna said. "Where is Abimányu? Why has he not come to meet me? I have heard that Drona formed the circular array today. Did you send the boy to pierce it? Has that mighty bowman, that slayer of enemies, fallen at last in battle?" Their silence told him that this was so.

"Alas," he said, "that dear son of Subádra, the favorite child of Dráupadi and Krishna, beloved of Kunti; if he is dead then I myself will die! That son with softly curling hair and eyes like a deer's; sweet of speech and wise for all his youth, generous, obedient, and fearless; if he is dead then I myself will die! What peace can my heart know if I never again behold his face or hear his voice? What can I say to Subádra and Dráupadi? For while he fought, surrounded by his foes, he must have thought, 'My father will come and rescue me.' Surely my heart is hard as the thunderbolt, since it does not break to pieces here and now."

As he sat there weeping for his son, none dared to speak to him save Krishna and Yudíshtira, whom he loved and reverenced most. Yudíshtira told him all that had happened: how Abimányu had broken the array, how they had followed close behind him but had been stopped by the King of Sind, and how at last Abimányu had been surrounded and slain by six great chariot warriors.

Then Arjuna, pressing his hands together with rage and sighing deeply, said, "You bulls among men, I swear here before you that tomorrow I will slay that King of Sind! Listen now to another oath of mine! If tomorrow's sun sets before I have slain that wretch I myself will mount the funeral pyre! You demons and gods and men, you birds and snakes, you wanderers of the night, do not protect my enemy, for if he goes under the earth or into the heavens I shall still, with a hundred arrows, before another night has come, cut off the head of Abimányu's foe!"

When he had said this, he rose and stretched Gandíva, plucking its string, and the sound of the mighty bow rose above his voice and touched the very heavens. Then shouts and the blare of conchs and trumpets rose in the Pándava camp, making the earth tremble. The spies of Duryódana heard it and told their master what had happened, as he sat among the assembled Kúrava warriors. The King of Sind, stunned with grief and fear, arose and said, "If Arjuna means to kill me, allow me, O lords of earth, to go back home and live! These shouts from the Pándava camp fill me with fear; I feel like a man drowning in the ocean. Therefore, give me leave, I pray you, to go where the wielder of Gandíva may not find me." But Duryódana, thinking always of his own victory, said, "Do not fear, O tiger among men! We shall surround you on all sides and protect you with our eleven armies. You yourself are a hero; therefore do not fear!"

Thus comforted, the King of Sind went that night to Drona, for he had been one of Drona's pupils. Touching the master's feet, he asked, "O illustrious one, tell me the exact difference between Arjuna and myself, in aim, in lightness of hand, and in strength." "Both of you," said Drona, "had the same teaching, but because of Arjuna's hard life and the discipline that he has undergone, he is better than you in every respect. However, do not fear to fight tomorrow, for I will protect you and form an array that the Pándavas cannot pierce. Do your duty, following the path of your ancestors."

In the morning Drona formed an array hard to be broken. First he formed one shaped like a cart and behind that another in the form of a lotus, and inside that lotus a dense array called the needle. At the eye of the needle stood Duryódana and Karna and behind them thousands of the finest warriors, while at the point of the needle the King of Sind took his stand. Drona stood at the head of the whole host, and Duryódana, beholding that mighty array teeming with chariots and men, horses and elephants roaring dreadfully, took heart and rejoiced.

On the other side, the ever victorious Arjuna, eager to achieve his great vow, clad in mail and decked with his golden diadem, brandishing Gandíva, placed his chariot at the very head of his army and blew his conch, while the ape on his banner opened his mouth and yelled. He attacked his foes like a pouring cloud of arrows, seeming to dance upon his chariot, drawing his bow so swiftly that no one could find the slightest chance to strike him.

Approaching Drona's chariot, he joined his palms and said, "Wish me well, O Brahman, and bless me! I wish to enter this unbreakable array and kill the King of Sind in battle. You are like a father to me, like the just Yudíshtira or Krishna, and I ask for your permission, as your son might ask it. Let me pass, O sinless one!"

The master, smiling, said to him, "O Arjuna, unless you vanquish me, you will not be able to kill the King of Sind. Remember your pledge to me!" Saying this, he covered the son of Pandu and his chariot with a shower of arrows, and Arjuna fought back, shooting his mightiest shafts, but so wonderful was Drona's skill that not one arrow touched him, although many of his troops were slain and wounded.

Krishna, anxious that Arjuna's vow should be kept, said to him, "We cannot waste time, for a more important task awaits us. We must avoid Drona and press on!"

"Do as you please," answered Arjuna, and Krishna, passing Drona on the left, drove onward while Arjuna turned round, shooting backwards.

"Why do you drive on, O son of Pandu?" shouted the master. "Must not a warrior go on fighting till he has beaten his foe? Are you leaving the battle?"

"You are my teacher and no foe of mine," answered Arjuna. "I am your pupil and therefore like your son. Besides, no one can vanquish you in battle." With these words he drove swiftly on, with two princes of Panchála guarding his wheels, and began to penetrate the Kuru host, careering over the field like an elephant among reeds, strewing the earth with the bodies of men and animals. Meanwhile the Pándava army, in full force, attacked the outer array where Drona was.

Duryódana, beholding the slaughter and confusion of his army, drove to the side of Drona and said to him, "Behold, that tiger among men has passed through our host. What can we do to prevent him from slaying the ruler of Sind? No one believed that he could pass you by; if you had not promised to check him, I should have permitted the King to return home, as he desired. Fool that I am to trust you, for you have always favored the Pándavas, even though you are supported by me! O sinless one, do not be angry with me; protect the King of Sind!"

"Krishna is the best of charioteers and his steeds the fleetest," Drona said. "I am too old to follow them so far and so fast. Besides, the whole army of the Pándavas is upon us and Yudíshtira, unprotected, may now be captured. Therefore I shall stay and fight here, while you must go and fight with Arjuna. You are a king and a hero, his equal in birth and education. Go then, and fight with him!"

"I, fight against Arjuna," asked the King, "when he has passed you by, when no one in the world can vanquish him?"

"I will enable you to stand against him and to stop him," Drona answered. Then, speaking certain incantations, he put Duryódana's armor on him in such a way that no weapon could penetrate it, and bade him have no fear; and the mighty-armed king, having confidence in that armor and surrounded by the Trigartas and thousands of other great chariot warriors, set out in pursuit of Arjuna.

The son of Kunti was already approaching the place where the ruler of Sind stood in his chariot; he made a path through the enemy army with his arrows, and Krishna drove the white steeds along that path. Passing through that part of the host led by Drona, they looked like the sun and moon coming out of the darkness. When at last they came in sight of the King of Sind, they shouted with joy and rushed toward him like two hawks swooping down on a piece of meat. Just then, however, Duryódana rushed past them in his chariot and, turning his horses sharply, stood between them and their foe. Both warriors were filled with joy and blew their conchs, eager to slay each other.

Arjuna, coolly and quickly, shot fourteen arrows whetted on

stone and winged with vulture's feathers, but these fell down from the armor of Duryódana without piercing it. Krishna was amazed to see this, but Arjuna knew that Drona must have put the armor on, for he alone knew the whole science of armor and had taught it to Arjuna. Therefore the son of Kunti attacked Duryódana's steeds, his driver and his bow, even shooting the gloves from his enemy's hands and piercing his palms. Thus he made Duryódana helpless and other warriors, coming to his rescue, bore the King from the field. But Karna and Ashvattáman and many other kings and warriors surrounded Arjuna, trying to protect the King of Sind, hoping that the sun would set before he should be slain, for they knew that Arjuna would keep his word and kill himself if he had not fulfilled his vow. But the ape-bannered son of Pandu, like a blazing fire, fought his way through them all, and at last reached with his arrows the King of Sind himself, piercing him with nine of them. The King, bearing the boar on his banner, was filled with rage and rushed against Arjuna, speeding from his bow many a polished shaft, and the fight became more fierce as the Kúrava warriors crowded round him to protect him.

The fearful fight had raged all afternoon; the sun was sinking on the western hills. Krishna said, "You cannot kill the King, O best of men, till you have slain these warriors. Therefore I shall shroud the sun in a cloud of darkness so that they will think that it has set and be less careful." Through his soul's power he created darkness that only those warriors perceived and they, thinking the sun had set, were filled with gladness and stood with their heads thrown back, looking at the sky.

"Now quickly drive them off, O mighty one!" cried Krishna. "Strike off the head of the King of Sind and fulfill your vow! Strike quickly, for the sun has touched the mountains!"

Arjuna sent forth a torrent of arrows, wounding every one of the warriors and slaughtering their troops, and they were so amazed that they fell back and many fled away, abandoning the King. Then the son of Pandu took up an arrow that looked like the thunderbolt of Indra, terrible and fiery, and fixed it on his bow, and that shaft, sped from Gandíva, snatched off the head of the King of Sind as a hawk snatches a smaller bird from a treetop.

Krishna removed the darkness that he had made; the Kúrava warriors, seeing that they had been deceived, wept with sorrow and wrath, while Krishna and Arjuna blew their conchs triumphantly. At that moment the thousand-rayed sun set behind the hills and Arjuna returned to Yudíshtira, to tell him that the victory was won.

Duryódana was filled with despair and breathed deep sighs, like a snake with broken fangs. He bitterly reproached Drona and then ordered the army out again to battle, even though night had come. In the terrible hours of darkness the fight went on, while the jackals howled round the field and owls perched, hooting, on the banners. A fearful din arose, for in the pitchy dark, no one knew which was friend or which was foe: shouts and the neighing of steeds and the clashing of weapons filled the air. Bima and Arjuna attacked the army of Drona and drove it back until the Kúrava warriors, terrified by the darkness and overcome with sleep, broke and began to flee in all directions.

Then Duryódana stopped them and rallied them with cheering words, crying, "Lay aside your great weapons and take blazing lamps into your hands!" And foot soldiers each joyfully took up a burning lamp and arrayed themselves again; on each chariot five lamps were placed, on every elephant three, and one on every horse. The army, thus made radiant with light, looked beautiful, like the summer sky flashing with lightning, like trees covered with fireflies at twilight. The flames were reflected from golden ornaments, from armor, and from bows, and flashed back from whirling maces and from swords. Beholding the Kuru host so radiant, the Pándavas bestirred themselves and lighted lamps. On each elephant they placed seven, on each car ten, and two on every horse, while the foot soldiers held blazing torches. Then the two armies clashed again and fought such a battle as never before was seen.

Midnight came while they fought. Animals and men were worn out and their eyes closed in sleep; the night seemed everlasting.

Some, blind with weariness, laid down their weapons and slept, on the backs of elephants, in their chariots, or on the ground, and many were slain before they waked and many slew those of their own side, so dazed were they. Arjuna, seeing this, shouted to his men, "All of you and your animals are worn out with fighting. Therefore rest, here on the field of battle, and close your eyes for a while! When the moon rises, you may fight again."

Hearing these words, the Kúrava warriors cried, "O King Dury-ódana, O Karna, stop the fight! The Pándavas are no longer attacking us." And both armies lay down on the field, each warrior with his animal. The elephants, heavy with sleep, looked like hills as they lay there cooling the earth with the breath blown through their snakelike trunks; the horses stood still in their trappings of gold, softly stamping the ground. Warriors lay against their elephants' necks or on their chariots, while many men, in their armor and with their weapons beside them, slept on the ground. All were motionless and silent, like a forest unstirred by the wind.

In the early morning the moon rose, that delighter of eyes, the lord of lilies. It came like a lion out of its eastern cave; slowly its rays drove off the darkness and filled the earth and sky with radiance. The two hosts were awakened; they rose up as the ocean rises when its tide is summoned by the moon, and tired as they were, they fought again. Soon the chariot of the sun, vanquishing the glory of the moon, reddened the east and blazed into the sky. All the warriors of both the hosts, alighting from their chariots or their beasts, stood with joined palms, facing the lord of day, and worshiped him, saying their morning prayers. Then, filled with joy and with new strength, they dashed into the battle.

The Death of Drona

The same soldiers who had fought each other before sunrise now fought again after the sun had risen, although some, weakened with fatigue and thirst and hunger, fell fainting on the ground. Bima drove his chariot close to Arjuna's and said, "Listen to these words of mine, O foremost of warriors! This is the day when we must put forth all our might and compass Drona's death." Beholding the master at the head of the Kúrava troops, handsome, blazing with energy in spite of his eighty years, the Pándava warriors attacked him together, while Duryódana, Karna, and Shákuni surrounded him to protect him.

Dráupadi's father and Viráta, those aged kings, supported by their armies, were the first to attack him. Drona, with three sharp shafts, slew three of the grandsons of the King of Panchála and then put to flight the army of the Matsyas. The two kings, filled with rage, covered him with their arrows and with iron darts, whereupon the master, with two well-tempered, broad-headed shafts, sent both those aged monarchs to the abode of Yama. Seeing his father fall, the high-souled Dyumna swore a great oath in the midst of all the warriors, saying, "May I lose the reward of all my deeds if Drona escape me with his life today!"

All the warriors rushed against each other like two stormy oceans meeting and it seemed wonderful that any could come out alive. There were single combats between Duryódana and Nákula, between Dushásana and Sahadéva, between Karna and Bima, who had already, during the night, slain eleven of Duryódana's brothers. Finally Drona and Arjuna met, and so wonderful was that battle between master and pupil that the other warriors lowered their weapons to watch it, for these two were the leaders, the refuge, and the saviors of their armies. The motions of their chariots, their swiftness, and sure aim, were beautiful to behold; whatever weapons, human or divine, were used by Drona, Arjuna destroyed, and Drona was pleased in his heart, for he was proud that the greatest bowman in the world had been his pupil. Beholding these two heroes, wheeling like two hawks in the sky over a single prey, the other warriors said, "Never has there been the like of this battle; no one can find any difference between these mighty ones. If Shiva, dividing himself in two, fought against himself, that fight would equal this one!"

When neither could prevail over the other, the battle became general again, and Drona attacked the Panchála army, slaughtering many and driving back the rest. Then the Pándavas despaired of victory and said to each other, "Drona will consume us all, like raging fire in a heap of straw. None can even encounter him in battle except Arjuna, and he, who alone can do it, will never slay the master."

Then Krishna said, "The gods themselves cannot vanquish this leader of leaders, this foremost of chariot warriors. He has told us, however, that if he lays aside his weapons, overcome by sorrow, then he may be slain. I think he would do this if he knew that his son, Ashvattáman, was dead. Therefore, you sons of Pandu, cast virtue aside and let some man tell him that Ashvattáman has been slain. Only thus can we win the victory!"

Arjuna did not approve of this advice, but others did, and at last, unwillingly, Yudíshtira gave his consent. Bima slew with his mace a huge elephant whose name was Ashvattáman, meaning the "horse-voiced." Then he approached Drona and, with some hesitation, cried aloud, "Ashvattáman has been slain!"

Hearing these words, Drona's limbs seemed to melt like salt in water, but, remembering the might of his son, he did not believe what Bima said. He turned to Yudíshtira and asked him if this was true, for he believed that Yudíshtira would never lie, even to gain the rule of the whole earth. Krishna quickly said to Yudíshtira, "If Drona fights for another half day, I tell you truly, your army will be wiped out. In this case a lie is better than the truth, for lying is no sin when it can save life."

Persuaded by Krishna and longing for victory, Yudíshtira said, "It is true. Ashvattáman is slain and lies on the bare ground like a young lion." After the word "Ashvattáman" he added under his breath, "the elephant." Before he said this, Yudíshtira's chariot had always stood above the surface of the earth, but after he had told that lie, chariot and horses stood upon the ground.

Then Drona, overcome with grief, laid down his weapons and called loudly his son's name. Sitting down in his chariot, his head bent forward and his eyes closed, he devoted himself to meditation, fixing his heart on God. Seeing this, Dyumna, frantic to avenge his father, leaped from his chariot with his sword in his hand and seized Drona's white hair. Shouts arose from all sides, "Do not slay Drona!" Arjuna leaped from his car, and ran toward Dyumna with upraised arms, crying, "Do not slay the master, but bring him here alive!" In spite of all these cries, the prince of Panchála cut off Drona's head and shouted with joy, whirling his bloody sword. Then he cast the head on the ground before the Kúrava host, and all the warriors, as if they themselves were about to lose their lives, despaired and fled from the field, crying, "Alas, alas!"

When Ashvattáman heard of his father's death he was mad with grief and rage. Pressing his hands together and sighing deeply, like a snake that has been trodden upon, he said to Duryódana, "I have heard how my sire was slain after he had laid aside his weapons, and I have heard how he was deceived by Darma's son. I do not grieve because he died in battle, for he met a hero's death and has surely gone to those regions where they dwell who never turn their backs in battle. I grieve because, while I was alive, his white locks were seized in the sight of all the army. This tears the very core of my heart. Shame on my might! Shame on my skill in arms; since Drona, having me for a son, had his white locks seized by that impious wretch! O tiger among men, I swear by the truth and by my own deeds that I shall slay Dyumna and wipe out all the Pándavas with the divine weapons my father gave me! Let them beware today!"

Hearing those words the Kúrava army rallied and the leaders blew their great conchs and had the drums beaten. The uproar made the earth and the sky echo, and the Pándavas, when they heard it, assembled to take counsel. Yudíshtira said to Arjuna, "When Drona was slain, O conqueror of wealth, the Kuru army fled. What mighty warrior is causing this terrible uproar, leading the enemy host back into battle?"

"He who rallies the Kúravas," answered Arjuna, "he who walks like an angry elephant and has a face like a tiger's, he who now roars so loud, O King, is Ashvattáman! He will never forgive Dyumna for seizing the master's hair; he will never rest till he has slain him or been slain himself, and all of us together will not be able to save Dráupadi's brother. You, O King, told your teacher a lie for the sake of a kingdom. Drona thought, 'The son of Pandu is virtuous and is, besides, my pupil; he will never lie to me.' Thinking thus, he believed you and this caused his death. Alas, we have committed a cruel and a heavy sin! I have already, O lord of earth, sunk into hell, overcome with shame, since we caused the death of one who was a Brahman, who was old in years, who was our teacher, who had laid aside his arms, and was engaged in prayer."

When Arjuna had spoken, the rest sat silent for a moment, and then Bima said angrily, "You are preaching like a Brahman or a holy man. We are Kshatrias, whose business is battle and whose purpose is victory, O son of Kunti. It is true that we have slain our teacher: that teacher who sat indifferently beside his son when Dráupadi was dragged into the assembly; that teacher who caused the child, Subádra's son, to be slain by six mighty warriors; that teacher who put Duryódana's armor on in such a way that he could not be slain while fighting with you! We need not fear the son of Drona. It is no sin to slay one's enemy, and Drona was our enemy."

Then Dyumna spoke: "O Arjuna, the duties of a Brahman are sacrifice, study, and the teaching of the Vedas. Which of these duties did Drona perform? Calling himself a Brahman, he performed all the duties of a Kshatria and did his utmost to slay us all in battle. Why should we not slay him? Long ago he wronged my father and I was born to avenge that wrong and my father's death. Why then do you not praise me instead of reproaching me? You slew the grandsire, and yet you reproach me now for slaying this enemy of mine. That is not right, yet I forgive your hasty words for the sake of Dráupadi and her children. Let us fight now. Victory will be ours!"

Then those warriors went out again to battle with the Kúrava host, led by Drona's son. Terrible was the fight between them, for the Pándavas felt new strength because of Drona's death, while Ashvattáman, filled with fury and eager to avenge his father, encouraged the Kúravas and led them on. When the two armies met, like two oceans or two mountains striking against each other, the son of Drona loosed his most powerful weapon: thousands of arrows with blazing mouths appeared in the sky, and also iron balls, which sorely wounded the Pándava host, slaughtering vast numbers of them, who lay piled up like hills upon the field. Then Krishna shouted, "Lay down your arms and lie down on the earth, all you that hear my words! Only so can this mighty weapon lose its power."

All those who heard him obeyed him, excepting Bima, who rushed furiously against Ashvattáman. Krishna and Arjuna, who had alighted from their chariot, ran swiftly after him and, seizing him, dragged him from his car and took his weapons from him, despite his roaring and struggling. When all were lying down upon the field, the terrible weapons of Ashvattáman passed harmlessly above them. Then they rose again joyfully, eager to fight again.

"Hurl that weapon speedily again, O son of our master!" Duryódana cried. "For there our enemies are arrayed in battle!"

"Alas," said Ashvattáman sadly, "the weapon can be cast but once and Krishna knew how to make it powerless."

"Then fight them with other weapons," said Duryódana, "and let these slayers of their teacher be slain by his son!"

Thus roused again to anger, Ashvattáman went forth and sought out Dyumna, whom he struck between the eyebrows with an arrow. The Panchála prince sank down on the floor of his chariot, holding the flagstaff for support, and his charioteer drove him from the field to tend his wound, while Bima and Arjuna and many others covered his retreat. Ashvattáman also slew Bima's charioteer, and the horses, feeling the reins loosened, galloped madly away, carrying Bima with them. But Arjuna and Krishna led the Pándava host and drove the Kúravas back, till night came and both armies withdrew to rest.

This was the fifteenth day of battle, the fifth day of Drona's command of the Kúrava host.

BOOK XIV

THE BATTLE ENDS

Bima Fulfills a Vow

AT the end of that day when Drona had been killed and his son had failed to avenge him, the Kúrava chiefs met with cheerless hearts in the tent of Duryódana. Drona's son proposed that Karna be made commander of the host and Duryódana received his words with joy, installing Karna with the usual rites. "I have told you already, O son of Gandári," said Karna, decked with ornaments and looking as resplendent as the sun, his father, "that I shall vanquish the Pándavas with all their sons and Krishna. Have no fear while I command your host."

At dawn, to the sound of joyful music, he arrayed the host in the hawk formation, placing himself in the tip of the beak; and Dyumna made a counter-array in the form of a half-moon. The two armies advanced against each other as if in a dance, and warriors rushed forth from the tips of the moon and from the wings of the hawk, eager to slay each other. Yet on that sixteenth day of battle neither side prevailed until the evening, when all the Pándavas turned upon Karna and drove his army back. He, fearing another night battle, ordered his army to retire, and the Pándavas retired too, jeering at their enemy with shouts and derisive sounds of their conchs and trumpets, hoping for victory the following day.

Early the next morning, before dawn, Karna went to Duryódana and said, "Today, O King, I shall fight with Arjuna and I shall slay him or be slain by him. Listen, O ruler of men! My knowledge of divine weapons is equal to that of Arjuna and in all else I am far better than he. Therefore rejoice, for I shall gladden your heart by slaying him today and the whole earth will be yours! There is only one way in which he is superior to me and that can be mended: he has Krishna for his charioteer. O King, Shalya, the King of Madra, is the only one who equals Krishna in knowledge of horses and skill in driving; therefore, O best of the Kúravas, give me Shalya for my charioteer and I will be superior in every way to the son of Pandu."

Duryódana heard these boastful words with a glad heart. He went to the King of Madra and approached him humbly, saying, "O ruler of the Madras, O hero in battle, O slayer of foes, I come to you today with joined hands and bowed head, to beg a favor of you. Today Karna wishes to contend in single combat with Arjuna, but there is no charioteer equal to Krishna—save you—to hold his reins. Therefore I beg of you, O foremost of warriors, to drive his chariot and to protect Karna, even as Krishna protects Arjuna. With you as his driver, the gods themselves could not defeat him, and we shall surely win the victory."

Shalya was filled with rage at these words. Frowning and roll-ing his eyes in anger, he answered, "You insult me, O son of Gandári, by asking me to drive the chariot of Karna, who is not my equal in battle or in birth. Give me a harder task, O lord of earth! I will, if you wish, fight the enemy singlehanded. Behold these arms of mine, as strong as thunder! Behold my excellent bow, this mace twined with hempen cords and decked with gold! I can split the very earth, dry up the oceans, scatter the mountains with my strength, O King! But I cannot hold the reins of a Suta's son. I cannot fight, having been so humiliated; therefore permit me to return home, O king of kings." Having spoken thus, that tiger among men stood up, meaning to leave the encampment.

Duryódana, however, held him and spoke sweet and soothing words: "Listen, O ruler of men! I do not think Karna superior to you. Indeed, there is none like you in might of arms and learning.

You are superior to Krishna himself and therefore I am asking you to do for Karna what Krishna does for Arjuna. This is no insult, O mighty hero."

Then Shalya said, "Since you say I am superior to Krishna, I am pleased with you, O son of Gandári, and I will hold the reins of Karna while he fights Arjuna. But let it be understood that I will say, in his presence, anything that I please." Duryódana and Karna both agreed to this and Duryódana joyfully embraced Shalya.

Then Shalya mounted the splendid chariot of Karna and took up the reins; Karna also mounted it, stretching his mighty bow, and those two heroes looked like Surya and Agni seated on a cloud. The Kúravas, filled with delight, raised a great shout and beat their drums and cymbals. "Urge on the steeds, O Shalya," Karna said, "so that I may slay Arjuna and Bima, the twins and Yudíshtira! If all the gods should protect the sons of Pandu, I shall still vanquish them!"

Remembering his promise to Yudíshtira before the battle, Shalya laughed aloud and answered, "Forbear, forbear, O Karna, from such bragging! How can you, O lowest of men, compare with Arjuna, who is the foremost? Who but he could have challenged Shiva himself to battle? Who but he could have vanquished all the Kúravas when they tried to seize King Viráta's cattle? Why did you not slay him then? Now another chance presents itself, but truly, if you do not flee from this battle, you yourself will be slain."

"Why do you always praise Arjuna?" Karna said. "If he wins this battle, then you may praise him, but not till then. Drive on!" Shalya, urging on the white steeds, drove him onto the field. As soon as Karna met the Pándava host, he said to the soldiers, "Whoever will show me where the ape-bannered son of Pandu is, to him I will give a cartload of gems and jewels. I will give a hundred cows, with brass milking vessels, to him who will show me that hero who has Krishna for his driver. Indeed, he who will bring me to Arjuna shall have all the wealth that son of Pandu leaves behind him after I have slain him."

"O Suta's son," cried Shalya, "do not give away jewels and centuries of cattle in order to obtain a sight of Arjuna; you will see him soon enough and repent of your folly. When you challenge Arjuna to battle, you are like a hare that challenges a mighty elephant; you are like a man who fights a furious black cobra with a piece of wood, or like a jackal yelling at a maned lion; like a frog croaking at a thundercloud, or a dog who, from the safety of his master's house, barks at the forest-roaming tiger."

Stung to fury by these words, Karna replied, "You are an enemy with a friend's face, trying to frighten me. I know my own might. I have here one shaft that lies alone in its quiver in sandalwood dust. It is terrible as a poisonous snake, it is steeped in oil, and well adorned; it has been worshiped by me for many years. This shaft I have saved for Arjuna and with this I shall slay him."

"Behold, O Karna," said Shalya, "yonder comes the son of Kunti, slaughtering his foes along the way! Yonder flies his banner, while yours is trembling on its staff! Hark to Gandíva and behold your army fleeing before him!"

Karna replied with rage, "See now, he is beset on all sides by those Trigartas whom he has not yet slain! He will escape me! He is sure to perish, plunged into that ocean of warriors!"

"Who would try to slay the God of Waters with rain or quench the fire by adding fuel to it?" answered Shalya. "Rejoice that you cannot fight him now and turn to some other foe; there stand the other sons of Pandu, eager for battle!"

While they were talking thus, the two armies mingled fiercely in battle, like the currents of the Ganges and the Jumna meeting. Piercing through the Pándava host, Karna attacked Yudíshtira and a fierce fight took place between them, while the warriors on each side surrounded their leaders to protect them. That mighty bowman, Karna, wounded them all with his blood-drinking shafts and was wounded in the brow and chest by Yudíshtira. Filled with rage, he cut Yudíshtira's armor from his body with sharp arrows and broke his bow, but he did not kill that king of men, because he remembered his pledge to Kunti. Yudíshtira, deeply wounded, retreated from the fight, while Bima and the

twins hurled themselves against Karna, shouting angry and taunt-
ing words. Bima, eager to make an end of Karna, drew his bowstring to his very ear and sped a fierce and mighty shaft against
him. It pierced through Karna's armor and that hero fell senseless
to the floor of his chariot. Then Shalya drove him quickly from
the field and Bima, triumphant, began to rout the Kúrava host.

Seeing the army terrified and sorely smitten, Dushásana fearlessly advanced against Bima, shooting showers of arrows. Blazing
with anger at the sight of him, Bima shouted, "O wicked one,
today I shall drink your blood!" Dushásana hurled an iron dart
and Bima whirled his terrible mace and flung it at his foe. The
mace shattered the dart and then struck Dushásana on the head,
throwing him to the ground. Bima, seeing him lying there, remembered how Dráupadi's hair had been seized, how she had been
shamefully dragged into the assembly, and how her clothes were
torn from her. His wrath blazed up. Leaping from his chariot, he
looked down on his fallen enemy; then, drawing his whetted
sword, he put his foot on Dushásana's throat and, cutting open
his enemy's breast, bent down and drank his hot life's blood. "The
taste of this blood," he said, "is sweeter than my mother's milk or
good wine mixed with honey." Looking again at Dushásana's
body, he laughed softly and said, "What more can I do to you?
Death has rescued you from my hands."

Arjuna and Karna

Meanwhile Arjuna had slain the last of those warriors who
had challenged him. Returning to battle, he encountered the son
of Drona and killed his charioteer. Ashvattáman took up the reins
himself, but Arjuna, smiling, cut the reins with his sharp arrows
and the horses ran wildly off the field, carrying their master with
them. Then Arjuna, gladdening the eyes of his own troops, came
among them and looked about to see Yudíshtira's banner, bearing
the device of the golden moon and the planets. Unable to find it,
he drove close to Bima, asking, "Where is the King?"

"He has left the battle," Bima answered, "sorely wounded by Karna's arrows, and may be no longer living." Arjuna, alarmed, asked Krishna to turn the chariot and drive the horses swiftly toward the camp.

In Yudíshtira's tent they found the King lying alone on his bed, the arrows plucked from his body and his wounds tended. Filled with joy at finding him alive, they touched his feet, and Yudíshtira, thinking that Karna must be already slain, welcomed them with delight, hailing their victory and praising them. "I have not yet encountered the Suta's son," Arjuna told him, "for I wished to come here to see that you are well. Now bless me, O lion among kings, for I shall slay Karna today with all his troops and all our foes!"

But Yudíshtira, shamed by his defeat and suffering from the wounds of Karna's arrows, became very angry and spoke harsh words to his brother, saying, "You have deserted Bima and come here out of fear of Karna! Long ago you promised me that you would slay him; why then have you left the battle? For thirteen years we have relied on you, O conqueror of wealth; will you betray us now? If you cannot encounter the Suta's son in battle, then give your bow, Gandíva, to someone else who can use it better."

Hearing these bitter words, Arjuna's anger blazed up. He drew his sword, ready to kill his brother, but Krishna stopped him, asking, "Who is there here whom you must kill, O son of Kunti? You came to see the King and he is well. Now let us go to battle."

But Arjuna, breathing heavily like an angry snake and fixing his eyes on Yudíshtira, said, "I would cut off the head of any man who said to me, 'Give your Gandíva to someone else!' Those words have been spoken by this king and I dare not forgive them. For this reason, O Krishna, I have drawn my sword."

"The King is tired," Krishna said, "and suffers from pain and grief, for Karna drove him from the field and wounded him. Therefore he spoke harshly to you, and because he wished to provoke you to fight with Karna."

Arjuna thrust his sword into its sheath, and hanging his head in shame, seized his brother's feet in his two hands and said, weeping, "Forgive me, O King! The task shall be no longer delayed. Karna seeks to fight with me today and I shall meet him and slay him. I live only for your good, O King; this is the truth."

Yudíshtira raised his brother and embraced him, saying, "In the very sight of all my troops I was put to shame this day by Karna. Forgive my harsh words, O mighty-armed one! Go forth and slay the Suta's son, and my blessing go with you."

The brothers wept together until their hearts were free of grief; then Krishna turned the white steeds and drove Arjuna out into the battle, where Karna's banner, with the elephant's rope, waved above his chariot.

When those two great bowmen met, with shouts and the clapping of palms and the twang of bowstrings, the warriors on both sides cheered them with shouts and the blare of conchs and trumpets. They were much alike, for both were born of gods and were godlike in strength and beauty. One had Krishna and the other Shalya for his driver; both had white horses and resplendent chariots; both had shining bows and swords, arrows and darts, and lofty standards. The Kúrava warriors crowded round Karna, for he was their stake in that game of battle, while the Pándavas stood by the high-souled Arjuna, who was their stake, and the soldiers of both sides were spectators of that game. Fiercely the two heroes challenged each other and each blew his conch. The mighty ape on Arjuna's banner leaped from his place and fell upon Karna's standard, tearing the elephant's rope with his teeth and nails, while the rope, hard as iron and decked with little bells, wrapped itself angrily about the ape. The horses, too, neighed at each other and stamped, eager for battle, and Krishna and Shalya eyed each other with keen glances.

Then to the sound of conchs and drums, the two warriors fought with each other, like two full-grown Himálayan elephants fighting for a mate, like two storm clouds or two mountains encountering one another. Showers of arrows, crescent-shaped and boar-toothed, fell upon both chariots like birds flying into a tree at night to roost there. Both warriors possessed divine weapons.

Arjuna sped the Fire God's weapon at Karna; it flew, blazing, through the air, setting fire to the robes of the warriors who drew back from its path. But Karna quenched it with the weapon of Váruna, God of Waters, and also covered the sky with black clouds, to blind his foe. These Arjuna dispelled with the Wind God's weapon and, taking up another whose use he had learned in heaven, he sent forth hundreds of arrows with golden wings, which sped beyond the chariot of Karna and slew the warriors and soldiers of the Kúrava host.

Then, filled with rage, Karna took out that keen and snake-mouthed shaft that he had kept so long within its quiver in sandal-wood dust and aimed it at Arjuna. Seeing it blaze through the sky and understanding its power, Krishna pressed the chariot down with his feet until it sank a cubit's depth into the earth. The horses, white as moonbeams and decked with gold, bent their knees and lay down on the ground, and that terrible weapon passed over Arjuna's head, sweeping off the splendid diadem—set with many jewels, famous in the three worlds—which Indra had given him. The diadem broke to pieces but Arjuna stood unmoved and bound his curling locks with a piece of cloth. Krishna dismounted and lifted the chariot out of the earth and the white horses rose to their feet again.

Filled with anger, Arjuna cut the bright and costly armor from Karna's body and pierced his vital parts with whetted shafts. Karna reeled, clutching his flagstaff and dropping his bow, but Arjuna, mindful of Kshatria honor, did not slay him then. Karna recovered and sped an iron shaft at his enemy's breast, and the son of Kunti trembled, like a mountain in an earthquake, and lowered Gandíva. In that moment, one of Karna's wheels sank in the earth; his chariot reeled and stuck fast. Seeing that Arjuna was hurt, he leaped from his car and tried in vain to pull the wheel out of the ground; then he looked up to see Arjuna drawing his bowstring to his ear.

With tears of rage in his eyes, Karna cried out, "O Arjuna, wait till I lift my wheel! You are both brave and virtuous and know the rules of battle: a brave warrior never fights with one who is in distress; one standing in a chariot never fights with one who is on the ground." Then Krishna spoke to Karna, saying, "It is well, O Suta's son, that you remember virtue! When the son of Kunti was unfairly defeated at dice, where was your virtue? When you laughed to see Dráupadi dragged into the assembly, where was your virtue? When the sons of Pandu returned after the thirteenth year, did you wish to give their kingdom back to them? When the boy Abimányu was surrounded by six warriors, where was your virtue then? Since you thought nothing of it then, why waste your breath by speaking of it now?"

Karna, furious and ashamed, took up his bow and fought from where he stood, while Arjuna, blazing with anger as he heard Krishna's words, took up a razor-headed arrow winged with gold and struck down Karna's standard, bearing the elephant's rope and hung with bells. Then, taking up another terrible shaft, he drew his bowstring to his ear and cut off Karna's head. Unwillingly that beautiful head left its body, as an owner unwillingly leaves a rich and comfortable house. Beautiful even in death, Karna fell to the earth, the blood flowing from all his wounds, as the thousand-rayed sun falls at the close of day. Clad in bright garments and golden mail, he lay on the ground like a mighty tree with flowering branches, like a heap of pure gold, or like a fire extinguished by the shower of Arjuna's arrows. Súrya himself, beholding his son slain and touching the body with his rays, sank into the western sea as if to take a purifying bath.

The Kúrava army fled away in fear like a herd of stampeding cattle, crying, "Alas, Karna! Alas, Karna!" As they fled they looked back at the lofty standard of Arjuna, each man fearing that the son of Kunti was pursuing him. Shalya, standing alone in the chariot of Karna, cried to Duryódana, "Turn back, O King! The foremost of your warriors has been slain. The sun is setting; let your troops retire! This is destiny, O lord of earth; remember the cause of it!" Duryódana, nearly senseless with grief, wept for the Suta's son, crying, "O Karna! O Karna!" And all the kings, trying to comfort him, returned to their camp with drooping heads and cheerless hearts.

Meanwhile Krishna and Arjuna lifted their snow-white conchs adorned with gold and blew them at once, piercing the hearts of their foes with the sound and gladdening Yudíshtira. Then turning the chariot, and looking like two risen suns, they entered their own encampment, surrounded by their friends, followed by the praises of all the warriors, and went to Yudíshtira's tent to tell him that the victory had been won.

Duryódana Enters the Lake

Next morning the Kúrava warriors, putting aside their grief and undaunted by defeat, made Shalya the leader of their army. Although Bishma and Drona and Karna, those mighty warriors, had all failed and had all been slain, the Kúravas hoped that Shalya would still vanquish the Pándavas, and he himself accepted the leadership with confidence, promising Duryódana that victory would be his that day. It was the eighteenth day of battle; both armies had lost many thousands of their troops and most of their bravest leaders. The Kúrava army was still nearly twice as large as that of the Pándavas, but the Kúravas had lost more of their great chariot warriors than the Pándavas had lost.

When the two armies were arrayed, and the fierce and awful battle began, Shalya said to his driver, "Yonder is King Yudíshtira, resplendent as the sun. Take me to him with speed and then watch my great prowess! The Pándavas cannot stand against me in battle." He approched Yudíshtira, and both kings, filled with rage, challenged each other and blew their conchs. Terrible was the encounter between them and both were wounded and bleeding from each other's arrows. Yudíshtira killed his enemy's horses and cut down, with one blazing arrow, the standard with the golden plowshare. The son of Drona, driving quickly toward Shalya, took him up on his own chariot to rescue him, but as they fled away, Shalya heard Yudíshtira's triumphant shout and he found another chariot and returned, roaring, to the fight.

In his turn he killed the steeds of Yudíshtira and then, leaping from his chariot, he rushed on foot against the son of Kunti. Yudíshtira, blazing with anger, took up a dart whose handle was bright with gold and jewels, a dart that the sons of Pandu had worshiped with perfumes and garlands, for it had been forged with care by one of the workmen of the gods. He hurled it now at the King of Madra and those who watched it saw sparks of fire fly from it as it sped like a meteor through the air. Shalya tried to catch it, but it pierced through his fair broad chest as if his body had been water, and entered the ground, carrying with it the world-wide fame of Madra's king. Covered with blood, he fell down with outstretched arms, his face turned toward his foe. The earth seemed to rise a little to receive him, as a wife rises to receive her lord, and the mighty Shalya, who had long enjoyed the earth, as one enjoys a dear wife, seemed now to sleep on her breast, embracing her with his arms.

Seeing their king slain, the warriors of Madra fell upon Yudísh-tira, eager for revenge, while Arjuna and Bima, the twins and all Dráupadi's sons surrounded the King and fought against the Madras, driving them back and slaying hundreds of them. Shákuni rallied them, shouting, "Stop, ye sinful ones, and fight again! What use is there in flight? Fight here with all your strength, while I engage the enemy from the rear."

With a strong force of horsemen armed with lances he rode swiftly to the rear and attacked the Pándavas, slaughtering many of their troops and breaking their ranks. Yudíshtira said to Saha-déva, "Behold how the gambler is destroying our forces in the rear! Take the sons of Dráupadi, the elephants, and horses, and slay Shákuni, while your brothers and I fight here against these chariots!"

Eagerly Sahadéva did as the King bade him. His forces, led by Dráupadi's sons, fell upon Shákuni's cavalry, routing them after fearful fighting and driving them from the field like frightened deer. Sahadéva, angry to think that Shákuni still lived, sought him out and found him fleeing, protected by his horsemen. The son of Madri pursued him on his chariot, striking him with many whetted arrows winged with vulture's feathers and calling out to him, "O fool, do you remember how you rejoiced in the assembly when the game of dice was won? I told you then that your dice were arrows that would wound you. Reap now, O dull of understanding, the harvest of your deeds! Today I shall cut off your head as a man plucks fruit from a tree. Be a man now and fight with me!"

Shákuni, filled with rage, turned and attacked Sahadéva with his lance, but the son of Madri cut the lance in two with one broad-headed arrow and pierced also, with two other arrows, the strong arms of his enemy. Then, with an iron arrow winged with gold, sped with care and power from his bow, he cut Shákuni's head from his body—that head which had hatched the evil plan of the gambling match and had sent the sons of Pandu to the forest. Seeing their leader lying headless on the ground, his troops fled, while the Pándavas blew their conchs, praising Sahadéva, rejoicing that the wicked Shákuni was at last dead.

Meanwhile the other sons of Pandu had slain the force against which they were fighting. In the Kúrava army, which had numbered many hundreds of thousands of famous chariot warriors, not one remained alive save Duryódana himself, Ashvattáman, the son of Drona, and two others. Arjuna, standing on his chariot and gazing over the field, which looked like a forest laid low by a tempest, said to Krishna, "Behold, O Krishna, the course of destiny! The army of Kuru's son, once as vast as the ocean, is now no larger than a pool caught in the hoofprint of a cow. If the foolish Duryódana had only made peace when Bishma fell, all would now be well; but he would not cease fighting. Nor when Drona fell, and Karna, would he cease, but still kept up the hopeless fight. But today our task will be ended, and King Yudíshtira will be free from all his foes, for today Duryódana will give up both his kingdom and his life."

On the other side of the field, Duryódana, sorely wounded, his horses slain, looked around him on all sides and saw the earth empty of his troops. He saw not a single warrior on his side, for Ashvattáman and his two companions were far off. Hearing his enemies shouting aloud in triumph and seeing himself alone, without a single companion, he left his steedless chariot and, taking up his mace, he fled on foot toward a lake to the east of the battle-field. That lord of eleven armies fled alone on foot toward the east. On his way he met Sánjaya, the trusted messenger of King Kuru, and said to him, "O Sánjaya, none are left alive but we two. Tell the blind king, my father, that I have lost all my friends, my sons, and brothers; tell him that I myself have escaped with life from the awful battle, but that I am sorely wounded and shall rest within the waters of this lake." With these words he entered the lake and, casting a magic spell upon the waters, he made a place for himself in their depths and lay there, resting.

While Sánjaya stood there, wondering, the three remaining warriors of the Kúravas, Ashvattáman and his two companions, came to that place, their horses weary and they themselves badly wounded. Seeing Sánjaya, they drove quickly toward him, saying, "Well met, Sánjaya! Is our king, Duryódana, yet alive?"

"He lives," answered Sánjaya, "though his heart burns with grief. Behold, he is resting now within the waters of this lake."

"Alas, alas!" cried Ashvattáman. "The King did not know that we are still alive. With him to lead us, we are still able to fight."

Approaching the lake, they addressed that ruler of men who lay within its waters, saying, "Arise, O King, and fight with us against the Pándavas! Their forces also have been slain by us, and those who remain alive are sorely wounded. They cannot stand against you, when we fight by your side."

Duryódana answered from the depth of the lake, "I am glad to see you alive, ye bulls among men. After we have rested a while, we shall meet and conquer the enemy. Your hearts are noble and your devotion is great, but this is not the time for bravery. Let me rest for one night, and tomorrow I shall join you and fight."

"I swear by all my good deeds, by the gifts that I have made, by my silent meditations," cried Ashvattáman, "that I will not put off my armor until I have slain the Pándavas. May my sacrifices be vain if this night passes away before I have slain my foes! Believe me, O ruler of men!"

While they were talking thus, some hunters came to the lake

to quench their thirst and to rest, for they were tired of carrying the weight of the animals that they had killed. These men went into the woods every day to provide meat for Bima. As they sat on the banks of the lake they heard every word that was said by the three warriors and Duryódana and they realized that the King was lying within the waters of the lake. They whispered to each other, "Let us tell the Pándavas that Duryódana is here and they will reward us with great wealth. Let us quickly tell Bima and he will pay us well. Why should we tire ourselves out with hunting every day?"

Filled with joy, they took up their burdens and hastened to the Pándavas' camp. Those mighty warriors had looked everywhere for Duryódana and had sent their spies in every direction, but no trace could be found of him, and Yudíshtira was troubled. Just then the hunters came to Bima and told him what they had seen and heard. Bima rewarded them richly and hastened to Yudíshtira to tell him the welcome news. Then the King and all his brothers were filled with joy and, mounting their chariots, drove speedily to the lake where Duryódana lay. A great noise arose in the Pándava camp, shouts and the blare of conchs and the rattle of chariot wheels. The sons of Pandu and the five sons of Dráupadi, Dyumna, and Shikándin, with all the warriors that were still alive, with the elephants and horsemen and foot soldiers, all rushed toward the lake, raising a cloud of dust and making the earth tremble.

Lying beneath the water with his mace beside him, King Duryódana heard the noise of the approaching army, sounding like thunder. The son of Drona and his two companions heard it and said to the King, "The Pándavas are coming here; therefore, with your permission we shall leave." And Duryódana answered, "So be it."

Sorrowfully the three warriors took leave of the King, and driving far away into the forest, they stopped under a banyan tree, for they were greatly tired. Sad at heart, anxious about the King, they loosed their horses from the yokes and lay down to rest.

The Duel with Maces

When the Pándavas arrived at the lake, Yudíshtira dismounted from his chariot and stood on the bank, looking over those waters that Duryódana had enchanted and within which he lay. Then he addressed that wicked king, saying, "Why, O Duryódana, after you have caused and seen the slaughter of your sons and brothers, your kinsmen and friends, have you entered into this lake today, in order to save your own life? Arise, O King, and fight with us! Where are your pride and honor? Men speak of you as a hero, but they speak falsely, for heroes never flee at the sight of their foes. Surely you forget yourself! Arise, O prince; cast off your fears and fight! Either vanquish us and rule the wide earth, or be slain by us and lie on the bare ground. Remember the duties of your caste, O mighty warrior!"

Still lying beneath the water, Duryódana answered, "It was not to save my life, it was not from fear, it was not from grief, O King, that I entered these waters. My horses were killed, my quivers were empty; I was alone without a single follower to stand by me in the battle. I was tired and came here to rest. Do you also, O son of Kunti, rest a while with your followers; then I will rise from this lake and fight you all in battle!"

But Yudíshtira said, "We have no need of rest although, while you were lying here, we were searching for you far and wide. Rise even now, and give us battle, Duryódana!"

"All those for whose sake I desired the kingdom—my brothers and my friends—lie dead on the field," Duryódana said. "This earth has become like a widow, bereft of her wealth and her pride. Take it, O Yudíshtira! Who could desire a kingdom without friends and without allies? I shall go into the forest, dressed in deerskins, for I have no further desire for life. Go, O King, and rule this empty earth as you please!"

"What folly is this?" answered Yudíshtira angrily. "When you ruled the entire earth, you would not give me even as much of it as could be covered by the point of a needle, and now, when you have lost it, you wish to give the whole of it to me. I do not wish to take the wide earth as a gift from you, but I shall enjoy it greatly after I have vanquished you in battle. Rise, rise, O wretch, and fight!"

Duryódana could not bear these words, as a high-bred horse cannot endure the whip. Breathing long and heavy sighs from within the water, like a snake within its hole, he answered, "You Pándavas, all of you have friends and chariots, horses and weapons. I am alone without a chariot or horse and with only one weapon; I cannot fight on foot against you all. Therefore fight me one at a time. I do not fear any of you and shall fight you all in turn. As the year meets with all the seasons, I shall meet you one after another; as the sun destroys the light of the stars at dawn, I shall destroy you all."

"Well said, O Duryódana!" cried Yudíshtira. "At last you know the duties of a Kshatria; at last you speak like a hero and, singlehanded, challenge us all to battle. Fight any one of us and choose your weapon! The rest of us will be spectators of the fight."

Churning the water, the King rose like a prince of elephants from the lake, breathing hard with anger and shouldering his mace. Frowning and biting his nether lip he stood there, dripping with water and with blood. Then, in a voice as deep as thunder, he said, "This mace that I hold in my hand is the weapon that I choose. Let any one among you who thinks that he is a match for me come forward and fight on foot, armed with a mace! You must encounter me one at a time, for it is not proper that one should fight with many at the same time, especially when that one is tired and wounded, without armor, chariot, or horse."

"Why did you not remember that, O Duryódana, when six great warriors together slew the boy Abimányu?" Yudíshtira said. "Take whatever armor you need, O hero; and bind your hair! I shall grant you still another advantage: if you can slay any one of the five Pándavas, you shall be king. Otherwise, slain by him, you shall go to heaven."

Duryódana clad himself in golden armor and put on a diadem

adorned with gold. While he was doing this, Krishna spoke angrily to Yudíshtira. "What rash words are these, O King?" he said. "Why did you say, 'If you slay any one of us, you shall be king'? Do you not know that for these thirteen years Duryódana has practiced with his mace on an iron image of Bima so that he might slay him? Bima is the only one of you who is a match for Duryódana, and even he, though he has great might and courage, is not so skillful as the King. In a contest between might and skill, he who has skill always wins. And what if he should challenge you or Arjuna, or one of the twins? You have placed yourself in great danger, O best of kings."

Meanwhile Duryódana, having prepared himself, addressed the Pándavas, saying, "Let any one of you five brothers fight with me now, armed with the mace. Today we shall reach the end of this long battle, for I think that no one is a match for me in an encounter with the mace, and I shall slay you one after another. Within this very hour my words will be proved true."

The mighty Bima addressed Yudíshtira, saying, "I wish to accept this challenge, O King. Today I shall pluck out the thorn that has stayed so long in your heart; today I shall win back your wreath of glory, for today Duryódana shall yield up his life and his kingdom." With these words he stood up for battle and the Pándavas, seeing him standing there like a mountain peak, were filled with joy. Duryódana also stood, like a prince of elephants separated from the herd, and felt no pain or fear.

Bima addressed him, saying, "Remember now, O wicked one, all the wrongs that you have done us! Remember what happened at Varanávata! Remember how Dráupadi was dragged into the assembly and how Yudíshtira was unfairly defeated at dice! It is because of you that Bishma, the grandsire of us all, lies now upon a bed of arrows. Drona has been slain, and Karna and Shalya, and there Shákuni lies, the root of all this evil. Your heroic brothers and your sons have all been slain. You alone, the destroyer of your line, remain alive, and you shall die today."

"What use is there in words?" answered his foe. "Do you not see that I am waiting here to fight you? Up to this day I have never been vanquished in fair fight on the field of battle. If you vanquish me unfairly, your name will be forever dishonored. Do not roar any longer, like an autumn cloud that holds no rain, but put forth all the strength you have and fight me now!" All the Pándava warriors who stood there watching applauded these words with shouts and the clapping of hands and Duryódana's heart was gladdened.

He rushed furiously against Bima with a roar and they met each other like two charging bulls, while the clash of their maces sounded like thunderbolts and sent out showers of sparks. Both were skillful in the use of the weapon and were beautiful to watch. They moved in circles; they advanced and retreated. They dealt blows and warded them off; they avoided blows by sometimes crouching low and sometimes leaping over the other's weapon. Now they ran to the right and now to the left, now straight at one another. It seemed as if they were playing with each other. They rested a while and then returned to the fight.

Circling to the left and whirling his mace, Duryódana struck Bima on the chest and stupefied him for a moment. Then Bima, filled with rage, struck his cousin on the side and made him fall on his knees. A great shout arose from the Pándavas, and Duryódana, hearing it, rose up furious, breathing like a great snake, and seemed to burn Bima with his glance. Rushing at his foe, he struck him on the head, but Bima, though his blood flowed down, stood immovable as a mountain. Each struck the other down again, and at the last blow Duryódana broke Bima's coat of mail. Seeing this and seeing Bima rise, wiping the blood from his face and steadying himself with a great effort, fear entered the hearts of all the Pándava warriors who were watching.

Arjuna said to Krishna, "Tell me, which of these two is the better?" "They received the same teaching," answered Krishna. "Bima is the stronger and Duryódana has the greater skill. Bima will never win if he fights fairly; therefore he must be unfair. Even the gods have been known to deceive their enemies. At the time of the gambling match, O son of Pandu, Bima vowed that he would break the thigh of Duryódana with his mace. Let him keep that vow now, even though the blow is a foul one! Yudíshtira has put you all in danger again by saying that only one of you need be vanquished. Your foe is a great warrior and doubly dangerous because he is desperate. If Bima does not slay him unfairly, Duryódana may yet keep the kingdom."

Heeding these words, Arjuna caught Bima's eye and touched his own thigh, and Bima understood him. Both the cousins were sorely bruised and bleeding from many wounds. They rested for a moment and then Bima rushed furiously against the King, whirling his mace, eager to strike him down. Duryódana leaped into the air to avoid the blow and as he leaped, Bima hurled his mace with mighty strength and broke the two thighs of the King, who fell to the earth like a great tree uprooted by a tempest.

Bima, holding his mace on his shoulder, approached him and said, "O wretch, you who laughed at Dráupadi in the assembly, bear now the fruit of that insult! We use no poison or fire; we do not cheat at dice, but by the might of our own arms we fight our foes." With these words he touched the head of Duryódana with his left foot, then turned and stood before Yudíshtira, saluting him with joined hands. Proud of his victory, filled with joy, he said, "The earth is yours today, O King, without brawls to disturb its peace, without a thorn! Rule over it with all its forests and mountains and seas, for now you have no living enemy."

Beholding Duryódana struck down, like a wild elephant killed by a lion, the Pándava warriors rejoiced: some blew their conchs and beat their drums; they shouted and laughed aloud with joy. But others of righteous soul were displeased when they saw Bima strike the head of the fallen king with his foot, and one said angrily, "Shame on Bima! O shame, that in a fair fight a foul blow has been struck! In an encounter with the mace, no limb below the navel should be struck. This is the rule and Bima knows it well."

Krishna soothed him, saying, "He and his brothers suffered many cruel wrongs from this king. Great was the grief in Bima's heart because of these wrongs. Remember, too, the vow that he had made. Now he has paid his debt and kept his vow."

Hearing these words, Duryódana was so angry that he tried to rise. Sitting up and leaning on his hands, he looked angrily at Krishna and said, "Have you no shame, O sinful one, that you justify this deed that you yourself advised? Do you think I did not see the sign that Arjuna gave his brother at your behest? You, too, caused the death of Drona by persuading Yudíshtira to tell a lie. When Karna's wheel was sunk in the mud, you caused him to be slain. If you had fought fairly with us, the victory would never have been yours. Are you not ashamed of these unrighteous deeds?"

"O son of Gandári," answered Krishna, "you have been slain with all your kinsmen and your friends because of the sinful path on which you trod. You met your death when, from greed, you refused to give the sons of Pandu their rightful share of the kingdom. Bear now the fruits of all your evil deeds."

Duryódana said, "I have performed sacrifices and made gifts and governed the wide earth with its seas; enjoyments worthy of the very gods have been mine. Who is so fortunate as I? I have conquered hostile kingdoms and laid my commands on great kings; I have given wealth to my kinsmen and have pleased my friends. Who is so fortunate as I? My life has passed in happiness, and death in battle, the death desired by all Kshatrias, is mine. Who then is more fortunate than I? With my friends and brothers I am going now to heaven, while you, torn with grief, will live in this unhappy world."

Hearing these words and remembering those heroes who had been slain unrighteously, the Pándavas were grieved, and wept, but Krishna said to them, "Those four great warriors, headed by Bishma, could not have been slain in fair fight by the gods themselves. If I had not advised deceitful ways of battle, you would never have won the victory, your kingdom, or your wealth. Do not take it to heart that this enemy has been slain deceitfully. All that he has suffered he brought upon himself. We have won the victory and it is evening; let us return to our tents and rest, and let the troops and elephants and horses also rest."

Those kings and warriors returned to their encampment, filled with joy and blowing their conchs on the way. Having loosed their animals, they rested for a while, and then Krishna said to the Pándavas, "Tonight, in order to purify ourselves, let us bathe in the sacred waters and sleep on the bare ground." Therefore, for that night, they slept on the bank of the Ganges.

BOOK XV

THE NIGHT ATTACK

Ashvattáman's Revenge

A MESSENGER brought the news of Duryódana's fall to the son of Drona and his two companions, as they rested under the tree. Mounting their chariots, they drove swiftly back to the banks of the lake, where they found the King lying on the bare ground, covered with dust and blood, and writhing in pain. Around him were fierce animals, which he kept off with his arms. The three warriors alighted and sat on the ground beside him, and their anger blazed up as they saw him in such a plight.

Wringing his hands, his voice hoarse with rage, Ashvattáman said, "My father was slain cruelly and unjustly by those wretches, but even that does not grieve me as deeply as it does to see you here, O King. Listen to me! I swear by all my gifts and good deeds, by truth itself, that I will send the Pándavas and all the Panchálas this very day to Yama's realm. Give me leave to do this, my lord!"

Now one of Ashvattáman's companions was a Brahman and therefore able to perform the rites. "Bring a pot of water from the lake, O Brahman," said Duryódana, "and make the son of Drona the commander of my forces." The ceremonial water was brought, and Ashvattáman was solemnly installed as commander. He rose and raised a mighty shout that rang through the air in all directions; then he embraced the King and drove away with his companions, leaving Duryódana to face the fearful night alone.

Those heroes drove toward the south and secretly entered a forest near the Pándava camp. Going deeper into the woods they came upon a gigantic banyan tree with thousands of branches; there they loosed their horses and said their evening prayers. Seated under the tree, they talked sorrowfully of all that had happened, while around them the night-wandering animals began to howl and darkness fell. They were wounded and very tired. They lay down on the ground and Ashvattáman's two friends soon fell asleep; but he, burning with anger and the desire for revenge, could not close his eyes, and lay wide awake, sighing deeply.

As he looked about him in the forest, he saw thousands of crows roosting in the branches of the banyan tree, perched side by side and sleeping trustfully. Suddenly an owl appeared, with a huge tawny body, green eyes, and long beak and claws. Flying swiftly and uttering little cries, it came secretly among the branches and, alighting, slew several of the sleeping crows. It tore the crows' wings, cut their heads off, or broke their legs with its sharp beak, and soon the ground was strewn with the limbs and bodies of the slain. Then the owl was filled with delight, like a warrior who has vanquished his enemies.

Ashvattáman said to himself, "This owl has taught me a lesson. I cannot slay the Pándavas in battle, and yet I have sworn, in the presence of the King, to slay them. If I were to fight openly with them, I should lose my life at once; yet with guile I may still defeat them, as this owl has done to the crows. Tonight the Pándavas, with the Panchálas, will sleep deeply, filled with joy because of their victory and worn out with fighting. I shall attack their camp and slay them all while they are sunk in sleep." Having made this wicked plan, he woke his companions and told them what he intended to do, but neither of them could answer him for shame.

At last the Brahman said, "O mighty one, do not do anything that you will repent of afterward. It is a wicked thing to kill sleeping men, or those who have surrendered or those who are disarmed. Our enemies will be sleeping trustfully, their armor laid aside; anyone shameless enough to attack them would suffer for that deed in this world and the next. You have never done a dishonorable deed; rest tonight and sleep happily; tomorrow morning, in broad daylight, go to their camp, proclaim yourself, and slay them all in battle, with our help!"

"How can I sleep," answered Ashvattáman angrily, "when my heart is burning with rage and grief? I cannot sleep until I have killed Dyumna, who slew my father, unarmed and seated in meditation. The Pándavas have broken every rule of battle and have torn down the barriers of virtue; why should I not do likewise? If I can slay them in their sleep, I do not care what happens to me. Until I have done it I cannot rest."

With these words, he yoked his steeds and mounted his chariot, and his two friends, seeing that they could not dissuade him, followed him to the Pándava camp. When they reached the gate, Ashvattáman whispered to the others, "Wait here and let no man escape, while I enter the camp and sweep through it like Death himself. It will not be hard to kill this remnant of the army when it is fast asleep!"

Casting off all fear, he entered the camp and went very softly to the tent of Dyumna. The Panchálas were tired out, sleeping side by side in perfect confidence. Ashvattáman entered the tent and saw his enemy lying on a perfumed bed, strewn with flowers. He woke him with a kick and, when he tried to rise, seized him by the hair, threw him down, and began to strangle him. Dyumna gasped, "Slay me with a weapon, O son of my teacher, quickly, so that I may die a Kshatria's death!"

"O wretch," answered Ashvattáman, "those who slay their teachers have no right to a happy death." With this he slew Dyumna, and going out of his tent, set up a mighty shout. Then he sought out the other Panchála warriors.

The guards and warriors, wakened suddenly, began to put on their armor, shouting, "Who is this?" "What is this noise?" "Is it a demon or a man?" "The King is slain!" All were dazed and did not know what had happened or what they should do. Blinded by sleep and possessed by fear, thinking that the camp had been attacked by demons, they ran hither and thither and did not know who were enemies and who were friends. Elephants and horses broke their tethers and ran about, trampling upon men and raising dust that made the night more dark. Meanwhile Ashvattáman sought the tents of Dyumna's brothers and slew them like animals in a sacrifice. Carrying his bright shield with a thousand moons upon it, and his splendid sword, he went along the different paths of the camp, one after another, slaying the unarmed, tired warriors who lay within the tents.

He came at last upon the sons of Dráupadi, who had heard the alarm and knew that Dyumna had been killed. They rose, seizing their weapons, and fought against him, but Ashvattáman, remembering his father's death, roared with rage and fought with the strength of a demon. One after another he cut down Dráupadi's sons and then went on to attack Shikándin, whom he cut in two with his sword. Then he careered through the camp like Death himself, cutting down all who came in his way with his mighty sword, covered with the blood of his enemies.

In the darkness and confusion, the Pándava and Panchála warriors, unable to recognize anyone, began to slay one another; some, full of fear, threw away their weapons and ran out of the camp, but they were met at the gate by Ashvattáman's friends, who slew every man that tried to escape and let not one get by. Then those two set fire to the camp in three places; the flames gave light to the son of Drona as he finished the slaughter, killing those who lay huddled on the ground and those who tried to hide or flee. Not one escaped except the charioteer of Dyumna, who fled past the two warriors at the gate and out into the night.

At last the shouts and shrieks and the clash of arms died down; dawn came, and Ashvattáman, bathed in blood, with his hand stuck fast to his sword as if they were one thing, looked about him and strode out of the camp. It had been silent when he entered it, for all its warriors had been asleep: it was silent again when he left it, for all were dead. Having kept his vow and done what no man had ever done before, he forgot his grief for his father's death; he met his two companions joyfully, telling them all that had been done that night, while they told him how they had slain those who tried to escape. This terrible deed could not have been achieved if the sons of Pandu had been in the camp; but they, with Krishna, were sleeping on the bank of the river.

The three warriors mounted their chariots and drove swiftly to the place where Duryódana lay. Seeing that he was not yet dead, they dismounted and sat down beside him. "If there is any life left in you still, O King," said Drona's son, "listen to the good news I have to tell! Dyumna and his sons, and Dráupadi's five sons, the Panchálas, and the Matsyas have all been slain this night. The Pándavas are now childless! On their side only six remain alive, the five brothers and Krishna; on our side, only we three. Behold the vengeance that has been taken for all that they have done!"

Duryódana, hearing these welcome words and rallying his senses, replied, "You have done what Bishma and Karna and your father failed to do, since you have slain that low wretch who was the leader of the Pándava host, with his brother Shikándin. Now I consider myself the victor. Good betide you! We shall all meet in heaven." With these words, casting off his grief for his slain brothers and kinsmen, the King of the Báratas gave up his life.

His three friends took leave of one another and went their separate ways: the Brahman returned to Hastinápura; his companion went back to the land of the Yadus, whence he had come, and Ashvattáman turned his horses' heads into the forest, for he meant to take shelter in the hermitage of Vyasa, close to Kuru Kshetra.

The Last Debt Is Paid

When the day came, Dyumna's charioteer, who had escaped death within the camp, ran to Yudíshtira to tell him the evil tidings. The King, hearing that all his sons had been slain, fell down upon the earth, weeping grievously with his brothers and saying, "Alas, having vanquished our foes, we ourselves have been vanquished in the end; and the vanquished are the victors! Those great warriors who stood against Bishma and Drona and Karna have been slain through our carelessness!" He sent Nákula to bring Dráupadi, who was living in her father's household, while he and his other brothers went to the camp. When they saw their sons, allies, and friends lying on the ground, their bodies mangled and bloody, the souls of the Pándavas were overwhelmed with sorrow.

Before the day had passed, Nákula brought Dráupadi, who stood like a plantain tree shaken by the wind, her heart rent by the slaughter of her sons. Bima took her in his arms; weeping, she said to Yudíshtira, "It is a happy thing, O King, to obtain the whole earth when all your brave sons are slain! O son of Kunti, grief burns me as if I were on fire! If Drona's son is not made to reap the fruit of that sinful deed of his, if you do not take his life this very day—listen, you Pándavas—I shall sit here and fast until I die! I have heard that Ashvattáman was born with a jewel in his head; if that jewel is brought to me after that wretch has been slain, I can bear to live, but otherwise I die!" Then, turning to Bima, she said, "O Bima, you are always our refuge. Slay now that evil man!" With these words she sat down beside the bodies of her sons and concentrated her mind on her resolve.

Bima mounted his chariot, taking Nákula as his charioteer; his horses, fleet as the wind, carried him away from the camp, following the track of Ashvattáman's wheels.

When he had gone, Krishna said to Yudíshtira, "O son of Pandu, of all your brothers Bima is dearest to you, yet you have let him go off alone to slay the son of Drona. When Drona gave to Arjuna that weapon that can destroy the world, his son, always jealous of Arjuna, begged his father to give it also to him. His father gave it to him unwillingly, for he knew that Ashvattáman was restless and feared that he would not walk in the path of virtue. He commanded him never to use it against human beings even in the midst of battle, even when overtaken by the greatest danger. But he will use it now against Bima, unless Arjuna protects his brother."

Krishna mounted his splendid chariot, drawn by four swift horses and carrying a banner with the figure of a great bird; Arjuna and Yudíshtira mounted it also and sat beside him. The horses carried them as swiftly and easily as a bird flies and they soon caught up with Bima, who did not stop, but galloped on, following Ashvattáman's track. This led them to the bank of the Ganges, where they beheld the holy Vyasa sitting in the midst of a group of sages, among whom was Ashvattáman, his dust-stained body clad in a garment made of grass.

Bima, taking up his bow and fixing an arrow on the string, walked toward Drona's son, who, seeing that mighty bowman advancing and his two brothers standing on Krishna's car, thought his last hour had come. He remembered the heavenly weapon that his father had given him. Picking up a blade of grass, he changed it, by speaking the right spells, into that weapon. Then, burning with anger, he said, "Let this destroy the Pándavas!" and loosed the missile, which blazed with a fire that seemed able to destroy the three worlds.

Arjuna, leaping to the ground, summoned the same weapon. Blessing in his heart the son of Drona, himself, his brothers, and all the worlds, he loosed it, saying, "Let this weapon stop Ashvattáman's!" Then both those missiles blazed up with terrible flames within a huge sphere of fire; peals of thunder were heard; the earth trembled and all living creatures were terrified.

Beholding these two celestial fires scorching all the worlds, Vyasa and the great sage Nárada, who was beside him, rose and stood between the two warriors in order to protect the worlds. "What rash act is this, you heroes?" they cried. "The great warriors who fell in battle knew the use of many heavenly missiles but never used one like this against a human foe. Why have you done so?"

Arjuna, joining his hands humbly, answered them, "I used the weapon to baffle Ashvattáman's; if I withdraw it, he will consume us all."

The son of Drona said with a cheerless heart, "I used it to protect my life from Bima, you holy ones. Bima slew Duryódana in a sinful way; I wished this weapon to destroy him and all his brothers."

"Arjuna also knew its use, my child," Vyasa said, "yet he

loosed it, not from anger or the desire to destroy you, but only to baffle yours. Any place where this fearful power is let loose suffers a twelve years' drought. Therefore withdraw it and cast off your anger! Give to the Pándavas the jewel that is in your head and they, in turn, will give you your life."

"This jewel," said the master's son, "is worth more than all the wealth heaped up by both the Pándavas and the Kúravas. He who wears it need not fear any weapon or disease or hunger; neither gods nor demons can slay him. Nevertheless, you holy ones, I must obey you. Here is the jewel; this blade of grass, turned into such fearful power, I withdraw."

Both warriors withdrew their weapons. Ashvattáman gave Bima the jewel from his head, then turned and went into the forest, with despair in his heart. The Pándavas and Krishna, taking the two great sages with them, drove speedily back to the camp and went to the place where Dráupadi sat. Bima gave her the jewel, saying, "The slayer of your sons is vanquished, O beautiful one! We did not slay him, because he is a Brahman and our teacher's son. Rise now, cast off your sorrow and remember the duties of a Kshatria princess! Remember the bitter words you spoke when Krishna went on his mission of peace to Hastinápura and you desired war! The last debt that we owed our enemies has now been paid."

"I desired only to pay the debt of injury that we have suffered," answered Dráupadi. "I respect the master's son as I did the master himself. Bind this jewel on your head, O son of Kunti!" The King, taking the jewel, bound it on his head, and Dráupadi, who was strong of soul, rose and took up her life.

Lament for the Dead

In Hastinápura, King Kuru had been told by his messenger and charioteer, Sánjaya, all that took place on the battlefield, day by day. When Duryódana was slain and the battle ended, Sánjaya came to the King and said, "The kings who came from many lands, O monarch, have all gone to the realm of the dead, together with your sons. Duryódana, who refused all offers of peace, who wished to end his quarrel with the Pándavas by slaying them all, has made the earth empty of warriors and is dead himself. Now, O King, perform the funeral ceremonies of your sons and kinsmen."

Hearing these terrible words, Kuru fell down on the ground like an uprooted tree, lamenting for his century of sons, his friends, and kinsmen. "Cast off your grief, O King!" Sánjaya said. "Your own mind, like a sharp sword, has wounded you. You always listened, out of greed, to evil counselors, refusing to follow the advice of the wise and good. Your son was foolish, proud, and quarrelsome. His friends were men of wicked souls: none of them cared for virtue; battle was the one word on their lips. You were as an umpire between them and the Pándavas, but you did not give them one word of good advice; you held the scales unevenly, doing always what Duryódana desired. You must repent of that now. Therefore do not grieve for what has happened: the man who carries a burning coal in the folds of his dress and then weeps when he is burned is called a fool. Grief of the mind must be cured by wisdom as grief of the body is cured by medicine."

Vídura also came to the King and comforted him with wise words. At last Kuru rose from the ground and ordered his chariot to be yoked. He sent for Gandári and Kunti and all his sons' wives, who were wailing loudly in their sorrow. Followed by those weeping women in their chariots, he set out from the city, while cries of woe arose from every house. Merchants and workmen and many other citizens followed them and all of them together went out to the field of Kuru Kshetra.

Yudíshtira, hearing that Kuru had set out from the city went with his brothers and Krishna to meet him; Dráupadi also, and the women of Panchála, all grieving for the loss of sons, husbands, and fathers, went with him. Near the banks of the Ganges they met. The women of Hastinápura surrounded Yudíshtira with their arms raised aloft in sorrow and cried to him, "Where is the virtue of the King, where are his truth and his pity, since he has slain fathers and brothers, teachers and sons and friends? What good is the kingdom to you, O son of Kunti, when your sons have all been slaughtered?"

Passing them, Yudíshtira went to his uncle and touched his feet; his brothers did likewise, each uttering his own name as he did so. Kuru, his grief burning within him, unwillingly embraced Yudíshtira and spoke words of comfort to him. Then he sought for Bima and his wrath blazed up as he thought of the death of Duryódana. Krishna, understanding what was in the old king's mind, pulled Bima aside and put in his place the iron image of him, on which Duryódana had practiced with his mace for thirteen years. Seizing that image in his two arms, the King, strong as an elephant, broke it to pieces, but also bruised his own breast, and fell, bleeding, on the ground. Sánjaya lifted him and the King, coming to his senses, thinking that he had slain his nephew, wept and cried aloud, "O Bima, Bima!" Krishna told him how he had put the iron image in Bima's place and Kuru, repenting of his anger, embraced Bima and Arjuna and the two sons of Madri, blessing them.

Then the Pándavas with Krishna saluted the faultless Gandári, naming themselves to her as they had done to the old king, for her eyes were always bandaged. Gandári, sorrowing bitterly for all her sons, wished to curse Yudíshtira, but Vyasa, who was with them, read her mind and said quickly, "Hold back the words that are on your lips, Gandári; forgive instead of cursing. Do you remember how your son Duryódana, before he went to battle, beseeched you, saying, 'O Mother, bless me now, and pray for my victory!' and how you always said to him, 'He that is righteous will have the victory'? Remember your own words and withhold your anger, O Queen!"

Gandári said, "I do not wish ill to the Pándavas, O holy one, for I know that they were not in any way to blame for the slaughter of all the Báratas. But my heart is sorely troubled because of the death of my sons, and there is one deed of Bima's, done in the very presence of Krishna, that I cannot forget. Knowing that Duryódana was more skillful than he was with the mace,

Bima struck him a foul blow, below the navel, and slew him. Why should heroes, in order to save their own lives, do what is wrong?"

Bima, looking frightened, answered her, "Right or wrong, O Queen, I acted out of fear and in order to defend my life. Your mighty son could not have been slain by anyone in fair battle. He defeated Yudíshtira unfairly at dice and always behaved treacherously toward us. He was the only warrior left, opposing us; until he was dead we could not regain our kingdom. Therefore I acted as I did. You, who never corrected his evil ways, should not blame me, but forgive me."

Gandári was pleased that Bima had praised her son's might, but she still reproved him, saying, "You have slain a hundred sons of this old man. O, why could you not have spared one son to this old couple, who have lost all they had; why could you not have left one child to guide this blind old pair? Yet, even though you slew them all, I should not grieve so if you had done it righteously." Her anger blazed up again and she asked, "Where is the King?"

Yudíshtira came near to her and stood with joined hands. "Here is the King," he said, "that cruel slayer of your sons. O curse me, for I am the cause of this great slaughter; I have no further need of life or wealth or kingdom."

Gandári, who knew the way of righteousness, said nothing to Yudíshtira, but sighed deeply, and looking down under the folds of cloth that bandaged her eyes, she saw the tip of his toe, as he stood, trembling and humble, before her. Her glance burned his toenail, which pained him ever after. Beholding this, Arjuna stepped behind Krishna and the other sons of Pandu moved from one place to another, uneasily. But Gandári's anger passed; she embraced the Pándavas and comforted them, for she had always thought of them as her own sons.

Last of all, the Pándavas presented themselves to their mother, Kunti, who had not seen them for all those thirteen years, and had grieved so long for them. She covered her face and wept; then, seeing the scars of many wounds on their bodies, she embraced and stroked them and could not see enough of them. She welcomed Dráupadi and wept with her for the loss of all her sons.

Then Kuru, with Kunti and Gandári and all the wives of his sons, drew near to that terrible battlefield that was strewn with thousands upon thousands of dead bodies of men and elephants and horses. Jackals and wolves prowled about, howling; vultures and crows flew here and there, feeding on the bodies of the dead. The women who had lost their husbands, sons, brothers, and kinsmen, shrieked at the sight and, alighting from their chariots, ran hither and thither over the field, seeking the bodies of those who had been slain. Some of them, with disheveled hair, threw themselves upon the bodies of their lords, weeping piteously; others fell senseless on the ground. Some could not find the bodies of those they loved, while others ran from son to husband, from brother to father, distraught with grief, striking their heads with their hands.

Gandári, accompanied by Krishna, was led from one of her dead sons to another and came at last upon the body of Duryódana. She threw herself beside it and embraced it, weeping bitterly, even though she knew that all this slaughter had come about because of his evil ways. Remembering all her sorrows, she allowed anger to fill her heart again and, turning to Krishna, cast all the blame on him.

"The Pándavas and the Kúravas, O Krishna, have both been destroyed," she cried. "Why did you not care? You could have prevented this destruction, for you had a vast army and many followers, and yet you did not stop it! Nay, more—all those unrighteous acts whereby the Pándavas slew Bishma and Drona, Karna and Duryódana, they did at your behest, urged on by you. Therefore you should reap the fruit of those acts. With the soul power that I have gained through dutifully serving my husband, I curse you, O wielder of the discus and the mace! Since you did not care to stop the slaughter of these cousins, you shall be the slayer of your own kinsmen: thirty-six years after this, O Krishna, you shall cause the death of your sons and friends and kinsmen, and perish in a shameful way yourself. The women of your realm shall weep and cry even as the women of the Báratas are weeping now!"

Krishna answered, with a faint smile, "You have cursed well, O Queen, for none but myself could ever slay the Yadus. It will be as you have said, even though you are blaming me for what is truly your own fault. Duryódana was wicked, jealous, and exceedingly proud, but you never restrained him. Now arise, Gandári, and do not grieve, for he who grieves for what has already happened brings upon himself more grief. A Kshatria mother bears sons in order to have them killed, and all your sons have died bravely in battle, facing the foe."

When all the women had had their fill of lamentation and had seen all that they desired to see of that dreadful field, King Yudíshtira said, "Now perform the funeral rites of all the slain, which number thousands, so that no one may perish from lack of care." At his command, Vídura, Sánjaya, and many others fetched sandal and aloe wood, oil and perfumes, and costly silken robes. Great heaps of dry wood were raised and strewn with perfumes; on these the bodies of the slain kings were laid, in proper order according to their age and honor. Those among the dead who came from distant countries and were unknown and friendless were laid together on heaps of wood, by the thousands, and burned with the proper rites. The funeral fires, smokeless and bright, burned far into the night, while the Brahmans chanted the hymns of death and the women wept for the slain.

When that was done, Yudíshtira, giving Kuru the place of honor, and followed by his brothers and all the women and citizens, went to the Ganges and in that holy river with its vast bed, its high banks, and broad shores, they performed the water rites for their sons and lords and sires.

There Kunti, overtaken again by sorrow, said to her sons, "That great bowman who battled with you and all your followers, that warrior who loved glory better than life, who shone like the sun himself as he commanded the host of Duryódana, that hero whom you took for a Suta's son and whom Arjuna slew, was your eldest brother. Therefore make offerings of water to Karna, also, who was born of me by the God of Day!"

These words, like sharp arrows, pierced the Pándavas' hearts. "O Mother," cried Yudíshtira, "was that mighty warrior whose might held us in check, whom Arjuna alone could vanquish, truly our eldest brother? How could you hide him from us, like one who hides a burning fire in his hands? Alas, because you hid him, we have been undone, for if we had known him, this battle would never have taken place. If he had been with us, if I had had both him and Arjuna to help me, I could have stormed heaven itself. Now I have caused my brother to be slain and my heart burns with a greater grief than I have ever known."

Weeping, his mother said, "Do not give way to grief, O righteous one! I told Karna that he was your brother and Krishna did the same. All that could be said was said to him, but he would not reveal himself to you or fight for you. He hated you and was bound to hurt you all; therefore I tried no longer to persuade him."

But Yudíshtira would not be comforted and said again, "Because you hid him from us, this great misfortune has overtaken us." And he put a curse on all the women of the world, saying, "Henceforth let no woman be able to keep a secret!" Then he summoned Karna's wives and the other members of his family and performed with them the water rites in honor of his brother.

Yudíshtira's Sorrow

When they had finished the water rites for all their friends and kinsmen, Yudíshtira, following the old king up the bank of the Ganges, suddenly fell down like an elephant pierced by the hunters. Bima raised him up and his brothers, seeing him overcome by grief, sat down around him, sighing deeply.

Turning to Arjuna, Yudíshtira said, "O scorcher of foes, if we had stayed in the forest, if we had been content to beg our food, we should not have had the sorrow today of having slain our kinsmen! Fie upon power and strength and bravery, since they have brought us this misfortune! Blessed are forgiveness and self-control, humility and truthfulness, which forest dwellers practice! These who have died should not have been slain even to gain the whole earth—no, not for the three worlds! I have committed great sins because I desired the things of this earth; therefore, with your leave, I shall now abandon my kingdom and go to the woods, leaving all things both dear and hateful, harming no creature, casting off desire, fear, and anger, until I cast off life itself."

His brothers were deeply pained by these words of his; each of them spoke to him, urging him to take up the duties of his caste, to rule wisely the earth that he had so righteously won. Dráupadi added her words to theirs, begging him not to cast away all that they had suffered so much to gain. Yudíshtira, however, still burned with sorrow as he thought of the deaths of friends and foes: his elder brother Karna, Dráupadi's sons, and Abimányu, the noble Bishma, who had loved him as a child, and his teacher Drona, to whom he had lied on the field of battle, thus causing his death.

Arjuna, seeing him speechless, said to Krishna, "Comfort him, O sinless one! Once more we are in great danger. Save us yet again!"

Taking the King's hand in his own, the wielder of the discus said to him, "Do not yield to sorrow, O King! You think that you have slain all your enemies, but you do not yet know the enemies that lurk in your own heart. It is not fitting that you should brood now upon the deaths of those warriors whom you can by no means bring back to life. The time has come when you must fight the battle that every man must wage in his own mind. In this fight there will be no need of weapons or friends or followers, for each one must wage it alone. If you should die before you win the victory, then, in another life, you will have to fight these foes again; but if you win, you will have reached the goal of life. Therefore fight that battle this very day, O son of Kunti. Give your whole mind to finding out the right path and the wrong."

253

Unto King Yudíshtira, still plunged in grief, the island-born Vyasa came and spoke: "O child," he said, "why do we, again and again, scatter our words upon the wind? You know the duties of a Kshatria, who lives by warfare. A king who has righteously played his part should not be overcome by grief. The time has not yet come for you to go to the woods.

"There are four steps in life, O Yudíshtira, which are like a ladder or a flight of stairs leading to heaven.

"A man spends the first part of his life as a student: he lives with a teacher, whom he serves reverently while he studies the Vedas and the duties of his caste.

"When he has finished his studies and paid his teacher's fee, he returns home and becomes a householder. He marries and lights the sacred fire of his home; he has sons and grandsons. In this second part of his life he earns wealth in honest ways; he never turns a guest from his door or refuses food to a Brahman.

"When the householder sees wrinkles on his face and white hair on his head, when he beholds his children's children, then he should go to the woods, carrying with him his sacrificial fire. The forest dweller eats only once a day; he sits and sleeps on the bare ground. Bearing with patience heat and cold, rain and wind, he burns his sins away as with fire and purifies his heart.

"When the fourth or last part of life is reached, a man may leave the forest dweller's life for the last step—the way of freedom—the search for God. He casts away the sacred fire, for his sacrifice is then performed in his own heart and his very self is the offering. He calls nothing his own; he eats what is barely necessary and roams over the earth, sleeping at the foot of trees. He fears no creature and no creature fears him; he beholds all things in himself and himself in all things. Cheerful, fearless, and silent, his mind fixed on God, he frees himself from death and birth and enters the regions of everlasting bliss. This last way of life is very hard to attain, O best of kings; few men are able to reach it.

"Your duty now is to live the life of the householder, O Yudíshtira. It is the best of all the ways of life, for all the others—the student, the forest dweller, and the seeker of God—depend on the householder. As the footprints of all the smaller animals are contained in that of the elephant, so the other three ways of life are contained in that of the householder.

"There are four castes, O King. The Shudra serves, the Vaisya lives by farming, herding, or trade, the Kshatria fights and governs, while the Brahman teaches and performs the sacrifices. As the footprints of the smaller animals are covered by that of the elephant, so the other three castes are sheltered by the Kshatria, O lord of earth, for the Kshatria protects and supports the Shudra, the Vaisya, and the Brahman. The highest duty is that of the Kshatria.

"It behooves you, therefore, O Yudíshtira, to live the life of your caste and to bear like an ox the burden of your ancestral kingdom. Cast off your grief, O King; take up your life."

"I do not doubt your words, O holy one," answered the King. "Everything is known to you. But my heart can find no peace since, for the sake of a kingdom, I have caused so many people to be slain. This sin burns and consumes me."

"O Bárata," answered Vyasa, "is God the doer, or is man? Is all that happens the result of chance, or do we enjoy and suffer the results of our own actions? The Kúravas sinned and have been slain by you. When a tree is cut down, the ax is not blamed, but he who wields it. You were the ax in the hands of Destiny, O King, and have no cause for grief. Arise, and perform the great Horse Sacrifice, O best of the Báratas, as your ancestors have done, for that sacrifice cleanses the hearts of kings."

Comforted by his words, Yudíshtira said, "Tell me, O first of Brahmans, all the duties of a king. It is hard to be a king and to practice virtue; my mind is always bewildered by this problem."

"If you wish to know the duties of a king," Vyasa answered, "go to Bishma, O mighty-armed one, and ask the old grandsire of the Báratas, before he dies; for nothing is unknown to him. Behold now, these brothers of yours and Dráupadi, who stand before you, beseeching you as men beseech Indra for rain at the close of summer! The people of all castes in your kingdom await you. O slayer of foes, do what they desire and what is best for the whole world!"

Then Yudíshtira rose from his seat for the good of the whole world and cast off his grief. Surrounded by his brothers and his friends as the moon is surrounded by stars, he set out for Hastiná-pura, placing Kuru before him. He mounted a new white chariot covered with blankets and deerskins and drawn by sixteen white bullocks. Bima joyfully took up the reins; Arjuna held over the King's head a canopy bright as a sunlit cloud, while Nákula and Sahadéva fanned him with yak tails as white as moonbeams and adorned with gems. Kuru and Gandári were borne in litters at the head of the procession; Krishna rode in his own golden car, and the women followed in excellent chariots. Behind them came more chariots, elephants, foot soldiers, and horsemen.

As they approached the city, the hum of innumerable voices could be heard. The streets were decked with flowers and count-less banners and thronged with citizens waiting to see the King. The palace was fragrant with powdered perfumes, flowers, and sweet-smelling plants, and hung all over with wreaths and garlands. Accompanied by friends and Brahmans, praised by sweet-voiced bards, the son of Pandu entered the city through its principal gate and passed through the streets and squares, where the crowds swelled as the ocean swells at the rise of the moon. Shouts of joy arose; the city was in an uproar. On the terraces of all the houses the ladies stood, with soft voices praising the Pándavas. They also said: "Worthy of all praise are you, O blessed princess of Panchála! Your deeds and prayers have borne their fruit, O Dráupadi!"

Thus Yudíshtira, graced with victory and the blessings of the people, entered the courtyard of the palace of the Báratas and descended from his chariot.

BOOK XVI

THE HORSE SACRIFICE

The Death of Bishma

THE royal son of Kunti, after the grief and fever of his heart had been healed, was seated on a golden throne and crowned with due ceremony the king of the Báratas. He made Bima his heir and Vídura his chief minister. Sánjaya, the friend and charioteer of Kuru, was given charge of the treasury, and Nákula charge of the army, to see that the troops were well trained and cared for, while Arjuna, as commander of the forces, protected the kingdom from all foes. The King kept Sahadéva always at his side, for he could not do without the knowledge and advice of his youngest brother.

To Bima, with the consent of Kuru, was given the beautiful palace of Duryódana, and to Arjuna the palace of Dushásana, abounding in wealth. Nákula and Sahadéva were given two equally splendid mansions belonging to two of Kuru's sons. The King always treated Kuru and Gandári with the same honor that they had had before, and commanded all his ministers to consult the old King in everything they did. He provided for all those women who had lost their sons and husbands in the battle; he made rich gifts in the names of all the dead, and gave food and clothes and shelter to the helpless and the blind.

As soon as this was done, he bethought himself of Bishma, the grandsire of the Báratas, who lay upon his bed of arrows, waiting till the sun should turn into the north. Yudíshtira ordered his chariot to be yoked and, with his brothers and Krishna, drove swiftly to the field of Kuru Kshetra. They dismounted on that field, where so many high-souled Kshatrias had cast away their bodies, and went on foot to the spot where Bishma lay. On the plain there was many a hill formed by the bodies and bones of elephants and horses, while human skulls lay scattered over it like conch shells. With the remains of countless funeral pyres and heaps of armor and weapons, the vast plain looked like the drinking garden of Death himself, as if he had been reveling there and had just departed.

Bishma lay where he had fallen, stretched on his arrowy bed. He was surrounded by the holiest of the sages, Nárada, Vyasa, and many others, while at a distance stood the warriors who guarded him night and day. The Pándavas approached the grandsire with joined hands, but none of them dared to speak to him, so Krishna spoke.

"O best of men," he said, "have you passed the night happily? Is your mind unclouded and your heart without pain?"

"All fatigue and pain have left me, O wielder of the discus," answered Bishma. "Strengthened by meditation, I feel as if I had become a young man again. My mind is unclouded; all that is past, present, and future I see as clearly as if it were a fruit placed in my hands."

"The son of Pandu has come to question you," Krishna said, "about the duties of a king, but, overcome with shame because he caused your death, and fearful lest you curse him, he does not dare to address you."

"A Kshatria," answered Bishma, "should slay sires and grand-sires, brothers, teachers, and kinsmen if they fight against him in an unjust war. Let the son of Pandu, who is ever devoted to peace and to truth, ask me whatever he desires."

Hearing these words, Yudíshtira came forward and took in his two hands the feet of Bishma, who caressed him lovingly and said, "Do not fear, my son, to question me."

Saluting with joined hands the eldest of the Báratas, Yudíshtira asked, "What are the duties of the four castes of men; what way of life should be taken up by each of them? What are the special duties of the king? How does the kingdom grow? How do the king himself, his citizens, and his subjects grow? Whom should the king trust? What evils should he fear? Tell me all this, O wisest of men!"

Then Bishma, remembering all that was declared in the Vedas, all that he had heard from learned and righteous persons, and all that he had seen and known himself, began to answer Yudíshtira's questions. He told him about the origin and the duties of the four castes, about the four ways of life and the four purposes—duty, wealth, pleasure, and the final purpose, the freedom of the soul. He told Yudíshtira all the duties of a king and said to him, "Kingly duties are the highest of all, for all the castes and those who follow all the ways of life depend upon the power and the protection of the king. The protection of his subjects is the first and highest duty of the king.

"Remember, O Yudíshtira, that power is given to you in order that you may protect the weak. Never make enemies of them, for it is said that no man can bear the eyes of the weak, the eyes of a snake, and the eyes of a saint, when they are angry. Take care that the eyes of the weak do not scorch you like a burning fire, for they can destroy a people to the very roots.

"When you are enjoying your power, do not take wealth from the poor. Tax your kingdom as bees take honey from the flowers, as a good cowherd takes milk from a cow, without hurting her udders and without starving her calf. Treat your subjects as a tigress does when she carries her cubs, holding them but never piercing them with her teeth."

With these and many other wise words Bishma made clear to the King all his high duties, enlivening his talk with many tales of gods and men, of animals and birds. Day after day the Pándavas sat round him in the company of the holy sages, asking him more and more questions, listening with rapt attention to his answers and storing in their hearts the wisdom that would vanish from the world when Bishma left it. At last the sun drew near to the end of its southward course, and one day the grandsire said, "My mind, my eyes, and ears are dulled today; the time is near when I shall cast off my body. I have answered all your questions, O king of men; return now to your city, and when the sun turns north, come here again."

When the day came for Bishma's departure, Yudíshtira took garlands, perfumes, and silken cloths, sandal and aloe wood, and jewels; with the old king and queen, with Kunti and Vídura, the Pándavas went again to Kuru Kshetra and stood beside that mighty hero, who lay with closed eyes, looking like the setting sun, like a fire about to go out. When he opened his eyes and beheld them all, he took the strong hand of Yudíshtira and said in a voice as deep as thunder, "I wish to cast off my body now, O King. Pray give me leave." Then he embraced them all and, as they watched him, they saw his spirit come forth from his head and flash up into the sky like a meteor, disappearing at last from their sight. Thus, that mighty hero of the Báratas was united with eternity. They built a funeral pyre of fragrant woods, and wrapping his body in silken cloths, they laid it on the pyre and burned it there, Kuru and Yudíshtira standing at the feet.

An Heir Is Born

When the Pándavas returned to Hastinápura, after the death of Bishma, Vyasa said to the King, "It behooves you now, O Yudíshtira, to prepare for that greatest of sacrifices, the Horse Sacrifice, even as your ancestor, the exceedingly mighty King Bárata, that lord of the earth, performed it. Only a monarch who has conquered the whole earth is worthy to perform this king of rites. It will cleanse your heart of any grief or sin, and because of it your empire will prosper and endure."

"Without doubt," answered Yudíshtira, "the Horse Sacrifice purifies and blesses kings. But, O sinless one, in this sacrifice the wealth of the whole earth must be given away and, since I have caused this great slaughter of my kindred, I cannot make even

small gifts, for I have no wealth. For the sake of wealth Duryódana laid waste the earth, but now his treasury is empty. I cannot
ask tribute from the young sons of the kings who were slain, for
they are in distress and their wounds are yet green; I cannot levy
taxes when the whole world has been destroyed. Therefore, counsel me, O righteous one."

Vyasa thought for a while and then said to the King, "This
empty treasury shall be filled. O son of Kunti, in the Himálaya
Mountains there is a great heap of gold, left there long ago by the
Brahmans after a famous sacrifice, because they could not carry it
all away. A king in olden days, who was righteous and of great
renown, celebrated a sacrifice on the northern side of the Himálayas, on a huge golden hill. He caused his goldsmiths to make thousands of shining golden vessels and bowls and seats and ornaments,
so many that not a half of them could be carried away. Now, O
King, you must collect that gold that was left and, worshiping the
gods with due ceremony, perform the sacrifice. I will show you
where it lies."

Yudíshtira was delighted to hear these words and summoned his
brothers to go in quest of the treasure. Leaving the kingdom in
the care of their chief minister, they set out with joyful hearts,
guided by the island-born sage, and accompanied by men and
animals in high spirits. They filled the earth with the clatter of
their wheels, while the tread and the voices of the soldiers who
followed them seemed to fill the sky. Yudíshtira, with the white
canopy held over his head, shone with beauty like the full moon
and received the blessings and shouts of his people as he went on
his way. The host crossed many rivers, forests, and mountains,
reaching at last the northern side of the Himálayas. Vyasa led
them to the place where the gold was buried; there the King
pitched his camp, and the sons of Pandu, fasting, laid themselves
down on beds of grass.

When the cloudless morning came, they worshiped Kúvera, the
lord of treasures, with flowers and cakes; then, under Vyasa's direction, they caused the digging to begin. Countless vessels and
seats of varied and delightful shapes were dug out, thousands of

jars of golden coins and ornaments of every sort, wrought of fine gold. Some of this wealth was carried on men's shoulders, on yokes of wood with baskets slung like scales at either end; some was carried on the backs of camels and elephants and in carts drawn by mules. When it was loaded on countless carts, on thousands of animals, and on the shoulders of hundreds of men, the sons of Pandu set out for the city called after the elephant, making short marches each day, for the host was sorely burdened by the wealth that they carried.

It was at this time, while the Pándavas were absent from the city, that Uttara, the daughter of King Viráta and the wife of Abimányu, gave birth to the son who alone could carry on the line of the Báratas. Since all the sons of the Kúravas as well as the sons of the Pándavas had been slain in that awful battle, the hopes of all the Báratas depended on this child. Kunti, Dráupadi, and Subádra, like shipwrecked people who finally reach the shore, were filled with joy as they saw Uttara, with a delighted heart, holding the child in her arms. Poets and musicians, astrologers and actors praised the young prince and the citizens raised a shout of joy that seemed to fill the earth.

When the baby was a month old, the Pándavas came back to their capital, bringing the treasure with them. The citizens decked the city with garlands of flowers and beautiful flags and pennons. It was filled with the hum of thousands of voices that sounded like the distant roar of the ocean; the sound of singing and stringed instruments rose from various parts of it. The officers of the government, proclaiming that this was to be a day of rejoicing for the entire kingdom, went out to meet the King and to announce to him the happy news of the birth of Abimányu's son. Then the Pándavas with rejoicing hearts entered the city.

After they had celebrated, with due ceremony and festivity, the birth of the young prince, Yudíshtira addressed the holy sage Vyasa, saying, "O wisest of men, this treasure that you have brought to us I wish to devote to the Horse Sacrifice. I pray you to initiate me when the proper hour comes and to perform the sacrifice, for we depend upon you for its success."

"O son of Kunti, I shall perform every ceremony at the proper time," Vyasa answered. "You shall be initiated on the day of the next full moon. Now let Sutas expert in the knowledge of horses, and Brahmans also, select a horse worthy of your sacrifice. Then let the horse be loosed to wander over the earth freely at its will for a year, as the scriptures ordain. Let Arjuna, that mighty-armed one, follow and protect it. He will, according to the scriptures, allow it to roam and graze as it will, but if the king of any country where it roams attempts to stop it, then Arjuna must challenge him to battle and make him acknowledge you as lord of the earth. When the horse returns and all the earth is subject to you, the sacrifice will be performed."

Yudíshtira summoned Arjuna, saying to him, "Do you, O hero, follow the sacred steed, for you alone are able to protect it. If any kings come forward to challenge you, O sinless one, do not slay them! Invite them to this sacrifice of mine and make friends of them!"

Arjuna Follows the Horse

When the full moon came, the King was initiated, and the year-long preparation for the sacrifice began. The beautiful black horse that had been selected was let loose; and Arjuna, in his chariot yoked with white steeds, Gandíva in his hand, followed it. All the citizens and the children came out to behold him and loud was the noise that arose from that crowd as they cried, "There goes the son of Kunti and that steed of blazing beauty! There is the famous Gandíva of terrible twang! Blessings go with you, O son of Kunti! Go safely and return, and may all dangers fly from your path!" The horse then roamed over all the earth already conquered by the Pándavas, and Arjuna followed it in his chariot.

The horse wandered first into the north and then eastward, Arjuna following it slowly. It entered the kingdoms of many monarchs, and many of them stopped it and challenged Arjuna to battle, because they had lost their kinsmen on the field of Kuru Kshetra. Those Trigartas, who had long been enemies of the Pándavas, fought against him, and so did the young Prince of Mágada, the son of Jarasánda, but Arjuna, mindful of the words of his eldest brother, did not kill them but said, "Rise up and return to your city, and when the full moon of the month of Chaitra comes, go to the sacrifice of King Yudíshtira in Hastinápura!"

Worshiped by those kings and shaking his beautiful mane, the horse turned toward the south, where it was received with due honor, and entered all the kingdoms there. In the southern forests Arjuna fought against many tribes of barbarians, vanquishing them easily, and then the horse turned into the land of the Gandáras.

There occurred a fierce battle between Arjuna and the son of Shákuni, who had a bitter memory of the long feud between his sire and the Pándavas. He fought fiercely until his mother, with the ministers of state, came out of the city and bade him lay down his arms, while they offered food and gifts to Arjuna, and water for his feet. Arjuna, remembering Gandári, the sister of Shákuni, treated the prince kindly and bade him come to the sacrifice.

Following the horse into the west, he came into the land of Sind, whose ruler he had slain; there again the horse was seized and the men of Sind fought fiercely, for they could not bear the sight of the son of Pandu. But no one could stand against the wielder of Gandíva: at first he cut off their weapons before they could reach him; then, growing angry, he began to slay those warriors.

Now it happened that the only daughter of Kuru had been married to the King of Sind. She came forth from the city with her grandson, a young child, in her arms and said, weeping, to Arjuna, "Behold this child, whose father and grandfather and kinsmen have all been slain! Just as the son of Abimányu is the only one to carry on your line, so this child is our only hope. See, he bends his head before you and asks for peace!" Then she forbade her warriors to fight any longer, and Arjuna comforted her, promising her that there would be peace between their kingdoms.

When the steed had wandered over the whole earth for a year, it turned toward the road that led to Hastinápura. When Yudíshtira heard from his messengers that it had turned back and that

Arjuna was well, his heart was filled with joy. He summoned his brothers and said to Bima, "Your younger brother is coming back with the horse. The time for the sacrifice is come. Let learned Brahmans look for a place where it can be successfully accomplished."

Bima, with a glad heart, summoned those men who knew the rules for laying out the sacrificial grounds and buildings. The surface was leveled and the altar was erected; columns and wide triumphal arches, brightly adorned with gold, were raised, and mansions built for the many kings and their ladies and their attendants who were expected to come from many and diverse realms. Stables were filled with grain and sugar cane for the animals that would come with the guests. Many of the great sages came to that sacrifice and all the foremost Brahmans who were then alive came with their disciples.

When all was ready, the invited kings arrived and Yudíshtira, casting off all pride, took each of his guests to the pavilion that had been prepared for him, while the kings looked with wonder at the splendor of that sacrifice. It seemed that the whole population of the world had assembled there from all its realms and provinces. Thousands of men, adorned with garlands and golden earrings, distributed food to the Brahmans and attended to the needs of all the guests.

Krishna came with many of the warriors of the Yadus and was joyfully received by the Pándavas. "A messenger of mine," he said, "has come to me, telling me that Arjuna is very near. He saw that hero and says that he is very thin and worn because of the many battles he has fought."

"Alas," answered Yudíshtira, "it pains my heart that Arjuna always seems to bear the greatest burden and hardly ever has any rest or comfort. Why should that be? His body bears every fortunate sign."

Krishna said thoughtfully, "I see nothing imperfect in him except, perhaps, that his cheekbones are a little high. Perhaps it is for this that he rests so little."

When he said this, Dráupadi looked askance at Krishna angrily,

THE HOST CROSSED MANY MOUNTAINS

for she could not bear to hear a word against Arjuna; but Krishna was pleased at this sign of her love for his friend.

While they were talking, a messenger came who bowed before the King and announced that Arjuna would soon arrive. Two days later he appeared at the gate and a great shout arose as the people saw him, standing in his chariot in a haze of golden dust raised by the hoofs of the sacrificial horse. He was welcomed joyfully by the King and Bima, his younger brothers and Krishna. Saluting them all, he entered the palace and took his rest, like a shipwrecked man who has at last reached the shore after tossing for a long time on the waves.

On the third day after his return, since the full moon of the month of Chaitra was at hand, the sage Vyasa said to Yudíshtira, "The time has come, O son of Kunti, to begin your sacrifice. Since you have such a wealth of gold, you may give away three times as much as is usually given. Thus you will have the reward of three Horse Sacrifices, which will free you from every sin."

The high-souled King gladly agreed, and the three days of the great sacrifice began. On the first day Yudíshtira was anointed and made abundant gifts of food and other pleasant things to all those who were there. In the great enclosure the sacrificial stakes were set up; the priests moved about in all directions, performing every ceremony in the proper way, never swerving from the rules laid down in the Vedas. Vyasa was the high priest and directed the different acts of each day.

On the second day, Yudíshtira, clad in armor and carrying his weapons, entered the enclosure in his chariot, drawn by the sacrificial steed and three others. He took his place on his throne, surrounded by his brothers and by all the kings of the earth, adorned with royal robes and flashing jewels. Three hundred animals and birds, both tame and wild, were tied to the stakes and assigned to all the gods, while the black horse that had roamed all over the earth was bound in the center. After the other animals had been sacrificed and cooked, that beautiful steed was slain and its body cut into pieces, according to the scriptures. The Brahmans took the marrow of its bones and cooked it; then they presented it to

Yudíshtira and his brothers, who breathed the smoke of that marrow, which cleanses one of every sin.

On the third day the ceremony was completed and the King took the bath of purification. He accepted the homage of all the kings of the earth and was acclaimed their emperor, the sole lord of the whole world. When he had given away to the Brahmans hundreds of thousands of golden coins, he gave the earth to Vyasa. The sinless Vyasa, accepting the gift, said, "O best of kings, the earth that you have given me I now return to you. Give me the price of it in gold, for Brahmans need wealth and have no use for the earth." Yudíshtira and his brothers were glad of soul and gave the holy one three times the wealth that was ordained to be given at the Horse Sacrifice. Accepting it, Vyasa gave it to the sacrificial priests, who divided it among the Brahmans, giving each what he desired. After they had taken all that they wished, the wealth that remained was given to the Kshatrias and Vaisyas and Shudras, and to the barbarian tribes. The holy Vyasa gave his share, which was very large, to Kunti.

Among the assembled guests, none could be seen who was unhappy or hungry or poor. The sons of Pandu gave to all the kings jewels and gems, elephants and horses, and ornaments of gold. There were food and drink and sweetmeats in abundance, and the spacious grounds echoed with the sound of drums and flutes and stringed instruments. The vast space was filled with happy men and women; people speak of that sacrifice in all the different realms to this day.

King Yudíshtira, when he had given away all that untold wealth and had dismissed the assembled kings with due honors, returned to his capital, cleansed of his sins and with his purpose fulfilled.

The Mongoose's Story

Listen now to a most wonderful thing that happened at the end of that great sacrifice. After all the Brahmans and the kings, all the poor, the blind, and the helpless had received abundant gifts, and everyone was praising King Yudíshtira, a blue-eyed mongoose with his head and one half of his body turned to gold came into the sacrificial enclosure and spoke in a human voice that was as deep as thunder. He said: "You holy ones, this great sacrifice is not equal to one handful of powdered barley that was given away by a kind Brahman who lived at Kuru Kshetra."

The Brahmans were filled with wonder at these words and, approaching him, they asked, "Whence do you come? What knowledge and power is yours that you thus belittle our sacrifice? Everything has been done here according to the scriptures; gods and men have been abundantly satisfied. You must explain your words to us."

The mongoose, smiling, answered them as follows: "O sinless ones, my words are true and I have not spoken them out of pride. I say again that this sacrifice is not equal to the gift of one handful of powdered barley. Listen attentively to me as I tell you something that I saw with my own eyes and that turned half my body into gold.

"In that holy place that is called Kuru Kshetra, where many righteous people live, there was a Brahman who had taken a very difficult vow. He ate only what he could pick up from the fields after the farmers had gathered in the harvest. He and his wife, his son and his son's wife lived thus like birds and ate but once a day. They were pure-minded, having cast off all pride and anger. One time there was a dreadful famine in the land. The grain and plants were all dried up and that righteous Brahman and his family had nothing stored away, for they picked up their food day by day. They had nothing at all to eat and passed the days in great suffering.

"One day he succeeded in picking up about a quart of barley. He and his family powdered the barley and, after they had finished their silent meditations and their daily worship, they divided that little measure of grain among them so that each one had about a handful. Just as they were sitting down to eat, a guest came to their house. They welcomed him gladly, bringing water to wash his feet, and offering him a seat of clean grass. Then the Brahman gave him his share of the barley to eat. The guest ate it all but was still hungry, and the Brahman tried to think of something else to give him.

"His wife said, 'Give him my share of the barley.' But the Brahman, seeing how weak and thin she was from hunger, said, 'O beautiful one, even among animals and insects, wives are fed and protected by their husbands. If I fail to do this, I shall certainly never go to heaven.' 'O blessed one,' answered his wife, 'all that I have is yours. All my life you have taken care of me; in return for that I pray you to take my share of the barley and give it to our guest.' So he took her share and gave it to the guest, who ate it and was still hungry.

"Then the Brahman's son said to him, 'O best of men, give my share of barley to our guest. It is the duty of a son to take care of his father when he is old. It is shameful to send a guest away hungry from one's door; let me save you, therefore, from that shame, by giving my share of the barley.' The father then took his son's share and gave it to the guest, who ate it all and was still hungry.

"His daughter-in-law, bringing her share of the powdered grain, came to him and said, 'Because you had a son, I have had a son, and through him I shall attain happiness in this world and the next. Take my share, therefore, and give it to the guest.' Her father-in-law accepted it and gave it to the guest.

"That guest was none other than Darma himself, the God of Righteousness, who now revealed himself to those four blessed ones and said, 'O best of Brahmans, I am exceedingly pleased with this pure gift of yours. Truly, the blessed ones in heaven are talking about your gift and flowers are falling thence upon the earth; the gods, the holy sages, and the heavenly messengers are praising you, struck with wonder at this deed. For hunger destroys wisdom and drives away courage; therefore he who can conquer hunger conquers heaven. Putting virtue first, you have overcome your love for wife and children and the craving of your own body. You have, by this act, conquered heaven.

" 'The door of heaven is difficult to open,' Darma said. 'Greed is the bar to that door and it is fastened by desire and affection. Those who have conquered anger and greed, who give according to their ability, are able to open it. It is said that he who has a thousand and gives away a hundred, he who has a hundred and gives away ten, and he who has nothing and gives away a cupful of water are equally rewarded. King Usinara, by giving away the flesh of his body for the sake of a pigeon, is rejoicing now in heaven. This gift of yours, O Brahman, is greater than those gifts that are made in many Rajasúya Sacrifices or many Horse Sacrifices. A heavenly chariot is here for you: ascend it now, with your wife, your son, and your daughter-in-law, and go to those regions that are unstained by any sorrow!'

"All this," said the mongoose, "I beheld from inside my hole. After that learned Brahman, with his wife, his son, and daughter-in-law, had gone to heaven, I came out of my hole, and the fragrance of that powdered barley and the heavenly flowers that had fallen turned my head to gold. As I came farther out, half of this broad body of mine became golden, because of the gift of that Brahman who held fast to virtue. Ever since that time, O foremost of Brahmans, I have gone to the hermitages of holy sages and to the sacrifices of kings so that the rest of my body might be turned to gold. When I heard of this great sacrifice, I came here with high hope, but behold, I have not been turned to gold. For this reason I said that this sacrifice cannot compare with that gift of powdered barley, and that is still my opinion." With these words the mongoose disappeared from the sight of those Brahmans.

This wonderful incident has been told so that no one may think too highly of sacrifices. Many a holy man has gone to heaven with the aid of his good deeds alone. To harm no creature, to be contented and true, self-controlled and generous is equal to any sacrifice.

BOOK XVII

THE FOREST DWELLERS

The Old People Go to the Woods

FOR many years the high-souled Pándavas ruled the earth justly, placing the old king, Kuru, at their head, and taking his counsel in all matters. Indeed, for fifteen years they asked his advice about everything they did, going to him and sitting beside him, after having touched his feet. Kunti also obeyed Gandári, her elder sister-in-law, while Dráupadi and Subádra behaved toward the old king and queen as they would have behaved toward their own parents. Wines, fish, flesh, and honey and many other delightful kinds of food, costly beds, robes, and ornaments were given to Kuru so that he might have everything that he had enjoyed in the days of his glory; for Yudíshtira desired that the old king, who had lost all his sons, might not die of his grief or be unhappy in any way. Indeed, the father of Duryódana had never been as happy with his own children as he was with the Pándavas, and Gandári, too, loved them as if they were her own sons.

There was one among the Pándavas, however, who did not follow the example of his older brother, and that was Bima. He could not forget all that had happened as a result of the gambling match, to which Kuru had invited them; he did not enjoy the sight of his uncle and reverenced him outwardly, but with a very unwilling heart. Secretly he did many things that were disagreeable to the old king and bribed the servants to disobey his orders. One day, remembering with rage the unhappy days of the past, Bima clapped his armpits and said to some of his friends, in the hearing of his uncle and Gandári, "All the sons of the blind king, although they were great warriors, were sent to the other world by these powerful arms of mine."

These words and others like them pierced Kuru's heart like arrows; after fifteen years, Bima's unkindness and harsh words drove him to grief and despair. Yudíshtira knew nothing of this; nor did Arjuna of the white steeds; nor Kunti, nor the renowned Dráupadi; nor the twin sons of Madri, who did everything to please the old king and never said anything that was disagreeable to him. One day Kuru said to his friends, with tears in his eyes, "You all know how the Báratas were destroyed, through my fault. All wise men gave me the same advice, but I did not follow it. Overwhelmed by love for my son, I made the wicked-minded Duryódana king of the Báratas and followed his evil counsels. Bitter repentance is now my lot, and I am trying to atone for my sins. Once a day I eat a little food, just to keep myself alive; I sleep on the ground and spend my time in silent prayers. Gandári knows this and does as I do, but I have hidden it from everyone else for fear of Yudíshtira, who would be greatly pained if he knew how I am living."

He spoke to Yudíshtira shortly afterward and said, "May you be blessed, O son of Kunti! I have lived these fifteen years very happily with you, for you are always devoted to virtue. Now, my son, with your permission I wish to retire into the woods with Gandári, clad in rags and the bark of trees. It is right, when old age comes, to give the throne to one's children and to live in the forest. I shall always bless you there and you shall have a share in any good acts that I may perform, for the king has a share in all the good and the evil deeds that are done in his kingdom." Then he told Yudíshtira of the penances that he had already performed.

"Alas, my brothers and I did not know that you were grieving so, fasting, and sleeping on the ground!" Yudíshtira said. "You are our father and our mother, the eldest of our line; how shall we live without you? You are the king and I am dependent on you;

how can I give permission to my superior? If you go to the woods, I will follow you, for this earth, with its belt of seas, so full of wealth, will give me no joy if I cannot share it with you."

"O delight of the Báratas," answered his uncle, "my mind is set on retiring to the woods, and it is fitting that I should do so. Therefore, give me your permission, my son."

And Yudíshtira, bowing low in humility before him, said gently, "So be it! I shall do all that you desire, O sinless one. I beg of you, however, to take some food now and afterward go to your forest retreat."

The old king took some food and then he summoned all the citizens to come to his palace. Brahmans and Kshatrias, Vaisyas and Shudras gathered together in the courtyard, and the King came out of the inner apartments and addressed them, saying, "We have lived together for many long years, each helping the other, wishing each other well. Now I have set my heart on retiring to the woods. The son of Kunti has given me his permission; now, I pray you, give me yours. Since Yudíshtira has ruled the kingdom I have enjoyed great happiness, greater, I think, than I could have known had my own son Duryódana been on the throne. Through the wicked understanding of that prince, and his pride, through my own foolishness as well, a great slaughter of warriors took place. Whether I acted rightly or wrongly, now, with joined hands, I pray you to erase that memory from your hearts. Say to yourselves, 'This one is old; he has lost all his children; he was once our king and is the descendant of former kings'—and try to forgive me.

"Yudíshtira the son of Kunti, with his four mighty brothers, will rule you like one of the gods and should be cherished by you all. I give him to you as a trust and I give you to him as a trust. I am worn out with the load of years upon my head and thin with fasting. What other refuge have I save the woods? You blessed ones, grant me the permission that I seek."

Thus addressed by the blind monarch, the citizens said nothing but only looked at one another, their eyes filled with tears. Gradually they began to talk, each telling the other what he felt, and finally they asked a certain Brahman to answer the King for them.

"O King," the Brahman said, "I will voice the answer that this assembly has asked me to make and do you listen to it. O foremost of men, follow the path that has been pointed out in the Vedas. If you leave us, we shall pass our days in sorrow, remembering your many virtues. We were well ruled and protected by King Duryódana, as we were by you and by Pandu, that lord of earth, and by your ancestors before you. Your son never did us any wrong. The slaughter that the Báratas suffered was not brought about by you or by your son; it was brought about by destiny and nothing could have stopped it. Eighteen armies were brought together, and in eighteen days they were destroyed. Who can think that this was not caused by destiny? Therefore, in your presence, we forgive you and your son Duryódana and give you our permission. Those mighty warriors, the sons of Kunti, will protect and cherish the people. Therefore, O king of kings, set your heart at rest and do as you desire."

Then Kuru, with joined hands, bowed down to that assembly of citizens and entered his own palace with Gandári.

The next morning Vídura came to Yudíshtira, saying, "The King will set out for the woods on the day of the next full moon. He asks you to give him some wealth, O lord of earth, so that he may perform a gift sacrifice for the souls of Bishma and Drona and all his sons who were slain."

Yudíshtira and Arjuna were pleased at this, but Bima grumbled, for he did not wish either to please his uncle or to help the souls of the cousins whom he had slain. Yudíshtira, however, answered, "Say to the King that he may take from my palace anything that he wishes in any quantity. Whatever wealth is here belongs to him; let him spend as largely as he likes and pay the debt that he owes to his sons and to his friends."

Kuru was highly pleased at these words; he ordered a great quantity of food and drink to be prepared and many chariots and robes, gold and jewels, elephants and horses richly decked, men and maidservants to be gathered together. These he gave away in the name of the dead, naming Bishma and Drona, Duryódana and all his other sons in due order as the gifts were made. Scribes and tellers constantly asked the old king, "What gifts, O monarch, do you wish to make? All things are ready to your hand." When the King spoke, they gave what he ordered, but if he said ten, they gave a hundred; if he said a hundred, they gave a thousand. This was done at the command of Yudíshtira. At last, after ten days, when he became tired of making gifts in such profusion, the blind king brought his gift sacrifice to an end. Everyone ate and drank all that they desired, while actors and dancers made merry, to entertain the guests.

On the day of the full moon, the old monarch put off his royal robes and dressed himself in deerskin. He honored with many excellent flowers the palace in which he had lived and had the sacrificial fire that he worshiped every day taken up so that he might carry it with him. He gave his servants rich gifts and set out on his journey. Kunti also desired to go to the woods, in order to take care of the King and Gandári, for he was blind and she, all her life, had bandaged her eyes in order to share all that her lord suffered. The sons of Kunti begged her to stay with them, but her heart was set on going. She walked ahead, bearing on her shoulder the hand of Gandári, while Kuru walked trustingly behind his wife, with his hand on her shoulder. Vídura and Sánjaya went with them, too.

Yudíshtira and his brothers, with all the ladies of the royal household, weeping and lamenting, walked with them out of the city, and all the citizens, with their wives and children, came out into the streets from every side. They were as much distressed at the old king's departure as they had been, years before, at the departure of the Pándavas after their defeat at dice. Ladies who had never seen the sun or the moon came out into the streets; great was the grief and uproar as Kuru, trembling with weakness, walked with difficulty through the principal street of the city and out of its gate. There he bade all those citizens to return to their homes and said farewell to the Pándavas.

The sons of Kunti, however, could not bear to leave their mother, and followed her, entreating her to remain with them. "When the kingdom is ours," said Bima to her, "and you are free to enjoy all that your sons have won for you, why do you wish to live in the woods? We were born in the forest; why did you bring us out of it when we were children if you desire to return to it now that we rule the earth? Relent, O Mother! Behold, the two sons of Madri are overwhelmed with sorrow. Do not go to the woods!"

"When you were unfortunate and had lost everything," answered Kunti, "I put courage and high thoughts into your minds so that you might not live, watching the faces of others, dependent on them for your food. I put courage into your hearts so that the fame of the sons of Pandu should be bright, so that the wrongs of this dear daughter of mine, Dráupadi, might be avenged; I put courage into your hearts so that the line of Pandu might not die out. But now that you have won wealth and happiness, I do not wish to enjoy them with you; rather, by my own efforts, I wish to reach those regions of bliss where my husband, Pandu, dwells. Therefore cease to follow me, O my sons. Be always devoted to righteousness, and let your minds be always great."

Then the Pándavas, ashamed, ceased to entreat her; they walked around the King and Queen and their mother, saluting them duly, and returned sorrowfully to the city.

On that day, Kuru reached a place far removed from the city, on the bank of the Ganges, and rested there for the night. Brahmans learned in the Vedas lit the sacred fires, including the sacrificial fire of the old king, who poured libations upon it and then worshiped the thousand-rayed sun as it was setting. Vídura and Sánjaya made a bed of grass for the King; near his bed they made another for Gandári, and close to her, the mother of the Pándavas, the excellent Kunti, laid herself happily down. Within hearing of those three slept Vídura and Sánjaya; the Brahmans who had come with the King chanted aloud many sacred hymns, while the holy fires blazed forth around them, and the night seemed delightful to them all.

The next morning they continued their journey to Kuru Kshetra, to the hermitage of the holy Vyasa. There Kuru was initiated into the forest dweller's life and began at once to train his body and his mind, fasting and meditating, clad in bark and skin, and with his hair unkempt. Gandári and Kunti dressed as he did and took the same vows; Vídura and Sánjaya also began to purify their hearts and minds of all sin.

The Dead Arise

After the retirement of those blessed ones, the Pándavas were very sad and talked constantly about them, wondering how they were bearing the hard life in the forest; they were so anxious about them that they took no pleasure in anything and did not even attend to their kingly duties. Finally they decided that they must go to the forest and see the old king; Dráupadi also longed to see Kunti once again. Therefore Yudíshtira gave the order: "Let my army, with all its chariots and elephants, prepare to march to Kuru Kshetra! Let all the carriages and closed litters for the women be prepared, and carts to carry the food and clothing and treasure that we need. If any of the citizens wish to see King Kuru, let them come with us."

After waiting five days for the citizens who wished to accompany him, he set forth with all his household, followed by a great number of chariots and elephants and carts, while many people from the city and the provinces followed on foot. Bima, that son of the Wind God, rode on an elephant as huge as a hill; the twin sons of Madri rode on two swift steeds, while Arjuna went in his chariot, drawn by white horses.

They traveled by slow marches, resting by the banks of rivers and lakes, until they reached Kuru Kshetra and, crossing the Jumna, saw at a distance the hermitage of Vyasa. They were filled with joy as they entered the forest; there they dismounted and went on foot to the hermitage, while the women, all their attendants, and the citizens followed them. The sages who lived there came out to see them and Yudíshtira, bowing humbly to them, asked, "Where has my sire, the eldest of the Báratas, gone?" They told him that the King had gone to the river to get water and flowers, and the Pándavas, walking quickly along the path that was shown them, saw the three old people coming toward them.

Sahadéva ran to Kunti and fell at her feet, weeping, and she raised him up and embraced him, for he had always been her darling; then she saw the others and hastened toward them, leading the blind Kuru and the Queen. The Pándavas knelt down before her, and the old king, recognizing them by their voices and their touch, greeted and comforted them. They rose, took the jars of water from their elders, and walked back along the path with them. The ladies and the citizens came forward to greet the King, and Yudíshtira presented each one to his uncle, telling him the name and the family of each. Surrounded by them all, the old monarch, with tears of joy in his eyes, felt that he was back in his own city, for the forest retreat was filled with crowds of men and women, all desiring to see him and to do him honor.

"Where is Vídura?" Yudíshtira asked. "I do not see him here. I hope that he and Sánjaya are well and at peace."

"Vídura is well, my son," answered Kuru. "He has taken hard vows and is living on air alone. He lives in the deep forest, but is sometimes seen by the Brahmans."

While he was speaking thus, Vídura was seen at a distance, coming toward the hermitage; but when he saw so many people there he turned and ran back into the deep forest. Yudíshtira followed him, sometimes seeing him, then losing sight of him, calling aloud, "Vídura, O Vídura! I am Yudíshtira, your favorite!" At last, with great difficulty, he caught up with Vídura in a solitary spot in the forest. His uncle was leaning against a tree; he was exceedingly thin, his hair was unkempt, and his body hardly clothed.

Bowing before him, Yudíshtira said again, "I am the eldest son of Kunti," but Vídura looked at him steadfastly and said nothing, for he was deep in meditation. Then the King saw that, while Vídura's body still leaned against the tree, the life had fled out of it. At the same time he felt stronger than before; he felt new virtue and power within him, and he understood that his uncle's life had entered into him, because of Vídura's love for him and the power of his soul. He returned and told his brothers and the old king what had happened and they were all filled with wonder. They talked long about Vídura, remembering his wisdom and his patience, his love for all his family, and his good counsel.

Then they ate the fruits and roots and drank the water that Kuru gave them, spread grass for their beds under a tree near their mother, and lay down to rest.

The Pándavas, with their troops and their households, spent about a month very happily in the forest. Toward the end of that time the holy Vyasa came to the hermitage. They all gathered about him, and there was excellent talk about things human and divine. When they had talked for a long time, Vyasa said to the blind king, "I know that you are burning with grief on account of your children, O king of kings; I know the sorrow that dwells in the hearts of Gandári and Dráupadi, and the grief that Krishna's sister Subádra feels because of the death of Abimányu. I have come here to grant you any wish that you desire, for I have gained enough soul power to fulfill the dearest wishes of your hearts."

"My mind," answered Kuru, after thinking for a while, "is always tortured by the memory of the wicked deeds of my son. Many high-souled kings sided with him and were killed. What has been the fate, O sinless one, of those men who were slain for their friend's sake? What has been the fate of my sons and grandsons? It is this thought that burns me day and night and gives me no peace."

Gandári also, with bandaged eyes, joining her hands, said to the sage, "O holy one, we too, the wives and mothers of those high-souled heroes, can have no peace. What has been their fate, O mighty seer? You alone can free us from our grief."

When Gandári had spoken, Kunti began to think of her secretly born son, that child of Surya. Vyasa, seeing her sorrow, said to her, "Tell me, O blessed one, what is in your mind."

And she, bowing her head to the sage, said shyly, "I cast into the water my infant son Karna, and although he knew me for his mother when he grew up, I never acknowledged him. For this reason he met his death. I pray you, O foremost of sages, to tell me the fate of this son of mine."

"Cast off all your doubts," Vyasa said. "You shall behold Karna, and you, O Gandári, shall behold your sons and brothers and kinsmen this very night, like men risen from sleep. Dráupadi shall behold her five sons, her father, and her brothers, and Subádra shall see Abimányu. Before you asked me, this thought was in my mind. Go now to the Ganges, for there you shall see all those who were slain on the field of battle."

Kuru with his companions, and the Pándavas with all those who had come with them, went to the bank of the Ganges and the day seemed to them as long as a whole year, so greatly did they long for the night to come. When the sun set, they bathed in the sacred stream and when they had finished their evening worship they approached Vyasa. Kuru, with purified body and mind, sat beside the sage with the Pándavas, while Gandári and the ladies of the royal household sat in a retired place, and all the people who had come with Yudíshtira took their places according to their ages.

Then Vyasa, entering the waters of the Ganges, summoned with mighty soul power all those dead warriors who had fought with the Pándavas and those who had fought with the Kúravas. At his word, a deafening uproar arose from within the waters, like that which had been heard on the battlefield, and those kings, headed by Bishma and Drona, with all their troops, rose by thousands from the waters of the sacred river. There were Viráta and the King of Panchála, with their sons and all their armies; there were the sons of Dráupadi, and Abimányu; there were Karna and the mighty Shákuni, Duryódana, and the other sons of Kuru, headed by Dushásana; there were the Kings of Sind and Madra and many others, the list of whose names would be too long to tell, with their sons and their armies. All of them rose from the Ganges with shining bodies, each one equipped as he had been on the field of battle, each one with his standard, but now they were clothed in heavenly garments and all wore brilliant earrings and fresh garlands. They were free from all anger, pride, or jealousy, and Gan-dárvas sang their praises.

Through the power of his soul, Vyasa opened for this night the eyes of Kuru: the old king beheld for the first time his children, and was filled with joy. Gandári, too, uncovered her eyes and beheld her sons and all her kinsmen that had been slain. All that were assembled there beheld, with steadfast gaze and wondering hearts, that amazing sight that made their hair stand on end.

Then those mighty men, free of anger and jealousy, met one another with happy hearts; sons met with fathers and mothers, wives with husbands, friends with friends. It was like a high carnival, so great was the rejoicing. The Pándavas met Abimányu and their sons by Dráupadi; with happy hearts they approached Karna and were reconciled with him. All those warriors meeting together were reconciled with one another and talked together in peace and friendship. Seeing their fathers and brothers, their husbands and sons, the women cast off their grief and were filled with delight. The whole night was passed thus in great happiness, as if the place were heaven itself, for no grief, no fear, and no reproach were there.

When the night had passed, those heroes and their wives, mothers, and sisters embraced and took their leave of one another, and the holy Vyasa dismissed that host that had risen from the water. In the twinkling of an eye they disappeared in the very sight of all those living people, plunging into the river with their chariots and their standards, their horses and all their followers, returning to their heavenly abodes. Some among them went to the highest region of heaven; some went to the regions of the gods who protect the earth; all had died in battle without turning their backs to the foe and therefore all had attained to regions of bliss.

After they had gone away, the mighty Vyasa, who was still standing in the waters of the sacred river, spoke to those women whose husbands had been slain, saying: "Let those among you who wish to share the blissful regions where your husbands dwell plunge now into the Ganges!" Those women then, trusting his words, plunged into the river; freed from their human bodies, in shining forms clothed with heavenly raiment and adorned with jewels and garlands, they joined their husbands in the happy regions where they dwelt.

When Kuru had beheld that exceedingly wonderful sight, the reappearance of his children, his heart was free of grief. He returned to the hermitage and, summoning Yudíshtira, said to him, "O sinless one, the purpose of my life has now been fulfilled. I wish to take even harder vows and I shall not live long. You have served me in every way that a son can serve his father; therefore go now, and do not tarry here any longer. The burdens of the Bárata realm have fallen on you, my son, and you know all the duties of a king. Depart now, either tomorrow or this very day, and my blessing go with you!"

Gandári and Kunti spoke in the same way, so the Pándavas, with the permission and the blessings of their elders, took their leave of them. Bima was reconciled to his uncle and showed his love and obedience to the old king, who comforted him and embraced him. Then the shouts of charioteers were heard, the grunting of elephants, and the neighing of horses, and King Yudíshtira, with his troops and his animals, his litters and carriages, set out for Hastinápura.

The Sacred Flame

Two years after the Pándavas had returned from the forest, the holy sage Nárada came to Yudíshtira, who received him with honor, asking him whence he had come. When he heard that the sage had recently come from the sacred Ganges, he asked him eagerly, "Have you seen my royal sire there, O holy one? Are he and my mother, are Gandári and Sánjaya well and at peace? How goes it with them?"

"Listen, O King," said Nárada, "with calmness, as I tell you what I have heard of them. When you left them the King took up his sacred fire and went deeper into the woods, with the two queens, Sánjaya, and the Brahmans who were with him. He took hard vows, fed on air alone, and spoke to no one. In six months nothing was left of him but skin and bone and he was greatly honored by all the others who dwelt within the forest. Gandári lived on water alone, while Kunti took a little food once a month and Sánjaya ate a little every sixth day. They had no fixed dwelling, but wandered through the woods, Sánjaya guiding them over the rough ground, Kunti leading Gandári, who led the old king.

"One day they came to the banks of the Ganges and the King had his sacrificial fire duly lighted. When he had performed his worship with it, the Brahmans cast the embers out into the woods and then went on their way. The smoldering embers set fire to the woods; a wind arose and fanned it into mighty flames that burned the forest all around that place. Animals and snakes hurried to the nearest marshes and rivers, but the King, as he felt the fire approaching from all sides, was unable to move, for he had taken no food. He said to Sánjaya, 'Go quickly where the flames cannot reach you. As for us, we shall let our bodies be destroyed, and our souls will be freed. Death by water, fire, wind, or starvation is good for forest dwellers. Therefore leave us, good Sánjaya.'

"Then the King sat down, facing the east, and concentrated his mind; controlling all his senses, he sat like a post of wood, and the highly blessed Gandári and Kunti, your mother, did likewise. They met their death thus, consumed by their own sacred flame. Sánjaya left them and escaped; I saw him in Vyasa's hermitage, but shortly afterward he departed, going toward the Himálayas. I heard from him all that I have told you. No one in that hermitage grieved for the King and those two queens, for they met the fire of their own free wills and died with their souls at peace. O king of kings, you should not grieve for them, but perform the needful ceremonies in their honor, with your brothers."

Nevertheless, the sons of Pandu grieved deeply for their mother, for the blind king, and the faultless Gandári. Thinking of his mother, Yudíshtira wept like a child and so did his brothers; in the inner apartments the women wailed and lamented, and all the people sorrowed for their king who had lost all his children and had then been burned to death. The Pándavas, the women of their household, and the principal citizens went to the Ganges, each wearing but one garment; they bathed there and made offerings of the sacred water to the King and to Gandári and Kunti. They sent into the forest and had the ashes of their bodies brought back and the funeral ceremonies were duly performed, with perfumes and garlands and the giving of many gifts.

Even so did King Kuru leave this world after spending fifteen years under the rule of Yudíshtira in the city called after the elephant, and three years in the forest.

BOOK XVIII

THE ASCENT TO HEAVEN

Gandári's Curse

AFTER his uncle's death, Yudíshtira sadly took up the burden of royalty, ruling justly over the earth for twenty years. In the twentieth year after Kuru's death, the thirty-sixth year after the great battle, that lord of men beheld many unusual omens. Winds, dry and strong, blew from every direction and birds flew in circles; the horizon seemed always to be covered with fog, meteors fell on the earth, and fierce circles of light were seen around the sun and the moon. These and many other omens, foreboding fear and danger, filled the hearts of men with anxiety.

Shortly afterward, a messenger came from Dváraka, the city of Krishna, to say that all the Yadu warriors had slain one another and that Krishna himself was dead; none remained alive but the old king, his father. This was the fulfillment of the curse of Gandári, uttered on the field of Kuru Kshetra. To the Pándavas, the death of Krishna was like the drying up of the ocean. They could scarcely believe it and were filled with sorrow and despair.

The messenger told them that Krishna, when his kinsmen had all been slain, summoned him and said, "Go to Hastinápura and tell Arjuna about this slaughter of the Yadus. Bid him come here quickly." Returning to Dváraka, he said to his father, "Arjuna will come soon; protect the women of our household until he arrives. He and I are but one person; he will do what is best for the women and the children, and he will perform your funeral rites. After he has gone, this city will be swallowed up by the ocean, with all its walls and palaces. As for myself, I shall retire to some holy place and await my hour." With these words, he touched his father's feet with his forehead and quickly left him.

Going into the forest, Krishna, who knew the destiny of all things, wandered thoughtfully for a while and then sat down on the earth in a solitary place. He knew that this calamity had been caused by the curse of Gandári, uttered in former days; he knew that the hour of his own departure from the world had come; therefore he concentrated all his senses and his mind and lay down in deep meditation. A fierce hunter came through the forest, chasing deer; when he saw Krishna lying there, clad in yellow robes, he mistook him for a deer and pierced his heel with an arrow. Then, running forward to seize his prey, he saw instead a man absorbed in meditation, and he was overcome by fear and remorse. Krishna, however, comforted him; then he cast off his body and rose into heaven, filling the sky with light.

When Arjuna received the message of Krishna, he set out at once for the city of Dváraka to see the old king, who was the brother of Kunti. Dváraka, bereft of its princes and warriors, looked like a woman just widowed, like a lotus flower in winter, its beauty wilted. Arjuna went quickly into the palace and touched the feet of the King, who said to him, weeping, "Krishna told me that you would come, O son of Kunti! Do now all that he asked of you. This kingdom, with all its women and children and its wealth, is yours now. As for myself, I shall cast my life away, for it is no longer dear to me."

"O Uncle, I can no longer look upon the earth when that hero of unfading glory has left it," Arjuna answered. "My brothers and Dráupadi feel as I do. The time for our departure from the world is also at hand; but I shall first take to Indra Prasta the women, the children, and the old people of this city. On the seventh day from today, at sunrise, we shall set out." Then he ordered all the citizens and the women of the palace to prepare themselves for the journey. He spent that night in the palace of Krishna, sorrowing for

CONSUMED BY THEIR OWN SACRED FLAME

his friend; at dawn he heard that the old king had given up his life.

After he had performed the funeral ceremonies of the King, he mounted his chariot on the seventh day and set out from the city, followed by the wives and children of the Yadu heroes, riding in litters and in carts drawn by bullocks and mules, while the citizens and the inhabitants of the country traveled on foot and on horseback, in chariots and carts, carrying with them all that they possessed. After they had all left the city, the ocean poured into it; whatever piece of land they left, the ocean immediately covered with its waters. Beholding this, they hurried on, following Arjuna. He traveled by slow marches so that the women could rest in pleasant woods and by the sides of streams.

When they came to the Land of the Five Rivers, he set up a camp, for the land abounded in grain and in cattle and other animals. A band of robbers saw those lordless ladies, escorted only by Arjuna, and the sinful wretches consulted together, saying, "Here is only one warrior, escorting a crowd of women and children, carrying much wealth. They are easy prey." Armed with clubs, they attacked the camp of the Yadus, frightening them with great shouts and slaying everyone they met. Arjuna, hearing the noise, took up his mighty bow and went speedily to meet them. He tried to string Gandíva and was barely able to do it, for he was old and his strength had left him. He summoned the heavenly weapons that Indra had given him, but they did not come to him, for it was long since he had used them. The foot soldiers and the other men of the Yadus were fighting furiously against the bandits; Arjuna, too, pierced them with his arrows, but his arrows were soon used up, while in former years his quivers had always been full. He did his best to protect the people who were in his care, but he was not able to drive the robbers off and he was deeply ashamed, feeling the loss of his power.

The camp was large; the robbers attacked it at different points, and, before the very eyes of Arjuna, they carried off many of the women with all their wealth.

Filled with sorrow and sighing deeply, he went on with those who remained and the wealth that the bandits had not been able to carry away. He settled some of the people in various cities and led the rest to Indra Prasta, where the Pándavas first had their kingdom. He gave that beautiful city to the great-grandson of Krishna and left there all the men who had come from Dváraka with him.

When he had taken care of all the people whom he had brought with him, he went to the hermitage of Vyasa at Kuru Kshetra to see that holy sage. He found the island-born one seated in a secluded place and he bowed before him, saying, "I am Arjuna." The holy one welcomed him and bade him be seated; then, seeing that he sighed deeply and was filled with despair, he asked Arjuna the cause of his unhappiness.

"Alas," answered that son of Kunti, "my friend of immeasurable soul—who wielded the discus and the mace, who was dark-skinned and dressed in yellow robes, whose eyes were like lotus petals—has cast off his body and risen to heaven, while his kinsmen have slaughtered one another in battle. Without him I no longer desire to live. But a still more painful thing has happened, O best of men, which is breaking my heart. Before my very eyes, many of the Yadu women were carried off by robbers in the Land of the Five Rivers. When I took up my bow, I could hardly string it; my weapons did not appear and my arrows were soon used up. The might of my arms seemed to leave me. Tell me now, O sinless one, what I must do, for I wander with an empty heart, having lost my friend, my kinsmen, and my power."

"Do not grieve for what has happened, O chief of the Báratas," Vyasa said, "for it was ordained and could not be otherwise. You and your brothers have now accomplished the purpose of your lives and have been crowned with success. The time has come for you to leave the world. Time brings everything to birth and, again, time withdraws everything from life, at its pleasure. One becomes mighty and then, losing his power, becomes weak. One becomes a master, ruling others, and then, losing this mastery, serves others. Your weapons, which brought you success, have now returned to the gods who gave them to you. Now you must leave your son's son on the throne and seek yourselves the highest goal of life, the freedom of the soul. Leave your home and cast away your sacrificial fires; calling nothing your own, fixing your minds on God, follow that path from which there is no return."

The Last Pilgrimage

Arjuna took his leave of the holy one and returned to Hastinápura, where he told Yudíshtira all that had occurred. The just king answered, "Time cooks all creatures in his caldron; time brings all things to pass. Let us now gladly follow Vyasa's counsel and leave the world!" Bima and Madri's sons agreed wholeheartedly with the King's resolve and they prepared for their journey, after providing for the welfare of the kingdom.

Yudíshtira placed Abimányu's son on the throne. To Subádra, the sister of Krishna, he said, "This son of your son is now the king of the Báratas. He will rule in Hastinápura, while the great-grandson of Krishna will rule in Indra Prasta. Watch over them and counsel them to follow always the path of virtue."

Then he summoned all his subjects from the city and from the provinces and told them what he desired to do, asking their permission. They listened anxiously and said to him, "This should not be done." But he did not listen to them, for his heart was set on leaving the world and at last he persuaded them to consent to it.

He cast off his royal robes and dressed in cloth made from the bark of trees; his brothers and Dráupadi, of bright fame, dressed themselves also in bark, just as they had done when they went out from the city after their defeat at dice. The women of the household, beholding them in that guise, wept aloud; but this time the Pándavas were happy to be starting on their journey. Yudíshtira gave rich gifts of jewels and robes, horses and chariots to the Brahmans in honor of Krishna, and asked the blessings of the gods on their journey. Then they cast their sacred fires into the water and took their leave of everyone in the palace.

The five brothers and Dráupadi, with a dog that followed them, set out from the city named after the elephant, Yudíshtira leading the party of seven. The citizens and the royal household followed them for a distance, but no one dared to ask the King to stay. Then those high-souled ones, fixing their minds on God, turned their faces to the east and began their journey.

Yudíshtira went first and behind him Bima; next walked Arjuna, and after him the twins, in the order of their birth; behind them all went Dráupadi, that best of women, large-eyed and beautiful, and the dog followed her. They traversed many countries and rivers until they reached the sea. Arjuna was still carrying his bow, Gandíva, and his two quivers, for he could not bear to part from them. Now, at the shore of the sea, the Pándavas beheld Agni, the smoke-bannered God of Fire, standing before them like a hill, blocking their way. The god said to them, "You heroic sons of Pandu, scorchers of your foes, listen to what I say. Let Arjuna now cast aside his great bow, for he has no longer any need of it. This Gandíva was given to me by Váruna, lord of waters, and I in turn gave it to Arjuna when the Kándava forest was burned. Let him return it now to Váruna."

Then Arjuna hurled into the ocean the bow and the two quivers, and Agni disappeared from their sight.

At the seacoast they turned their faces toward the south, then the southwest and the west, for they wished to go around the whole earth. In the west they saw how the city of Dváraka was covered by the ocean; thence they turned to the north. Controlling their senses and concentrating their minds, they strove to free their souls and to purify them in order to enter the blissful regions of heaven. They beheld the mighty Himálayas and crossed them, as they had done before; they passed the Gandamádana, where they had met Arjuna, and came to Mount Meru, that highest of all peaks, which rises from the center of the earth and leads to heaven. Each rapt in his own thought, the Pándavas began to climb that heavenly peak; Dráupadi, strong of soul as they, came after them and the dog followed her.

When they had climbed a long way Dráupadi weakened, fell down on the earth, and died. Seeing her fall, Bima spoke to Yudíshtira, who walked before him: "O lord of earth, this princess never did any sinful deed. Why has she fallen down on the earth?"

Yudíshtira said, "She always loved Arjuna better than the rest of us; because she was partial to him, she has fallen now." Saying this, Yudíshtira went on, his mind withdrawn into itself.

Then Sahadéva, the learned one, fell down on the earth and again Bima asked, "Alas, this son of Madri who has served us all with such humility, why has he fallen?"

"He thought that no one was his equal in wisdom," Yudíshtira said. "For that fault he has now fallen on the earth." The king went on, leaving Sahadéva there, and the others followed.

Seeing that both Dráupadi and his brother Sahadéva had fallen, Nákula, who loved his family dearly, himself fell down and died. And Bima said to the King, "This brother of ours, who was always righteous, who always obeyed us, and who was more beautiful than any other man, has fallen now."

"His soul was righteous," Yudíshtira said, "and he was wise; but he believed that no one equaled him in beauty, and for this fault he has fallen." And he went on, followed by his two brothers and the dog.

That slayer of foes, Arjuna of the white steeds, beholding Dráupadi and the two sons of Madri dead, fell down in great grief of heart and died. When he who was the equal of Indra fell, Bima said to the King, "I do not remember any time when this high-souled one spoke an untrue word; even in joke he said nothing that was false. For what reason then has he fallen on the earth?"

"Arjuna said that he would slay all our foes in a single day, and this he did not do," Yudíshtira answered. "He was proud of his heroism and thought himself better than any other bowman. For this reason he has fallen." With these words the King went on.

Then Bima fell. Lying on the earth, he cried to the King, "Lo, I, who am your darling, have fallen! Why has this happened? Tell me if you know."

"You were a great eater," Yudíshtira said, "and you boasted of your strength. O Bima, when you were eating you did not care about other people's needs. For this fault you have fallen." And

Yudíshtira went on without looking back, having only one companion, the dog that followed at his heels.

Then Indra, making the earth and sky tremble with his thunder, came to Yudíshtira on his shining chariot and asked him to mount it. But Yudíshtira said to that god of a thousand eyes, "My brothers have all fallen down upon this mountain; they must go with me. The delicate Princess Dráupadi, who deserves every happiness, must go with us. I do not wish to go to heaven without them, O lord of all the gods."

"You shall behold your brothers in heaven," Indra said, "for they have cast off their human bodies and have reached it before you. You shall see them all there with Dráupadi, in heavenly forms. But it is ordained that you shall go thither in this very body of yours."

"O lord of the past and present," Yudíshtira said, "this dog is devoted to me and my heart is full of compassion for him. Let him go with me!"

"You have attained today the highest goal," answered Indra, "eternal life and all the joys of heaven. There is no place in heaven for people with dogs; therefore leave this dog; there is no cruelty in doing so."

"It is a great sin," said Yudíshtira, "to abandon a devoted creature, or one who seeks protection, one who is suffering, or one who is terrified. Therefore, O mighty Indra, I shall not leave this dog even for all the joys of heaven; I cannot give him up as long as my own life lasts."

"You abandoned your brothers and Dráupadi," replied Indra. "You have given up everything. Why then can you not give up this dog?"

"It is well known that neither love nor hatred touches the dead," Yudíshtira said. "When my brothers and Dráupadi died, I left them because I could not bring them to life again; but I did not leave them while they were alive. O god of a thousand eyes, the dog still lives and I cannot leave him."

As he spoke these words, the dog vanished and Darma, the God of Justice, stood in his place and said to Yudíshtira, "I am well pleased with you, O king of kings, for you have compassion for all creatures. I tested you once, my son, in the forest, by the lake where all of your brothers seemed to have met their death. You chose that Nákula should be brought to life, in order that he might carry on the line of his mother, Madri. Now you have given up the very hope of heaven for the sake of this dog, whose shape I took to test you. Truly, no one in heaven is your equal and infinite happiness awaits you."

Then Indra and Darma, taking Yudíshtira with them, mounted speedily into heaven, making the sky blaze with their glory. The other gods and the holy sages came out in their chariots to meet him and all that concourse of gods welcomed and praised him.

Yudíshtira Enters Heaven

When Yudíshtira arrived in heaven, he beheld Duryódana seated on a throne, wearing all the glorious emblems that belong to heroes and shining like the sun. Then Yudíshtira's anger blazed up; he turned away and spoke to his companions in a loud voice, saying, "I do not wish to share eternal happiness with Duryódana, who was defiled by greed and stupidity. It was for him that friends and kinsmen, over the whole earth, were slaughtered. Ye gods, I do not even wish to see him; but wherever my brothers and Dráupadi are, there I wish to be."

Indra said to him, smiling, "Do not speak so, O king of kings! In heaven all hatreds cease. Duryódana poured forth his life as a sacrifice on the fire of battle; he fulfilled the duties of his caste and was never terrified by danger; therefore he has earned the reward of heroes. You should not remember any longer the wrongs that he did you. Meet him courteously, O lord of men! This is heaven, and there is no hatred here."

But Yudíshtira said, "If Duryódana, that sinful one for whose sake the whole earth was devastated, dwells in these blissful regions, I wish to see the regions where dwell those high-souled heroes, my brothers, who faithfully kept their promises, were always truthful in speech, and of great courage. I do not see here that son

of Kunti, the noble Karna, or the King of Panchála, or Viráta, or the sons of Dráupadi, or Abimányu, or all those other great chariot warriors who also poured their lives as sacrifices on the fire of battle and met their deaths for my sake. I do not see them here, O lord of heaven. If they have not been worthy to dwell in this high place, then know that without those brothers and kinsmen of mine I will not dwell here either. I wish to see Bima, who is dearer to me than my life, the godlike Arjuna, and the twins, who were mighty in prowess; I wish to see the righteous princess of Panchála. Ye gods, heaven is where they are: to me no other place is heaven."

The gods said, "If you long to go there, then go without delay, O son of Kunti, for we wish you to do what is pleasing to you." And they ordered a heavenly messenger to take Yudíshtira where his friends and kinsmen were.

Then the royal son of Kunti and the messenger set forth, the messenger going first and the King following. They went along a steep and dangerous path through murky darkness: the path was covered with moss and hair; it was slippery with blood and foul with the stench of rotting bodies. On trees whose leaves were sharp as swords sat crows and vultures with iron beaks. A river full of boiling water ran beside the path; its sands were hot as embers and its rocks were iron; thorn bushes grew beside it. Beholding all these frightful things, Yudíshtira asked the messenger, "What place is this, and how far must we go to reach the place where my brothers dwell?"

The heavenly messenger stopped and said, "The gods commanded me to bring you here, O king of kings, and then to return. If you are tired, you may return with me." Yudíshtira, dazed by the foul sights and odors, and sorely grieved at heart, turned back to retrace his steps, but just then he heard pitiful voices all around him. "O son of Darma, stay with us! When you drew near, delicious breezes blew upon us. Great is our joy at seeing you, O best of men; stay but a few moments more, that our joy may continue!"

These words, spoken with pain, made the King stand still; the voices seemed familiar to him, although he could not say whose they might be. Therefore he asked, "Who are you? Why are you staying here?" And they answered from all sides, "I am Karna!" "I am Bima!" "I am Arjuna!" "I am Nákula!" "I am Sahadéva!" "I am Dráupadi!" "We are Dráupadi's sons!" Even so did those voices speak in painful tones.

"What perverse fate is this?" Yudíshtira asked himself. "What sinful deeds were done by these high-souled ones that they should dwell in this dark and frightful place, while Kuru's son is enthroned in heaven? Am I asleep or awake? Is this a nightmare of my disordered mind?" Then he was filled with anger against the gods and against the God of Justice himself. He turned to the celestial guide and said, "Go back to those whose messenger you are! Tell them that I shall not return, but shall stay here, since my presence brings comfort to these suffering brothers of mine!" And the messenger went back and told Indra all that the King had said.

A moment after he had left, all the gods, with Indra leading them, came to the place where Yudíshtira stood. As they approached, the darkness vanished; the boiling river and the iron rocks, the thorn trees and the fearsome birds were there no longer, and a cool, pure breeze filled the air with fragrance.

Indra spoke comforting words to Yudíshtira, saying, "Come, come, O chief of men, this delusion is ended. Hell should be beheld by every king; I gave you a sight of it for your own good. On the battlefield you deceived Drona, telling him that his son was dead; therefore you, too, have been deceived by this sight of hell and by the voices of your brothers and kinsmen. They, too, have been shown that place of sinners; all of them have been cleansed of sin. They and all those kings who sided with you and were slain in battle have gone to heaven. Come and behold them, O chief of the Báratas! Come and enjoy the reward of all your good deeds, your gifts and sacrifices, and the labor of your soul. The place that you have won is far above that of kings; it is where Haris Chandra and the holy sages dwell. There you will live in bliss. Behold this river, called the heavenly Ganges, which flows through the three worlds. Bathe in this and your human form and nature will leave you; you will be free of grief and anger, and ready to mount into the highest heaven."

Then Darma, the God of Righteousness, also spoke to his son: "I am greatly pleased with you, O King! This is the third test that I have put you to and I find that you cannot be turned aside from the path of virtue. I examined you in the forest when, in the form of a deer, I carried off the Brahman's fire sticks, and you stood the testing well. I examined you once more, my son, when I took the shape of a dog, when your brothers and Dráupadi had fallen. This has been your third test, when you wished to stay in hell for the sake of those you love. You are cleansed of all sin; be happy now!"

Yudíshtira, led by Indra and Darma and the other gods, bathed in the heavenly Ganges, where he cast off his human body. Free of grief and anger, he appeared in a shining form, clad in heavenly garments, and went with the gods to the place where his brothers and kinsmen were. There he beheld Krishna, with his blazing celestial weapons, and beside him Arjuna, radiant and happy; there he saw Karna, as splendid as his father, Súrya. Bima stood beside the Wind God, his father, and the Storm Gods stood near them. With the beautiful Gods of Twilight and Dawn, the Ashvins, he beheld Nákula and Sahadéva; and he beheld also his beloved Dráupadi, adorned with garlands of lotuses. All of these welcomed him with great joy.

Indra said, "Behold Kuru, your eldest uncle, and the renowned Gandári, who have come to this place because of the power of the penances they performed in the forest. There is your father, that mighty bowman, Pandu, with his two wives, Kunti and Madri; he often comes to see me in his chariot. There is the royal Bishma, and there is Drona. The kings who fought for you and those who fought against you, O King, have slowly won their way to this happy place; they have conquered heaven by the virtue of their thoughts, their words, and deeds, and by the sacrifice of their lives in battle.

"All sin and grief is ended, O best of men, and everlasting happiness is yours!"